HEATHROW ATC

THE FIRST 50 YEARS

Brian Piket
Pete Bish

Published in the UK by Zebedee Balloon Service Ltd.
ISBN 0-9550042-0-9

Sales and all correspondence to
Pete Bish
Hayward Cross
Hungerford
Berkshire RG17 0QD
Tel / Fax 01488 681527
e-mail adverts@zebedeelist.co.uk

Cover pictures : Front cover : The current Heathrow Control Tower, opened in 1955.
This view was taken in June 1988 (Pete Bish)
Inset: The original Northside Control Tower used from 1946 to 1955. (British Airways via BAA)
Rear cover : Artists impression of the third Heathrow Control Tower. Height will be 87m, with operations
due to commence in October 2006. (BAA Heathrow)
Page layout and pre-press by Richard d'Alton.

CONTENTS

THE AUTHORS

BRIAN PIKET

Main text and accidents.

Brian was with ATC Heathrow for thirty seven years, arriving from Gatwick as an assistant in 1961. He was promoted to ATCO through the class to class system in 1965, and spent periods of time on 'B' 'C' 'D' and 'E' Watches before retirement on medical grounds in 1998. Since then his energies have been directed towards the research necessary to complete this book, together with some historical research for the Portuguese Instituto Nacional de Aviacao Civil, and the Portuguese national airline TAP - Air Portugal.

PETE BISH

Staff list, dates of interest, photograph selection and layout.

Pete came to Heathrow in August 1971 from No.14 Cadet Course having been aeroplane mad, including photography of same, since his school days in Windsor. He remained an operational ATCO on 'A' Watch until the split in October 1993 when he transfered to CCF (now Terminal Control) at LATCC. Still operational as a TC Heathrow Director Pete also organises the annual 'Heathrow Nostalgia' evening, now especially popular with retired staff and those working away from the Airport itself. Outside ATC Pete continues his photography, to fly his 1949 Piper Clipper and various hot air balloons.

The help of the following who contributed time and memories to the production of this book is gratefully acknowledged :-

Ernie Abery, Iain Alexander, Pete Allsopp, Ian Bailey (Tels items), Graham Bisset, Doug Bush, Bob Cook, Jez Cooke, Colin Coomber, Mike Crutch, Ian Culley, Roger Darling, John Davis MBE, Kevin Day, Mike Doyle, Tony Doyle (Accidents), George Dyer, Ted Elliott, Ian Finlay, Clive George, Phil Griffith, Alan Haines, Joe Hanbury, Chris Harris, Malcolm Hemming, Alan Hickman, Jack Hollis, Steve James, Graham Jarvis, Paul Johnson, Celia Kunert, Roger Kunert, Mike Martin, Eric Matthews, Brendan McCartney, Bill McColl, John MacDermot, Keith Meakin, Tony Merton Jones (and Propliner magazine), Rod Metcalfe, Keith Miller, Lucy Miller, Brian Milton, Gordon Morehouse, Angela Newman, Chris and Jenny Prentice, Eric Percival, Terry Quantrill, Brian Smith, Robert Spooner, Graham Stevens, Alan Watson, Bob Waud, Les West, Pete Wilde , Keith Williams, Bill Woodruff CBE, the staff of the CAA Library at Gatwick, AIS Heathrow and ATC Ops at Heathrow (Chris Wilson, Spike Bainbridge, Martyn Swann, Malcolm Judge, Kate and Karen).

In addition we are indebted to Dave Shawe, Gordon Bain and Chris Huggett who worked wonders on scanning the photos. Similarly to the many individuals who have taken or submitted photographs with credits as appropriate. Particular thanks go to Arthur Kemsley for making so many BAA Archive photographs available. Also to Roger and Celia Kunert who have spent many hours transforming the original document into 'Word' format. Last, but definitely not least, to Alan Carter and Bob Robinson for their support throughout.

INTRODUCTION

Heathrow. The busiest International Airport in the World. For most people the name conjures up images of a never-ending stream of heavily laden jets arriving from and setting off for exotic, far distant destinations and of heaving passenger terminals. But, of course, this has not always been the case. When Heathrow was handed over by the military to the Ministry of Civil Aviation on 1st January 1946 it was far from complete. Only one runway was ready for use, passenger facilities were minimal, and only one airline, British South American Airways, had been given approval to operate services. Dramatic changes took place over the next fifty years, not only to the Airport itself but also in the size, speed and numbers of aircraft that used it and the intention of this book is to show how Air Traffic Control adapted to this process. It is an unashamed nostalgia trip which we hope will bring back many happy memories to those who were there and paint a picture of the evolutionary process to those who have followed. The book combines two projects begun separately by the co-authors but which, together, hopefully form a comprehensive and accurate record of all that happened in the period to 1996 and it would be nice to think that there is someone in Heathrow ATC now with enough enthusiasm to continue our 'family history'. To assist with this some of the more notable changes that have taken place pending the book's somewhat delayed publication have been included in the appendices and the staffing details have also been brought up to date as far as possible. A book of this nature is, necessarily, most interesting to those who have been directly involved and know the people and equipment personally but we hope that it will also appeal to others who share our desire for Heathrow to maintain its eminent and envied status.

Bill Woodruff CBE FRAe S

FOREWORD

By Bill Woodruff CBE FRAe S

'those who watch at that midnight hour
From Hall or Terrace or lofty Tower'
Edward Lear

Histories have been written of most facets of civil aviation but there is a notable gap in the field of air traffic control. The history of Heathrow too has been well documented but again there is a gap in that same area. This book goes some way to filling the first gap and all the way to filling the second and I was delighted when Brian Piket asked me to write an introduction to it.

My association with aviation, civil and military, lasted, actively, from 1941 to 1988 and of that time thirty five years were taken up with air traffic control. Regrettably, only ten years were spent at airports but those ten years were among the most enjoyable and satisfying of my career. I suppose the reason was that of being at the 'sharp end' and of seeing the end product of aircraft arriving and departing. There was, too, a camaraderie among the various disciplines - ATC, Tels, aircrew, airport and airline staff - which could only exist at airports. I hope this still exists although I fear that the trend is toward less personal contacts. And the removal of the Approach Control function from Heathrow has substantially reduced the ATC presence. There was also, in the early post-war days, that 'esprit' which owed much to the fact that most of us had come out of the RAF or RN at the end of the war and had an approach to life that was bound to change, for better or worse, as the years went by.

My association with Heathrow started in a limited way - as a controller at Bournemouth (Hurn) in 1946-47 who used to cadge lifts to and from Heathrow in the BOAC Yorks, landing and taking off at what looked like a First World War battlefield. In 1947 I was posted to Northolt, which was then the busiest airport in Europe. These were pioneering days, learning how to handle at first without radar and from 1948 with radar, ever increasing volumes of traffic. We at Northolt were aware of the infant Heathrow six miles to the south, but we were contemptuous of its low volume of traffic.

I left Northolt in 1951 and following a brief spell at the area radar unit on the north side of Heathrow (opposite the Blue Diamond cafe!) I spent a few years behind a desk but in 1956 I was sent to Heathrow as ATCO i/c. Traffic levels were by now quite high and significant advances had been made in communications, radar and navaids. The nostalgia of those days is well reflected in this book. I have some clear memories of the four ATC watches - the team spirit and the many idiosyncrasies of some of the ATCOs, ATCAs and Runway Controllers. Traffic levels were now the highest in Europe and the IFR (bad weather) rates the highest in the world. Even FAA staff from the US came to study our methods of radar sequencing which achieved such landing rates. In the early 1960s Heathrow had occasional days approaching 1000 movements. Such rates are now regularly exceeded by 30% but I like to think that we laid some good foundations for today's operations.

But there were also, in those days before clean air legislation, pea-soupers and London 'Particulars' when, for several consecutive days, runway visibility barely exceeded double figures and no traffic moved at all. A brief and frightening trial of FIDO (burning petrol from a pipe along the side of the runway), the running of aircraft engines at high power to blow the fog away and other expedients all failed to shift the fog for more than a few minutes. The main problem for staff was travelling to and from home on roads where the visibility was often only a few yards.

Snow too, in those days, seemed more of a problem. The BAA was not yet in existence and responsibility for snow clearance rested with the Commandant and management and ATC. On Boxing Day 1960 for example, I was called in to help with a heavy fall which continued for several days. I returned home the next year having seen in 1961 sitting on a snow plough in the middle of Runway 28R drinking cocoa laced with rum 'borrowed' from the Commandant's hospitality bar. Fortunately that year the snow had come too late to interfere with the splendid Christmas parties given by a number of the airlines. Not only parties but food parcels and bottles sent to ATC for distribution among the watches. All quite harmless and friendly but no doubt classed as sleazy and incorrect today. It was the custom in those days too for senior staff to call in on Christmas Day bearing bottles, cigarettes and chocolates for the staff unfortunate to be on watch. Also now very incorrect I expect.

Reluctantly, I refrain from further reminiscences lest I trespass too much on the contents of the book. But, given the chance ......

The continuing efficiency of Heathrow ATC still amazes me. Here is one of the oldest and one of the smallest international airports serving a world capital. It has two parallel runways, quite close together and with severe environmental restrictions, it is hemmed in by three main roads, housed until recently a sewage farm, has four terminals with a fifth under construction and, in consequence, suffers serious ground movement problems. A third runway is available but presents even more problems. (In 1946 nine runways were planned, three of them north of the Bath Road!). And yet it remains the busiest airport in the world for international traffic, now handling over 400,000 movements a year.

In the late 1950s and early 1960s we thought we were doing well to handle, regularly, nearly 70 movements an hour. By 1997 the published rate had risen to 82 an hour and on one recent occasion 99 movements were achieved. In spite of the inevitable erosion of margins for error, the safety record remains second to none. Long may it stay this way but when any system operates for prolonged periods near to its maximum capability there must be anxieties about these decreasing margins.

The ATC staff who pioneered Heathrow in the early days and those who followed on may look back with pride and satisfaction at their achievements. This book gives some fascinating vignettes of the first fifty years of Heathrow ATC. I hope there will be a few younger readers who, in the late 2040s, will contribute to a second volume marking a hundred years of this outstandingly successful story.

BILL WOODRUFF

Written enthusiastically by Bill in 1999 on hearing of our project. Sadly Bill died in 2003 without seeing the final result.

The original northside Control Tower. (British Airways via BAA)

THE ORIGINAL CONTROL TOWER
(1946 TO 1955)

The desire for a rapid return to normality after a protracted period of hostilities saw a still unfinished Heathrow handed over by the military for civil use on 1st January 1946, followed by its official opening on the last day of May. The long haul operators who had been using Hurn Airport were, as might be expected, very keen to transfer services to the newly named 'London Airport' due to its proximity to our capital city and their pressure was rewarded when approval was given, despite the lack of facilities available. First day arrivals included a BOAC Lancastrian from Australia and Lockheed Constellations of Pan American and American Overseas Airways. Only one of the three runways which had been under construction was ready for use, a situation which continued until 1100 hours on Thursday 19th September when all three runways were declared serviceable. Runway 3 was, however, reserved primarily for aircraft parking.

DESIGN

The Control Tower, built to standard RAF design, was located on the north apron, to the west of the passenger terminal which was little more than a collection of tents and other temporary accomodation. It was a three storey brick building with a metal framed visual control room (VCR), glazed on all sides, sited on the roof. The geometry of this would undoubtedly have pleased anyone with a cubist bent. Single storey blocks extended east and west from this building, the former housing the briefing section and the Met office. Fifty years later the Met observer was still located within a short distance of this site. The ground and first floors of the Tower were primarily occupied by Tels staff and their equipment, although female ATC staff did use one of the ground floor rooms if sleeping during the night. On the second floor was Approach Control, facing south, behind which there were rooms for the W/T operators, the ATCO i/c, a bedding store, and another room where night duty staff could get some sleep. On the roof behind the VCR there was accommodation for the person who provided the commentary for the spectator's enclosure - he could easily walk through and find what movements were expected. The enclosure proved very popular, enabling people to see close up the new giants of the skies spawned by war time necessity, and the entrance fee of 3d (1.25p) per person and one shilling (5p) for a car raised in excess of £600 in the first three weeks which was put towards the Airport's operating costs.

Data transfer between the three ATC sections (Briefing, Approach and Tower) was by Lamson systems although, for a time, a pulley equipped with a paper clip was used for this purpose between Approach and the Tower, routed through a hole about one foot square cut in the dividing ceiling / floor. An enterprising member of staff constructed a cup holder out of a baked bean tin which hooked onto this lift for sending cups of tea up to the VCR on windy days when the clerk was unable to carry a tray up the outside staircase.

REFRESHMENTS

Facilities for passengers and for staff going outside the Control Tower were extremely limited to begin with, and staff would normally bring in their own food and drink, or make use of the tea swindle. Ted Elliott (1947): 'The only place to eat outside the Tower was in a canteen run by Airwork just inside the gates, and reached by duck-boards across the mud that constituted the northern passenger areas'. But by 1950 the situation had improved and allowed for varied tastes. Les West: 'Refreshment was provided by the MCA canteen (Greasy Spoon) alongside the Tower, also the 'Green Dragon' which was a large green corrugated hut that did teas and snacks for all Airport staff, drivers etc. 'Ben's, a transport cafe alongside the main gate was the best of all when open, even the BEA ground hostesses used it'. When the Green Dragon was demolished in the early 1960s over fifty cups were found in the space between the inner lining and the outside shell. The conclusion reached was that they must have been taken there over the years by a very contented family of rats!

manned by one runway controller (not an ATCO). The runway controller and Air Traffic Clerk grades would later be merged to form the Air Traffic Control Assistant grade, but at this stage the Clerks were locally employed, earning about £3.00 a week, and the runway controllers were ex RAF and receiving about £5.00 a week. The ATCO3, at age 25, had a salary of £428.00 pa and the ATCO2 £750.00 p.a., and generally the source of supply was the RAF where they could have been either ATCO or aircrew, although some also came from the Royal Navy. There was some rivalry over status in the Control Tower between the controllers and the W/T operators, who through their Union had negotiated pay rates in line with their Home Office colleagues above ATCO salaries, and who

Passengers disembark from an American Overseas Airlines Lockheed Constellation on the northside apron. The Tower is in the background. (BAA)

Accommodation in the form of a hostel for female staff was provided at Harlington Corner, catering for those who arrived without having made more permanent arrangements. Since many of the ladies coming to ATC were ex WAAF it served a useful purpose, which continued until the late 1960s.

STAFFING

Initially the VCR was manned by just one controller, an ATCO3, who was later assisted by an Air Traffic Clerk (graded TC3). In Approach were the ATCO2 Duty Supervisor and an ATCO3, again with a TC3 providing support duties. Briefing was manned by one TC3, and the runway caravans, sited by the threshold of each active runway, were each

therefore considered that they were the senior grade. Advances in radio communications would soon make them redundant.

A four Watch system was worked, based on a four day cycle - Day 1 from 1300 to 2000. Day 2 from 0800 to 1300 and then back on the same evening for a night duty from 2000 to 0800. The rest of Day 3 was a sleep day. Day 4 off. Staff shortages meant that controllers could be called in on their day off, to the extent that hours averaged 48 per week, and if they exceeded 50 hours over a period then a long hours gratuity of ten per cent of the salary could be claimed.

Among the first ATCOs to arrive at London Airport were Bob Waud, Ken Brown, Tommy Dalton, Len Graham, Bernard Ware, Dicky Manly, Bill Towers-Perkins, Phil Sargent, Bill Turnidge, Tim Wooldridge and Eric Matthews, with ATCO i/c Bill Rimmer. Training in Aerodrome and

Approach Controls was based on RAF procedures modified as necessary, since local instructions were not yet published, and validation times were very short by today's standards. Les West recalls being told that he 'had to go solo in the Tower in four weeks as they were about to start summer leave'. But because of the vast changes that were taking place in civil aviation in the immediate postwar years there was no guarantee that, having validated, an ATCO would stay at London Airport for any length of time. Some chose to return to the Air Force, or took jobs with International Aeradio abroad which seemed to offer better salaries and career prospects than did staying with the Ministry of Civil Aviation. There were also postings within the MCA. Bob Waud was one of the earliest departures, transferred out in 1950 because of his valuable knowledge of airways operation gained in the USA and Canada during the war, which could now be used in establishing an airways system in the UK. Average tour length was about five years although you might stay longer if you had a GCA ticket. The transition from military to civilian life, however, was not without its problems, and the i/c had to write a letter to staff in December 1946 urging them to improve their standards in keeping with their altered responsibilities.

ATCO i/c Bill Rimmer's 1946 letter to Bob Waud urging staff to improve standards. How management styles have changed......!

AERODROME CONTROL

Equipment in the VCR was fairly basic. There were desks for both the ATCO on duty and for the assistant who, at a later stage, logged movements and answered routine telephone calls. A loudspeaker enabled the Approach frequency to be monitored, and flight data came in or went out by the pulley (later Lamson tubes) mentioned earlier. Visual signals could be given to aircraft by Aldis lamp, Verey pistol or by Schermuly rocket launcher. This latter device was regarded with some distrust by staff, explaining why it was not often used. R/T was provided in the form of VHF

The visual control room, with its distinctive aerial array, situated on the roof of the box-like tower building. The open door and windows doubtless tells a story of temperatures within! From the contrail pattern above, the military clearly have the upper airspace to themselves.......(BAA)

frequency 118.1 Mcs and a standby HF frequency 5100 Kcs, which was of little use for traffic in the circuit but enabled you to hear the whole of Europe at night. One Christmas Day an Argonaut (DC4) had VHF radio failure and was working on HF, but could not receive landing clearance. The controller on duty had previously been exchanging Christmas greetings with Geneva, who could hear the aircraft concerned, and they relayed the landing clearance for him.

In the early hours of the morning there were very few, if any, aircraft movements so the Aerodrome controller would go down into Approach to split the Watch with his colleague, monitoring 118.1 on loudspeaker. But radio checks by BOAC maintenance technicians on the Approach frequency followed immediately after by the Tower frequency could mean nights of intense activity, dashing up and down the staircase, and so Tels were persuaded to provide a handset on a long cable which was lowered through the hole in the ceiling cut for the pulley. This was known as 'George'. One night when the VCR was unmanned another piece of equipment short-circuited and caught fire. Fortunately it was spotted by the Met observer, although the controller on duty thought at first that it was a poorly timed joke when the Met man burst through the door to tell him, and damage was confined to just the equipment concerned.

There was a small lighting panel on which the runway and taxiway lights were selected. To bring up these lights was not a straight-forward matter as it was necessary to 'pulse in' each section individually by holding down the selector button, otherwise there was a high risk of overloading the system. Since the panel was some distance from the controller's operating position switching on had to be delayed if there were any calls on the R/T, but it was not very long before a brick appeared as the solution to this problem. R/T could be answered while the brick looked after the pulsing process, but you had to remember to remove it afterwards of course. Approach lights were switched from remote sites to begin with, and it was a duty of the runway controller to accompany the engineers to ensure that the correct selections were made. All the lighting controls were later combined on a larger panel housed in a small extension to the VCR.

Use of London Airport in IFR conditions was governed by the regulations applicable to the Metropolitan Control Zone, within which it lay, and a flight plan had to be filed with Uxbridge ATCC (the controlling authority) at least thirty minutes before ETD. Revisions to route, or to the ETD if they exceeded ten minutes, had to be notified. For London departures three exit points from the Zone were specified, Woodley for traffic to the west and north, Dunsfold for southbounds, and Gravesend for eastbound flights. In January 1949 the altitude associated with each of these exit points was 2500 feet, with Northolt departures to Woodley and Gravesend and Croydon departures to Dunsfold being cleared at 1500 feet. A departure would call the Tower with its engines running and coordination would be effected with Uxbridge ATCC and then with Approach, to whom it would be transferred when airborne for separation against inbounds as far as the Zone exit points. There it was handed off to Uxbridge, although IFR flights which did not leave the Zone and VFR flights remained with London Approach. Because there were no maintenance facilities to begin with at London Airport aircraft of BSAA and BOAC would position out for maintenance between flights, BOAC using Hurn or Bristol Whitchurch for its own aircraft and Dunsfold for the Skyways Yorks which covered some of its schedules, whilst BSAA used Langley, which meant that as soon as an aircraft was airborne it was preparing to land.

Fog, or rather Smog, could cause severe disruption to schedules, with visibilities dropping to a few yards. Runway Visual Ranges (RVRs) did not exist as such and a Met observer was positioned at the runway caravan to provide visibility readings from reference lights. When more accurate assessment of visibility later became necessary the runway controllers took over this responsibility, counting 'Goose-neck' flares placed along the edge of the runway and converting the number seen to a distance from a table provided. 'Goose-necks' were genetically related to a watering can, oil filled with a wick in the spout, and care had to be taken when positioning them because if the wind was blowing towards the spout then a melt-down could occur. Later still black and white marker boards, positioned along the edge of the runway, were introduced for the measurement of RVRs and finally, before readings became automatic, dedicated RVR reference lights were installed. Caution had to be exercised when an aircraft wished to take off, since there was no Ground Movement Radar. An AFS vehicle was positioned at each runway intersection and the pilot was told 'the runway intersections are guarded, take off at your discretion'. Needless to say this was a procedure accepted less than enthusiastically by aircrew. Ground movements could also be affected. One night a call came to Approach from a BOAC driver who had been towing some steps when the tug broke down. It had taken him some time to get back and he had no idea where he had left the steps. Aircraft movements were suspended until they were retrieved.

APPROACH CONTROL

In Approach there were two working positions, one for the ATCO2 Supervisor and one for the ATCO3. R/T was available on 119.1 Mcs VHF, and bearing information could be obtained from an ex Royal Navy CRDF situated at the eastern end of the desks. W/T messages to aircraft needed to be converted into 'Q' code and were then handed through a hatch to the W/T operators for transmission, written on green printed cards. Similar cards printed in red were used for aircraft movements. Data transfer and the loudspeaker

This 1951 view of the Approach Control Room shows Les West (left) as the Approach Controller and Fred Every (right) as ATCO 2 Approach Supervisor. The big instrument at the end of the desk is the VHF Cathode Ray Direction Finder (CRDF) display, fed by receivers out on the airfield. (via Les West)

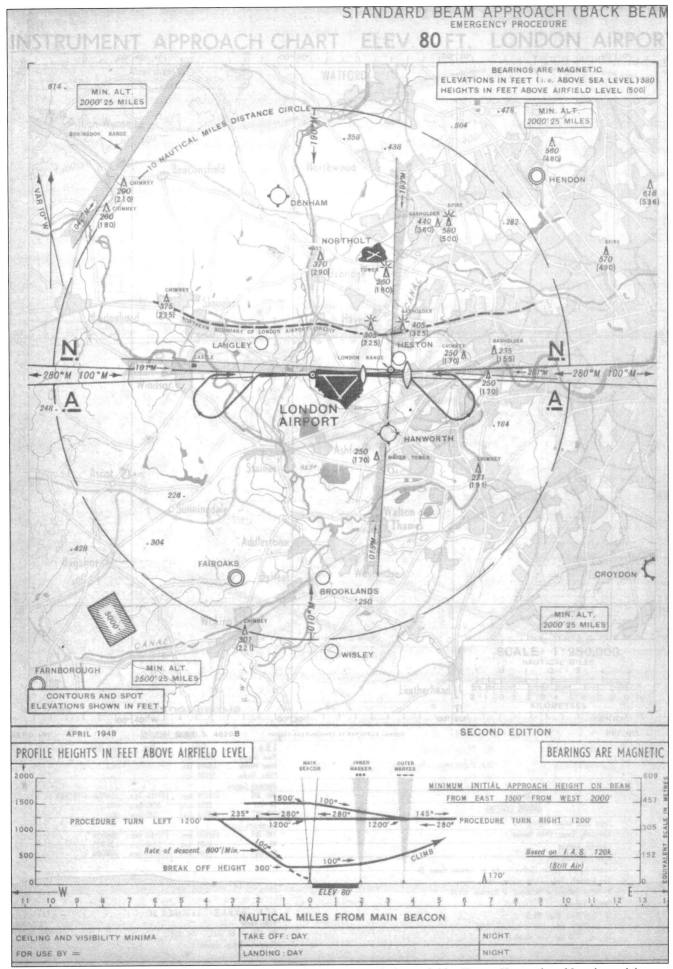

The Standard Beam Approach plate for April 1948. Note the close proximity of other airfields - Heston, Hanworth and Langley and the railway line used to divide Northolt and London Airport visual cicuits.

monitor of 118.1 Mcs have already been mentioned, and in addition there was a two-way 'squawk box' for communication with the Tower.

VFR and IFR flight was permitted. VFR inbounds were required, whenever possible, to arrange their flights to land without making a circuit. If this was not possible they were to make left hand circuits awaiting landing clearance, and were to keep to the south of the Slough - Southall - Ealing railway line to avoid confliction with Northolt traffic. If they were unable to comply with this latter requirement then they were to regard London and Northolt as one Airport and carry out a combined circuit during which both Airports were at all times on the left of the aircraft. IFR inbounds, like IFR departures, were governed by the regulations of the Metropolitan Control Zone and would be cleared in by Uxbridge ATCC through the same three points as were used by departures - Woodley, Dunsfold and Gravesend. On 1st January 1949 the altitudes allocated to London inbounds at Woodley were 3500 feet, 5500 feet, 7500 feet, and 9500 feet, and at both Dunsfold and Gravesend 4500 feet, 6500 feet and 8500 feet. Northolt arrivals through Woodley used 4500 feet, 6500 feet and 8500 feet, while Northolt arrivals through Gravesend and Croydon arrivals through Dunsfold used 3500 feet, 5500 feet, 7500 feet and 9500 feet. Pilots were required to specify the radio aid (SBA, ILS or Radio Range) they proposed to use when requesting Zone entry clearance from Uxbridge ATCC. After its transfer to them Approach would keep the aircraft separated from conflicting traffic inside the Zone, and whenever possible would issue the necessary clearances to enable the aircraft to land without holding. When this could not be done it would be cleared for the appropriate procedural approach.

The Spanish airline Iberia presented some problems to ATC when it first started operating into London as very few of their pilots could speak English. When one of their aircraft was due in, or ready to depart, the Iberia representative was called up from the passenger lounge to act as an interpreter. This often meant that the flight was given a priority so that a return to normal operation could be made as soon as possible.

The Beam Approach Beacon System (BABS), a responder system, and the Standard Beam Approach (SBA), which offered only azimuth guidance, were soon withdrawn from service leaving the ILS and GCA (introduced in 1948) as the primary landing aids. The first ILS was an SCS.51, transmitting on 109.1 Mcs and serving 28R. The back beam that it radiated was used by Pan American and American Overseas Airlines for cloud breaks from the west.

GROUND CONTROLLED APPROACH (GCA)

In 1947 talk-down staff started to arrive in preparation for the introduction of GCA. The equipment itself, Federal GCA, was mobile and would be positioned on the site appropriate to the runway in use. It was normally mains powered but had its own stand-by diesel generators, the fumes from which could get into the truck at times causing headaches and watering eyes. There were two elements, the talk-down radar itself being 3cm with a range of 10 miles, and the search radar 10cm with a range of 26 miles. For a while staff numbers were below requirement and you could find yourself summoned by telegram to appear on your day off if someone went sick. The complement was one talk-down

controller, two Directors and two Trackers (assistants), although the Trackers were reduced to one by 1950. While most of the GCA crews had previous Tower experience and could help out when required, this was not the case for the Tower controllers who over a period of two or three years were sent on GCA courses. Training consisted of a six week course at RAF Watton on basic theory and operating techniques followed by a six week course at Aldermaston adapting from RAF to civil procedures. Validation could then be achieved very quickly as there was no minimum time requirement and on one day of poor weather more than the required number of 'runs' could be achieved. For a couple of years only the morning and afternoon duties were worked (0800 to 2000), after which a full 24 hour service was provided. The facility was normally only used in poor weather conditions, but there were often requests for practice approaches. KLM, in particular, used the GCA service frequently and when they learnt that they had made the 5,000th run they presented the ATC staff with a beautiful iced cake decorated with a picture of a runway and a man with a megaphone representing 'talk-down'. There also exists a story about an Air France 'Postale de Nuit' DC3 which landed safely on 28L one night in thick fog following a successful talk-down. However, somewhere around block 85 it allegedly left the paved surface onto the grass, went around to the south of the GCA truck located in grass area 16, and found its way back onto the runway at block 83. None of this was known until the early morning inspection team found the aircraft's wheel tracks. After a while the search element began to be used to assist Approach with sequencing, although Southern Division did raise some objections to this usage initially, feeling that target persistence on the screens might not be adequate to provide a separation service. Nevertheless the search element came into increasing use, on one occasion helping to maintain a four minute landing rate over a five hour period of single runway operation. It was also used later for vectoring Croydon inbounds onto a five mile final.

On the social side Reg Bennett organized an archery class out at GCA with the target fastened to a ladder. Poor aim could, on occasions, result in arrows needing to be retrieved from the runway.

THE 1946 PLAN

The report of the London Airport Advisory Layout Panel was published in December 1946. Appointed fifteen months earlier they had been tasked with identifying the best layout for an international civil airport within a defined area, making maximum use of the three runways being constructed for (at that time) RAF purposes. The Chairman was A H Wilson CBE, and there were nine other members of varied qualifications reflecting wide ranging expertise. Guidance from experience elsewhere proved difficult to obtain as there was little knowledge of a multiple runway airport in civil operation. Among other layouts considered was a twelve runway tangential pattern which, it was claimed, could yield a movement rate of 360 per hour but this was not the one chosen. Instead the Panel recommended the retention of only two of the three runways now complete - runway three would be withdrawn and replaced by a new runway parallel to it and about a half a mile further to the west. A second triangle of parallel runways would then be superimposed on the first to form a 'Star of David' layout. By increasing the size of the

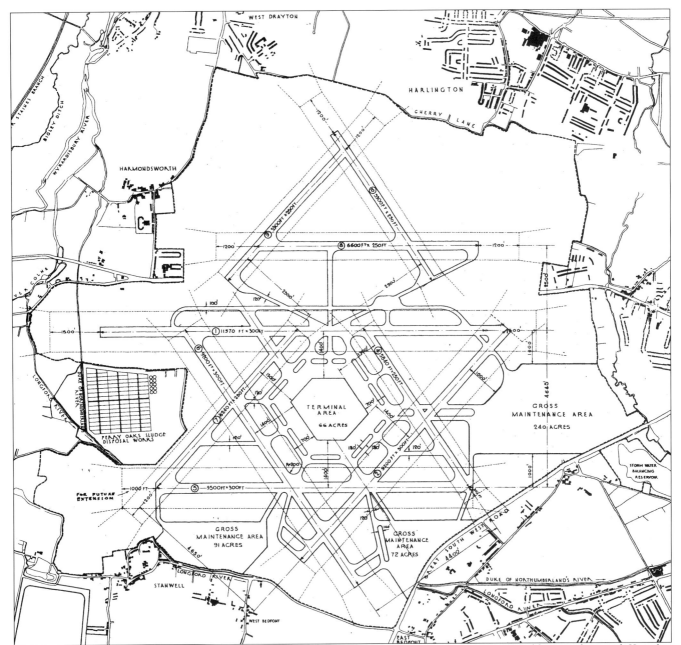

This is how the airport would have looked had all 3 stages of the 1946 London Airport Report of Layout Panel been implemented. How the BAA, over half a century later, must wish that concrete had been laid then north of the Bath Road!

triangle space would be created in its centre for passenger facilities reached by a road tunnel under one of the runways. At this stage they recommended development only to the south of the Bath Road, although the final stage of expansion envisaged the disappearance of Sipson and Harmondsworth and the building of a smaller, third triangle of runways to give a fair weather capacity of 160 movements or more per hour.

The implications to ATC were the necessary closure of runway 1 (28R/10L) for the construction of the tunnel, which would not be possible before the completion of the parallel runway 5, and a new control tower inside the runway complex. Work had progressed sufficiently by 1950 for runway 1 to be bisected by a huge ditch, within which the access tunnel was built. The section of runway to the east of this work was now used for parking, while west of the work the runway continued to be used for departure by those aircraft that could accept the reduced take-off distance in the westerly direction only.

INTRODUCTION OF AIRWAYS

Notam 36/1950 announced the intention to expand the UK Air Traffic Control Service by the introduction, in three phases, of an 'Airways' system. Phase One would consist of the introduction of one Airway only (Green One), designed mainly to serve trans-Atlantic traffic flying between Shannon and London. Phase Two would complete the Airway system within the South Eastern FIR, and introduce a revised Metropolitan Control Zone planned as an integral part of the Airways system. And Phase Three would complete the UK system by introducing further Airways in the Northern FIR. The first two phases were of particular importance to the operation at London Airport, affecting both inbound and outbound IFR flights. Standard departure routes were introduced as shown below, and a typical clearance now became BURNHAM above 2,000 feet, BEACON HILL at 3,000 feet (northbound) or CHERTSEY above 2,000 feet, DUNSFOLD at 3,000 feet (southbound), routing out on Amber One from runway 28 or 34.

DEPARTING FOR	VIA	ROUTE
London Airport - Runways 05 and 10		
N	Amber Two	Kilburn - Brookmans Park - Woburn
E	Red One	Epsom - Sevenoaks - Maidstone - Gl to North Foreland - R1
E	Green One	Epsom - Sevenoaks - Maidstone
SE	Red Two	Epsom - Sevenoaks - Ashford - SE FIR
S	Amber One	Epsom - Dunsfold
S	Blue One	Epsom - Sevenoaks - Crowborough - SE FIR
W	Green One	Chertsey - Woodley
London Airport - Runways 28 and 34		
N	Amber One	Burnham - Beacon Hill
E	Red One	Chertsey - Epsom - Sevenoaks - Maidstone - G1 to North Foreland - R1
E	Green One	Chertsey - Epsom - Sevenoaks - Maidstone
SE	Red Two	Chertsey - Epsom - Sevenoaks - Ashford - SE FIR
S	Amber One	Chertsey - Dunsfold
S	Blue One	Chertsey - Epsom - Sevenoaks - Crowborough - SE FIR
W	Green One	Direct

The controller issuing the clearance at Uxbridge was also responsible for ensuring that standard separation would be achieved and maintained en route, so clearances were also likely to contain a time restriction behind the preceding aircraft on the same route or possibly a restriction to climb rate.

The Metropolitan 'Inner' Control Zone was now replaced by the London Control Zone which extended from ground level to 11,000 feet within the area enclosed by straight lines joining the following points: 51.55N 00.35W, 51.40N 00.00, 51.15N 00.00, 51.25N 01.00W, 51.55N 00.35W. IFR flights wishing to enter the Zone needed to be able to maintain two way communication with the ATCC at Uxbridge (call sign 'London Airways'), and procedures also permitted Special VFR flight in IFR weather conditions for aircraft operating from aerodromes within its boundaries. VFR flights intending to fly within 5 nms of London Airport below 2,000 feet were required to call Aerodrome Control with details of their position and direction of flight, and to maintain a continuous listening watch, if necessary complying with any instructions issued.

Standard routes, all of which terminated at Epsom, were also laid down for inbound flights.

APPROACH FROM	VIA	ROUTE
London Airport		
N	Amber One	A1 to Chertsey - Epsom
E	Red One	R1 to Sevenoaks - Epsom
E	Green One	G1 to North Foreland - R1 to Sevenoaks - Epsom
SE	Amber Two	A2 to Ashford - R2 to Epsom
W	Green One	G1 to Woodley - R2 to Epsom

From there, if GCA Search Radar was not being used for sequencing, traffic was cleared to the outer marker for a procedural approach (or to hold if delay was necessary). If radar sequencing was in progress then a Range Departure Time and a heading on which to leave the Range was issued. The system was designed to ensure a minimum of five minutes longitudinal separation on final, and aircraft were required to declare their airspeed (120,140 or 160 knots IAS if possible) and to descend at a rate of at least 500 feet per minute. The GCA Director was really responsible for fine tuning to maintain the desired landing interval and would step in with variations to stack departure headings or adjustments to leg lengths when necessary. As far as possible the standard 1,000 feet vertical separation was maintained during intermediate approach. A special procedure existed for runway 23L, since a full instrument approach was not possible owing to confliction with the Northolt landing pattern. The procedure was basically the same as for runway 28R except that the final controller directed the aircraft along a track parallel to the extended centre line of 28R but 1,500 to 2,000 feet north of it. When one mile from touchdown the aircraft began a rate one turn to the left for a visual line-up and landing on runway 23L.

THE CIVIL RUN DOWN OF NORTHOLT

Aircraft movements at London Airport in 1950 were 37,746 and there were 523,351 passengers. Movements were increasing steadily with new carriers arriving from Croydon, although some Airlines were re-located from Croydon to Northolt. However, the military authorities had indicated that they wished Northolt to resume sole military status by 1954, so there was an added urgency to the construction work at London Airport. One carrier, Aer Lingus, actually moved out of London Airport in June 1948. Since the autumn of the previous year they had been using Constellations on the London - Dublin route, but at the same time as their UK terminal was changed to Northolt this type was replaced by DC-3s operating at a higher frequency. A significant event occurred on 16th April 1950 when British European Airways flew their first scheduled service from London Airport - a Viking bound for Paris. Transfer of Airline services from Northolt to London continued with the last scheduled service being flown by BEA DC-3 G-AHCZ to Jersey on 30th October 1954. During the eight years or so that Northolt had served as a London airport it had handled a considerable number of movements, both domestic and European, and as recently as March 1954 the monthly total was 1,531 compared with 3,959 at London. For a time facilities on the north apron were congested while fitting out continued in the new Terminal, but on the 17th April 1955 it was possible for the first commercial traffic to be dealt with by the (still incomplete) central Terminal. The reduced status of Northolt meant not only a large increase in London Airport movements (119,612 in 1955) but also allowed for two stack operation to be introduced at London Airport, using Watford as well as Epsom. Notam 773/1954 amended inbound routes so that traffic from the north (via Beacon Hill or Woburn) was now routed to Watford instead of Epsom if 10R or 28L was in use for landing. All traffic continued to use Epsom if 05R or 33L was in use, but for 15R or 23L all inbounds would now use Watford. Within a few months this use of Watford was further extended with the introduction of optional routes in from Green One eastbound and westbound and from Red One westbound when 28L or 10R were in use. Frequencies 124.9 Mcs and 125.3 Mcs were now allocated to Approach, the former

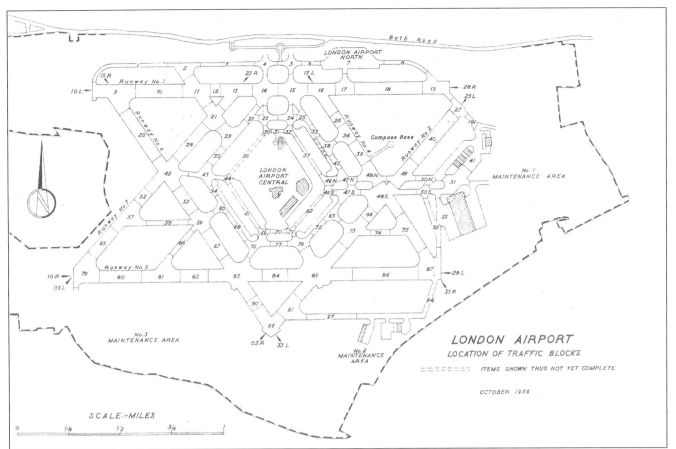

The introduction of block numbers in 1954 greatly eased reference to any point on the airfield. This diagram shows the layout in October 1956.

being used for traffic using Watford and the latter for Epsom inbounds. During two stack operation aircraft stayed on these frequencies until they were established on final approach, but when only one stack was in use they were put to the frequency appropriate to the stack in use for initial sequencing, and then handed off to the second frequency at the downwind - base leg position for vectoring onto final.

GROUND MOVEMENT CONTROL

In 1949 a study was made of London Airport's Ground Traffic Movement. A movement rate of 135 aircraft per hour was assumed which allowed 47 take-offs on each of two take-off runways and 41 landings on one landing runway in departure peaks, and 40 landings on each of two landing runways and 55 take-offs on one take-off runway during arrival peaks. To cope with this high level of traffic major improvements to taxiway lighting, which was then blue and amber edge lighting, were considered vital. With the complicated taxiway system that was developing pilots could no longer be allowed to choose random routes, and the problem would be aggravated by movements to and from maintenance areas. These factors pointed to 'the need for a positive, speedy yet flexible system of traffic direction, with some method of automatic position reporting to the controller, who in bad weather will not be able to see all the movement area'. It was felt that a control system should be devised that would satisfy the following requirements:-

(1)   To give a positive indication to aircraft of the route to be followed between starting point and destination.

(2)   To permit the selection of routes from any one point

on the aerodrome to any other.

(3)   To permit the selection, in sequence, of crossing routes, the information being 'stored' and released (in the order selected) as the previous traffic passes the intersections.

(4)   To provide automatic safety locks within the system to prevent aircraft colliding.

(5)   To report back automatically to the controller the progress along a path of an aircraft or vehicle.

(6)   To report back automatically to the controller any dangerous situation arising from the misinterpretation of signals.

(7)   To report from one phase of control to another the order in which aircraft would pass given points, to enable them to be marshalled into the correct stands.

It was apparent that radar could, at best, only provide a broad supervision of movements and that the solution would probably come from ground detection of an aircraft's position by electrical means, approximating closely to the railway block signalling system. The conclusions drawn were that a system based on green centre line lights with red stop bars at intersections, and a responder system using cabling laid in the bitumen joints of the concrete, would provide the necessary capability. Lights on the controller's mimic panel would glow to indicate the position of an aircraft or vehicle, and routes that conflicted would be resolved automatically.

By the beginning of 1952 green centre line lighting had been installed on all taxiways except to the north of 28R/10L where blue edge lighting remained. Red stop bars across taxiways were initially used only to guard runway 28R/10L, but after the move to the central area in 1955 were progressively introduced over the whole manoeuvring area. Arthur Ruffell was heavily involved with the introduction of the new taxiway lighting system and with the move to the central area the lighting panel was housed temporarily in a building beside the Tower known as 'Ruffell's Palace'. Coloured boards and Junction Indicators were also installed to improve day-time route guidance. The former were coloured according to the route being indicated and bore a superimposed outline arrow showing the direction to be followed. Boards directing aircraft towards the apron had the words 'TO APRON' inscribed within the arrow, and those directing aircraft to holding points bore the QDM number of the runway to which they referred. The Junction Indicators, later re-named Daylight Route Indicator Boards (DRIs), showed a diagram of the junction ahead with the correct route from the junction indicated by a white light on the appropriate arm. It was the responsibility of the lighting operator to turn these on and off as required, and to move the lamps at the back of the board to display the route required. The responder system meanwhile, known as Ground Traffic Indication (GTI) or Sintel, had been given the 'go-ahead' but nevertheless remained dormant for some time. The intention was to remove GMC from the VCR completely, with information from the system being fed back to the 4th floor of the new control tower and indicated on a huge display of the Airport. This area of the fourth floor would need to be extra high to accommodate the mimic board. The Airport lighting panels and their controls were to have been on this floor and their size was, therefore, of little significance. They were, in fact, stock railway signalling switches. However, in August 1951, Eric Matthews arrived at the Deputy Directorate of Control and Navigation Development and was put in charge of the project. Realising how misguided the plan was he argued and won the case for retaining GMC in the VCR. GTI was also abandoned because of its prohibitive cost. Modifications to the top of the Tower were necessary to accommodate the cabling which needed to be extended upwards from the 4th floor, and this resulted in the void which exists below the VCR floor. There was only just enough room for the lighting panels to be fitted in the VCR, and they had to be non-standard units.

The period of occupation of the first control tower drew to a close with two further developments related to ground movements. On 1st May 1954 the Aerodrome Control task was split with the introduction of Ground Movement Control on 121.9 Mcs. Eric Parker is believed to have been the first ATCO to operate this position. And at the end of the year block numbering was introduced. The complexity of the runway and taxiway layout made it necessary to provide a simple reference system which would enable any part of the manoeuvring area to be identified. So all runways and taxiways were divided into sections known as traffic blocks. Red traffic bars would be installed to separate blocks, and beside each of these bars Position Indicator Boards were placed showing two numbers, the block occupied and the block about to be entered. The highest numbered block at the time was 97, which was not yet complete.

Notice was also given in Notam 139/1955 of the intention to install a radar unit in Aerodrome Control which would supplement the outbound radar control given to departing aircraft by London Radar. Although it would not be brought into full use immediately it would be used to assist in the early identification of departures, and the service would be provided on 118.1 Mcs or 125.5 Mcs depending on frequency loading.

The current Control Tower Building taking shape in December 1953. (BAA)

THE SECOND CONTROL TOWER (1955 TO   )

The move to the new Control Tower in the Central Area took place (some might say rather appropriately) on 1st April 1955. The architect was Frederick Gibberd CBE, FRIBA, MTPI, and he was also responsible for the design of the Queens Building and of the South East Face Passenger Handling Building (now Terminal Two). The siting of the Tower meant that there was a good all-round view of the dual parallel runway system and its approaches from the VCR. The height of 127 feet 6 inches was necessary to give a view over the top of the other buildings, and the shape was determined by a number of practical considerations. The more important of these were the need to provide the view required by ATC, and the layout of technical equipment with an interconnecting vertical duct. In addition, the walls of the Tower were arranged on varying planes at angles to each other with the intention of minimising the interference which large flat surfaces might cause to radio aids. A central services core was included, extending to the full height of the Tower and containing the lifts, ventilation trunking and the pneumatic tube and cable duct. A false floor under all control rooms enabled tubes and cables to be run from the vertical duct to any position in the room, ensuring flexibility in the layout and ease of maintenance of technical equipment.

The ground floor of the new Control Tower provided accommodation for Tels staff and their equipment in the east wing, while in the west wing there was a medical centre. This was the headquarters of the Airport's medical services, and was fully equipped as a casualty clearing station. Aircrew medicals were also carried out here. The rest of the ground floor was given over to a kitchen, a staff cafeteria and a canteen for industrial staff. These facilities were open to all Airport staff, not just Control Tower personnel, and were busy day and night. It is rather sad to compare the high levels of security now necessary in the Tower with what existed in those early years. Casual visitors were known to have reached the VCR to ask if they could be shown around, and one day an opportunist job seeker arrived on the sixth floor outside Approach Control asking if there were any vacancies in Air Traffic Control.

Tels also occupied the east wing of the first floor, which was otherwise mainly administration offices. However there were further restaurant facilities - this time for the non-industrial staff - at the southern end of this floor, and outside this a roof garden. A welfare common room was also provided at this end of the building. The second and third floors were mainly further administration offices, although the Commandant's office and a conference room were located on the third floor. Further offices and a locker room were provided on the fourth floor, and a larger locker room on the fifth, but the major allocation of space on these two floors was for the proposed Ground Movement Control Room with a viewing gallery accessible from the fifth floor. The room needed to be two floors high to accommodate the GMC Airport mimic board which was planned, but as previously mentioned this project was cancelled and the space that became available was handed over to Tels, who installed their Telemove section. They were responsible for monitoring the various R/T channels and for sending relevant details to Airline offices and the Airport authorities for stand allocation etc. On the sixth floor was Approach Control, extending up into the seventh floor to accommodate a control information panel ('tote display') placed against the back wall in the widest part of the room. When it was first occupied only the northern half of the room was used, leaving the rest for future development. A viewing gallery for visitors was entered from the seventh floor, and early Approach layouts placed the radars so that the screens could be seen from here, with everything displayed symmetrically around the centre of the room. However, by the time the equipment was installed the radars had been turned to face the other way. Also on the sixth

No, not the new VCR! This is the Ealing Studios' mock-up built for the film 'Out of the Clouds', hence the strange 'exterior' lighting. Note the Lamson tube carriers stored in the desk (left) and the tube entry point in the desk sbove. (CAA Archives)

floor were three ATC offices and a Tels equipment room, while a library and male rest room were provided on the seventh. The ventilation plant and lift motor room were located on the eighth floor, and here too was an external viewing balcony. Finally, on the ninth floor was the VCR.

AERODROME CONTROL

The layout and design of furniture in the new VCR received unexpected help from the film industry. In 1954 Ealing Studios were involved in the making of a film titled

The new VCR on 19.5.55 shortly after opening. Just look at the size of that Lighting Panel....(BAA)

A fully staffed view in the new VCR. Left to Right: 'Teddy' Filmer (ATCA), John Overton (GMC), Harold 'Robby' Robbins (ATCA with binoculars), Alan Smith (Air Controller),Eric Parker (either assisting, training or listening in with Air Controller), Nedda Nedbolsky (ATCA) and Grahan Stevens (ATCO peering into the ASMI bucket). Note the crash grid on the left. (BEA via Graham Stevens)

'Out of the Clouds', and they needed interior shots of a modern control tower for one of the scenes. They were given the plans of the new London Airport VCR, which they built full size in every detail, providing a useful model for the ATC planners. Many of the photos of the VCR taken at that time were of the mock-up with non ATC personnel filling the operating positions, and in some shots the interior of an 'aircraft' can be seen in the background.

The requirement was now for a Supervisor and five staff, two controllers (Air and GMC) and three assistants including the lighting operator. The Air desk was aligned north - south in the centre of the flat floor, with GMC located on the eastern side of the VCR looking down onto the new Central aprons. This siting of GMC was found to be unsatisfactory, however, and within a year or so it was moved to a position at the southern end of the Air desk, with both positions raised onto a dais to improve lines of sight. An ASMI (Airfield Surface Movement Indicator) was provided to assist GMC in periods of reduced visibility. This important addition to the VCR inventory was under development by Decca, an eight millimetre Q-band radar derived from their Mark 4 marine radar, and was still at prototype stage. Early results, with the radar located on a wooden pile beside the Thames, were very encouraging and a further demonstration to ATC representatives was arranged, to take place on top of the uncompleted Control Tower, despite a lack of enthusiasm from Tels. The first photographs showed a blind area of 15 to 20 degrees to the north, but this was found to be caused by a water header tank placed there as a temporary requirement by the building contractors. Following this demonstration the radar was given the 'go-ahead', even though it was a prototype.

Increases in traffic levels meant that two assistants were now needed to provide operational support for the controllers. One of these was primarily involved with obtaining airways clearances for outbound flights from the 'D Outbound' controller, who was now located in the newly occupied Southern ATCC (Uxbridge ATCC closed in March 1955), situated on the northern perimeter of London Airport. D Outbound could be very busy issuing clearances to a number of ATSUs, so delays could occur in obtaining clearances which were still basically procedural, and which were passed and read back in full including any restrictions. It was normal for aircraft to start up before contacting ATC, the first call being for taxy clearance, but this meant that the airways clearance was not always available when the aircraft had completed its run-up. For this reason, as the turbo-prop Vickers Viscount which needed no run-up entered service in increasing numbers, a call for start-up was made to avoid holding point delays. The other assistant attended to the Lamson tube system, receiving and distributing incoming flight progress strips, met. reports etc. and despatching the finished strips. The tube system linked a number of sections, identified by an alphanumeric code that was set on a selector on the tube itself, A1 for the VCR, B1 for Tels, C1 for Approach, E1 for Flight Clearance and E2 for Met. The tube, 2.5 inches in diameter and 8.75 inches long, travelled through the system at 30 feet per second, and the destination code was detected by means of electrical contacts on the body of the carrier. With use the locking clip at the end of the tube became loose and could come undone in transit, allowing the contents (not always the approved, routine ATC messages) to fall out, causing the system to block. Unblocking the system could take some time and would be preceded by a stream of tubes arriving at the terminals as they were released by the engineer. When this happened it was easy to assume that the system was restored and to start sending tubes out again, much to the annoyance of the engineer involved.

The lighting operators were, in fact, the first ATC staff to move into the new Control Tower. Services, fixed routes, had been selected from the temporary accommodation outside the Tower for some time and as fitting out progressed so sections were transferred to the VCR. To ensure that these items of equipment were not tampered with the lighting operators were required to do guard duties in the VCR until the new Tower became operational. On one particular night, when traffic had died down, Frank Butler decided to take a few minutes horizontal rest on one of the work surfaces. Hearing a noise he sat up, stretching, and gave a workman, who had expected no-one to be in the VCR, the fright of his life.

Although the Aldis lamps were retained for giving visual signals to aircraft it was obviously impractical for the Verey pistols and Schermuly rocket launchers to remain because of the location of the new Tower. An AD210 direction finder was now installed on top of the Air desk.

APPROACH CONTROL

Original plans were for just two radar controllers and an assistant in Approach - with a Supervisor - but the case was successfully argued for two additional ATCOs, one as the Approach procedural controller and one to carry out telephone liaison which included taking releases and passing flight level vacations. A Cossor ACR6 ten centimetre (S-band) radar, under development by the Ministry of Supply to a joint Civil/Military specification, was available from the start of operations in the new Control Tower. Only three prototypes had been produced at this stage, one purchased by the Swiss, one retained by the Ministry of Supply, and this one supplied to civil ATC. Naturally Tels were somewhat reluctant to accept a prototype for day-to-day use but were eventually convinced of the necessity, and of course there was always the GCA search radar as stand-by. Rotation rate was 15 rpm, and the data was displayed on 12 inch screens. A recurring phenomenon, which was never acceptably explained, used to occur on this radar around dawn and came to be known as the 'Winkfield Explosion' or 'The Bomburst'. A series of concentric circles centred on the village of Winkfield (near Windsor Great Park), where incidentally there was a satellite tracking station, would slowly radiate outwards and break up as the diameter of the circle increased. Attempts to attribute this to the daily migration of birds, which even included the use of the Ministry's de Havilland Dove with ATCO John MacDonald on board, were never convincingly successful. This radar was warmly welcomed by ATC, allowing the Approach Radar service to be provided from within the Tower using improved equipment.

Further reductions in the service provided from the GCA truck also occurred. Increases in traffic levels meant that radar vectoring was becoming the norm, and from 1st April 1955 it became mandatory for aircraft to carry ILS (unless special permission was obtained) in order to reduce the GCA Talkdown workload. Pilots were now expected to complete

The sixth floor Approach Control room during the late 1950s. Suits, non mobile chairs and a hard floor set the scene. Bernard 'Mac' McDonnell is believed to be in the centre of this line up. (CAA Archives)

their approaches either on the ILS or visually, leaving GCA just a monitoring function most of the time. This enabled the GCA crew to stay in the Tower on stand-by, only going out to the truck when required.

FLIGHT CLEARANCE

The intended accommodation for Flight Clearance inside the Queens Building was not ready when the move was made to the Central Area, and so for a time temporary arrangements were made. The office on the north side remained open for airlines still using the north apron - these included BOAC, middle and far eastern airlines and the Queens Flight - while a new office was opened at the northern end of the new Central Terminal, overlooking the slope between the Terminal and the Queens Building. The assistant on the north side and the three in the Central Area office had to check and manually address flight plans that were received, pass details to the Southern ATCC and to the Tower, and then despatch the Departure Plan when the aircraft was airborne. Unusual routeings and destinations could be quite time consuming, but the repetitious nature of most flights meant that addressing could be done from memory after a short time. It nevertheless found the staff very busy during departure peaks.

Flight Clearance was one of the first offices made available for use in the Queens Building, sharing space with AIS. Its location, conveniently next to BEA Crew Briefing, meant that many flight plans were delivered by hand, with others arriving by teleprinter or via a tube system linking Flight Clearance with BEA. Departure times were obtained from a ticker tape.

RUNWAY CONTROL VANS (CARAVANS)

Only a brief reference has been made so far to the

Runway Control Vans, ATC outposts positioned close to the threshold of active runways. By 1955 manning in each had risen to two (ATCAs), their main function being to act as a second, remote pair of eyes for the Air Controller by checking various aspects of operational safety which might be missed, or not be visible, from the VCR. Outbound flights were inspected for control locks left in, flat tyres, hatches left open etc. and inbounds for alignment with the correct runway, undercarriage lowered and tyre bursts on landing. A general watch for unauthorised vehicles and personnel near the runway was also maintained, and in those days, before security fencing had been erected, was often necessary. A favoured route was from the north apron to the BOAC maintenance area, passing through the undershoots of 28R and 23L, but intruders could appear anywhere. The RCV was equipped with R/T, Aldis lamps and Verey pistols, and on one occasion a Verey was fired to deter a cyclist from crossing an active runway. The flare actually hit the bicycle and burned out lodged in the wheel (Frank Butler strikes again!). The siting of the 28L caravan was such that aircraft lining up from the north of the runway were often upwind of its position, and to fire a Verey in these circumstances in order to stop a take-off, particularly if there was a strong wind, was to invite the flare to assume the characteristics of a boomerang and gracefully return towards the caravan. The firing of Vereys could also highlight differences of perspective between the VCR and the caravan, with Air Controllers on occasions upset that their instructions had been over-ridden. Alan Wright, a lighting operator at Heathrow until 1998, would distinguish himself by unintentionally firing a Verey inside the caravan, fortunately without serious results. The movement logs were maintained in the RCVs, and RVR readings taken when necessary. Fog, and night time on the remoter sites at the western end of the Airport, made the caravan feel quite isolated (which is why very few of the female ATCAs opted for duties out there), but at other times the vehicle became

Delightful view of the 10R Runway Control Van with the Tower in the background. (Maurice Peall)

quite popular with people who had reason to be out on the manoeuvring area. Motor cycle police patrolling the Airport perimeter road would often call in for a short break, occasional visits would be made by the Airport Commandant particularly if he was out supervising snow clearance, and brief stops might be made by the Control Van during runway or lighting inspections. These vehicles were provided by MT with regular drivers, Messrs Goodhand, Budd and Nuth, and were used for routine and non-routine ATC tasks as required. The BAA Manoeuvring Area Safety Unit took over many of their duties when the Authority was created, including braking

action checks from which the Control Drivers appeared to take a rather sadistic pleasure if a member of ATC was on board. But the Control Drivers must also be credited with the large quantities of mushrooms that they picked from the abundant crops that used to appear on the Airport, and which they would deliver to Approach for ATC consumption. Mention must also be made of the vehicle which arrived every day to service the very basic outdoor toilet facilities that were provided. Its driver was always surprisingly cheerful despite his job and was given the nickname of 'Elsan Neddy' by ATC after a well-known bandleader. His R/T callsign was 'Sandan', and

Interior of a Runway Control Van, showing R/T, phone equipment and various crib sheets. Big letters on the right hand sheet say the Police are on Ext 7214! (CAA Archives)

whenever he called for a radio check he was told 'strength five with a strong background hum'. At that time aircraft were more susceptible to cross winds and so runway changes were more common. This, of course, involved moving the RCV. Two cables had to be unplugged and stowed, not enjoyed on wet and windy days, and then a route taken across the Airport to the new site. On days when weather conditions were changing rapidly it could seem that you had only just arrived when another move was required. Not all of the runway controllers possessed full driving licences, so they could only drive airside, but in 1963 management overcame this problem by arranging and paying for those concerned to have driving lessons with the Kenning Garage at Hatton Cross, and for the subsequent test.

THE TROLLEY

Although there were ample refreshment facilities in the new Tower, with more available across the road in the Terminal and the Queens Building, a tea trolley service was soon provided through the building in true Civil Service fashion. Its 1030 and 1500 arrival with tea, coffee, rolls and cakes was announced by the shout of 'Trolleee...' from the Approach door or from the foot of the VCR stairs, and was usually rewarded with a sizeable order. Cheese and onion rolls became very popular despite the problems of working in close proximity, and custard tarts were also highly prized. After the arrival of the stack monitor CCTVs they often appeared on the displays, occupying several flight levels, to provoke comment from the controllers at the ATCC. The trolley service continued for twenty years, which says a lot for the tolerance of ATC management, Tels and the equipment itself to the spillage of drinks on the work surfaces. Staff not needing to re-fuel in their breaks could walk over to the Queens Building where, just inside the entrance, there was a cartoon and news theatre although this did not survive very long.

INCREASING TRAFFIC AND NEW ROUTES

The opening of the Central Area made it possible to close the aircraft park which had existed at the eastern end of 10L/28R since the closure of the runway for construction of the tunnel, and to re-open the runway for full operational use (although ILS and a GCA service were not immediately available). Notice was given that when both 28R/10L and 28L/10R were available for use then 28L or 10L would normally be used for landing and 28R or 10R for departure. Movement rates were continuing to climb, and changes were becoming necessary if ATC was to remain efficient. From 11th March 1956 radar separation between known inbound aircraft was reduced to 3 nms, although the existing 5 nms separation continued to be applied between inbound traffic and other flights. This was done to keep pace with the increasing demand, and pilots were asked to help make the new procedure as efficient as possible by clearing the runway quickly after landing. The ACR6 radar, with its improved picture quality, also enabled the introduction soon afterwards of the surveillance radar approach (SRA), which terminated at 0.5 nms from touchdown. Eight VFR entry points were published for aircraft bound for London Airport, at Woodley NDB, Beacon Hill MKR, Watford RNG, Epsom RNG, Dunsfold RNG, Guildford, High Wycombe and Crystal Palace. Pilots were warned, however, that during busy arrival periods cancellation of an IFR flight plan might be inadvisable due to the density of traffic. In the VCR, meanwhile, the workload of the Air Controller, particularly the high level of liaison required, was causing concern. Not only was he constantly receiving updates of the landing order from Approach, he also needed to obtain a release for each departure from the appropriate radar controller at the Southern ATCC. This would be given as a time separation based on the route and speed of the preceding aircraft, and would vary from 'when the dust settles' or 'airfield separation' upwards. From 1957 an ATCO was made available to assist him with liaison during busy spells, either on request or when directed by the Supervisor, releasing valuable extra time for his main controlling tasks.

Late 1950s view of the recently opened Central Area with car park between the Tower and Europa building. Most cars were black then!
(CAA Archives)

A number of revisions to the airways system in the London area and south east England became necessary, primarily to increase capacity but also to integrate a new control zone for Gatwick Airport (due to re-open in 1958) within its framework. These were implemented in two phases, on 1st May 1957 and in May 1958, with further minor revisions later that year. Departure routes from, and inbound routes to, London Airport were both affected. Standard departure routes now became

DEPARTING FOR	VIA	ROUTE
Runways 05, 10 and 15		
N	Amber Two	Kilburn - Brookmans Park - Woburn
NE	Red One	Kilburn - Brookmans Park - Clacton
E and SE	Green One and Blue Three	Epsom - Malling - Cranbrook - Dover*
		Hornchurch - Malling - Cranbrook - Dover*
S	Amber One	Epsom - Dunsfold
SW	Red One	Epsom - Dunsfold
W	Green One	Chertsey - Woodley
Runways 23, 28 and 33		
N	Amber One	Burnham - Beacon Hill
NE	Red One	Burnham - Watford - Brookmans Park - Clacton
E and SE	Green One and Blue Three	Epsom - Malling - Cranbrook - Dover
S	Amber One	Chertsey - Dunsfold
SW	Red One	Chertsey - Dunsfold
W	Green One	Woodley
* alternative routes at discretion of ATC		

Two additional 'on request' reporting points, Fairoaks Intersection and Biggin Intersection, were also introduced for use by outbound aircraft.

Inbound procedures were standardised so that aircraft were now routed to Epsom or Watford depending on the direction from which they approached and not, as previously, on the direction of the runways in use at London Airport. Watford served traffic inbound through Beacon Hill, Brookmans Park and Woodley while Epsom was used by those routeing in through Cranbrook and Dunsfold. Minimum stack level was 5,000 feet.

APPROACH FROM	VIA	ROUTE
London Airport		
N	Amber One	A1 to Beacon Hill - Watford
NE	Red One	R1 to Brookmans Park - Watford
E	Red One	B29 to Clacton - R1 to Brookmans Park - Watford
E*	Green One	G1 to Cranbrook - Epsom
SE	Blue Three	B3 to Rye - A2 to Cranbrook - G1 to Epsom
SE	Amber Two	A2 to Cranbrook - G1 to Epsom
S	Amber One	A1 to Dunsfold - R1 to Epsom
SW	Red One	R1 to Dunsfold - Epsom
W	Green One	G1 to Woodley - Watford
* non-standard route at discretion of ATC		

Changes were also made to the boundaries of the London Control Zone, which was now the area enclosed by lines joining the towns of Hambledon (near Henley), Coleman Green (near Wheathampstead), Waltham Cross (near Enfield), Godstone and Three Mile Cross (near Reading).

GATWICK RE-OPENS

Gatwick Airport duly re-opened at 0700 on 30th May 1958. A number of staff from London Airport were present and took with them as a gift the 'Courage Cockerel' plaque which had graced the London Approach room wall for some years. Its sentimental value, however, led to plans being drawn up to restore it to its rightful spot in London Approach and a few weeks later a raiding party set out one evening comprising the Commandant Jimmy Jeffs, the ATCO i/c Bill Woodruff, Jimmy Matthews, Ray Pepal and others. Having visited a number of pubs on the way they broke into Gatwick Approach and made off with the plaque. Mission triumphantly accomplished, except that details reached an evening paper and, to quote Bill Woodruff, 'they received a slight strip from the Permanent Secretary' as a result!

Aeroflot, the Soviet airline, was becoming a regular visitor, but their aircraft presented similar problems to those caused by Iberia a decade or so earlier. One of the early flights carrying Mr. Gromyko made two GCAs to runway 05 but had to be instructed to overshoot from both as it was going well below the glide path. A diversion to Manchester was suggested but the aircraft had insufficient fuel. In these critical circumstances the decision was made for the GCA to be moved to a main runway site, which was accomplished with remarkable expedition, and a satisfactory approach and landing followed. A major problem was that the Russian crews spoke very little English and any instructions had to be passed through an on-board interpreter. He was normally an RAF liaison officer seconded to Aeroflot, and connected with the British Embassy in Moscow. This meant, of course, that there was a delayed response to any instructions that were passed - far from acceptable in a talk-down.

BRAKING PARACHUTES

The Tupolev Tu104s of Aeroflot and CSA and early series Caravelles carried braking parachutes which were used to enhance braking performance when there were adverse weather conditions - particularly days of heavy rain. In most cases a warning was given to ATC that the parachute would be used but sometimes it came as a complete surprise and only quick action would prevent it from being dropped on the runway creating an instant obstruction. The procedure was for it to be released after the aircraft cleared the runway for collection by a Leader vehicle or perhaps by the Control Van or Pixie if they were out on the field. But it was not that easy or pleasant to load a large, soaking wet parachute into the back of a van in driving rain, and its return could be a less than welcome surprise to the ground staff attending the aircraft who, at times, were completely unaware that it had been used.

1959 saw the GMC position coming under increasing pressure due to R/T congestion which, it was decided, would be relieved by opening a new frequency 118.5 Mcs for clearance delivery, available H24. This was introduced on 1st June 1959 and was used at ATC discretion during peak periods for passing airways clearances to outbound flights.

CROYDON AND BLACKBUSHE CLOSE

1959 also saw the final closure of Croydon Airport, at 2130 on 30th September. London Approach remained involved with Croydon's airways inbounds through Epsom to the end, positioning them onto a 5nm/1,500 feet final for runway 12. They were then transferred to Croydon Approach to continue approach to that runway by means of SBA or VDF bearings down to the appropriate critical height, or to descend to the minimum altitude for a visual approach to another runway. Eight months later, at 2300 on 31st May 1960, Blackbushe Airport was also declared permanently closed, the majority of its larger commercial aircraft - Vikings, Hermes etc - following Croydon's Doves, Herons and Dakotas to Gatwick.

The increase in movement rates generated by Northolt's closure as a civil Airport at the end of 1954 is very obvious in these figures for the second half of the nineteen fifties.

Total Aircraft Movements

1954	79,649
1955	119,612
1956	122,952
1957	131,160
1958	129,497
1959	129,641

HELICOPTER ROUTES

A major re-shaping and reduction in size of the London Control Zone was promulgated by Notam 404/60. This took place on 12th June when the irregular five-sided Zone was replaced by a race-track shape centred on London Airport and extending fourteen miles east and west, and eight miles north and south. The vertical extent, however, remained unchanged, from ground level to flight level 110. In the same month helicopter routes were introduced, within and outside the Control Zone, which helicopters were required to follow in IMC but were also advised to follow in VMC. The routes, known as helicopter lanes, were not numbered at this stage and were simply referred to as 'the route to the south' etc. Flight without ATC clearance was permitted in IMC and VMC on the small section of route inside the Control Zone east of Battersea, although pilots were advised to communicate with ATC Westland Heliport. West of Battersea, however, it was necessary to obtain a special VFR clearance from Approach to use the routes in IMC, and in VMC pilots using the helicopter lane to the south were requested to communicate with Approach so that they could be identified on radar. It was also necessary to obtain a clearance in VMC to use the routes that passed north and south of the Airport since they involved flight within five miles of and below 2,000 feet above London Airport. The freedom to fly VFR in the new Control Zone was, however, short lived. Rule 21 of the Rules of the Air and Air Traffic Control Regulations 1960 was applied to the Zone from 1st March 1961, effectively requiring all aircraft to

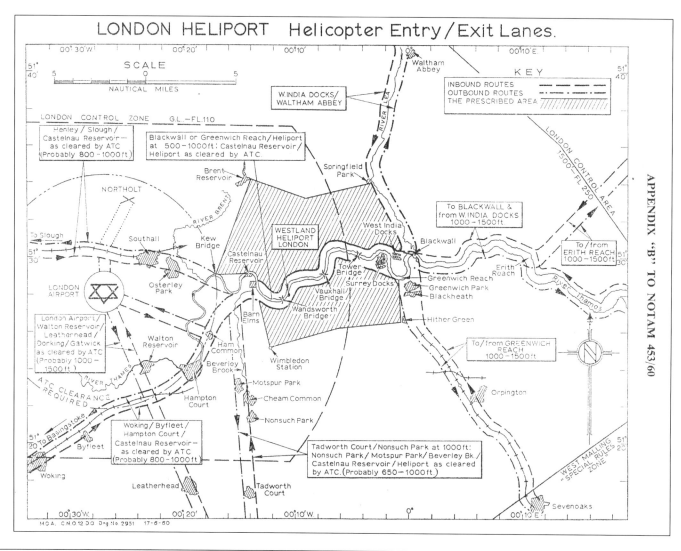

adhere to the full IFR requirements in all weather conditions unless exempted by a special VFR clearance.

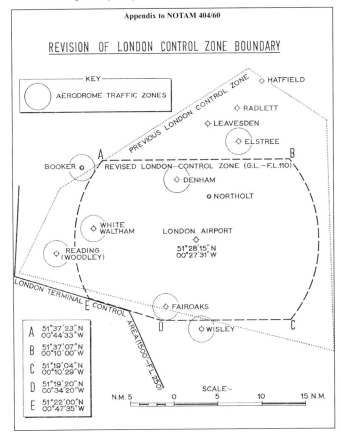

Appendix to NOTAM 404/60

REVISION OF LONDON CONTROL ZONE BOUNDARY

— KEY —

AERODROME TRAFFIC ZONES

PREVIOUS LONDON CONTROL ZONE

◇ HATFIELD

◇ RADLETT

◇ LEAVESDEN

◇ ELSTREE

A

B

BOOKER ○

REVISED LONDON CONTROL ZONE (G.L. – F.L. 110)

◇ DENHAM

○ NORTHOLT

◇ WHITE WALTHAM

LONDON AIRPORT
◇
51°28'15" N
00°27'31" W

◇ READING (WOODLEY)

LONDON TERMINAL CONTROL

E

AREA (1500 – FL 250)

◇ FAIROAKS

D

◇ WISLEY

C

A	51°37'23" N 00°44'33" W
B	51°37'07" N 00°10'00" W
C	51°19'04" N 00°10'29" W
D	51°19'20" N 00°34'20" W
E	51°22'00" N 00°47'35" W

N.M. 5   0   5   10   15 N.M.

SCALE:-

EXTENDING 28L/10R

Work began in mid 1960 to extend 28L/10R to the west, increasing its length from 9,576 feet to 11,000 feet. To protect the work force a ten feet high blast screen was erected 100 feet west of the existing 10R threshold, and since the in-line localiser for 28L could not be used a temporary localiser was provided from an off-set transmitter south of the runway. The effect of this two degree off-set was to keep aircraft slightly north of, but converging on, the runway's centre line to the middle marker where they came in line with the runway. 10R and 05L were restricted to daytime use only, the former being subject to weather conditions better than a cloud base of 500 feet and visibility one mile. So that the work could be completed the runway was closed on 15th September, allowing the existing runway lights and pit covers to be upgraded at the same time. A number of other works services were also undertaken. But the closure meant that, for a time, only 28R/10L and 23L/05R were available for use. On its return to service in the Spring of 1961 there were still certain temporary restrictions necessary to the use of the runway, due to the culverting of the Duke of Northumberland's and Longford rivers which lay approximately 300 feet west of the stub at the end of the runway. Cranes associated with the work caused displacement of the landing threshold of 10R and restrictions to take-off weights on 28L, and the rivers themselves presented a potential hazard to any aircraft over-running the runway to the west until the culverting was complete. Initially it was made clear that the extension had been added primarily for the use of larger jet aircraft and a warning was given that its indiscriminate use by other types might adversely affect the

movement rate by reducing ATC flexibility. But later in 1961, when all work on and around the runway had been finished, this restriction was removed in order to alleviate noise nuisance to communities east of the Airport.

1960 also saw the declaration of a Clearway of 500 feet available for take-offs on 28R, extending the take-off distance to 9,812 feet. By informing ATC and the Police one hour before ETD pilots could arrange for the closure of the perimeter road, enabling them to use the maximum possible take-off distance. Aircraft were not only becoming larger they were also increasing in numbers, and the movement total for 1960 was 146,506.

MINIMUM NOISE ROUTEINGS

In a further effort to reduce noise disturbance to local residents a noise abatement exercise was carried out in May and June of 1961 during which all aircraft departing from the Airport in certain directions followed specified routeings. This established that significant reductions in noise levels could be achieved, and so a system of minimum noise routeings was developed and introduced on an experimental basis on 21st August 1961. These applied to all aircraft but were laid down only for the main runways (10R, 28R, 28L) from which the large majority of departures took place. Departures from the two preferred departure runways, 28R and 10R, generally used the reciprocal ILS middle marker for the start of their turn, with subsequent headings chosen to keep the aircraft away from the more populated areas, and pilots were advised that use of these routeings did not absolve them from carrying out the noise abatement take-off techniques in current use. Although the routeings were compatible with normal ATC requirements they could be varied when considered necessary for individual aircraft. With just two minor detail changes the minimum noise routeings became permanent in July 1962.

ATCO CADET SCHEME

Another important landmark in 1961 was the introduction of the ATCO Cadetship scheme. Until then the majority of ATCOs came directly or indirectly from the Services, with only a very small number of assistants able to satisfy the requirements of promotion boards, but this source of supply was drying up and a new approach to recruitment was vital. In fact the employment of so many people of similar age from the Services after the War would also present problems related to promotion prospects and a retirement 'bulge', but a feeling of continuity existed among the ATCOs at London Airport where most, if not all, had been Air Force pilots or navigators. The assistants, however, were from more varied backgrounds which allowed a certain class barrier to exist. It was not unusual to go on a break and to find the controllers sitting at one table in the canteen and the assistants at another, though this may at times have been a deliberate effort to avoid having to listen again to a particular ATCO's oft repeated reminiscences of Service escapades. But as the progeny of the Cadet courses began to arrive, many of them ex ATCA grade, so the gap became less and less noticeable. Among the first Cadets to arrive at London Airport were Chris Barrows and Dave Carney from course 2 and Colin Ward and Alan Hickman from course 3

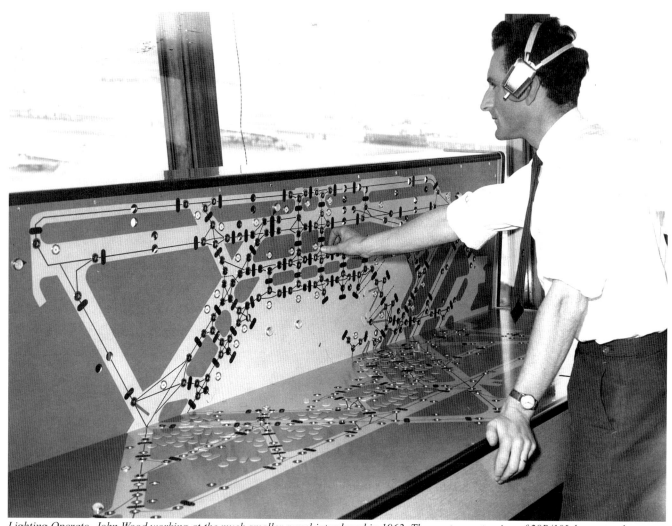

Lighting Operato, John Wood working at the much smaller panel introduced in 1962. The western extension of 28R/10L has yet to be constructed. (via John Wood)

NEW EQUIPMENT

The early 1960s saw a number of significant equipment changes in the VCR and Approach Control, some reflecting improved technology and some made necessary by increased operational demands. June 1962 saw the start of work to replace the original lighting panel with a much

Following the introduction of the smaller lighting panel the Tower ATCAs were relocated to the south east corner of the VCR, together with the Lamson tube terminal. ATCA Margot Trickett is seen here in 1963. (CAA Archives)

smaller unit on which route selection was made by pressing buttons flush-mounted on a diagramatic presentation of the Airport. The change-over, as might be expected, took several months and at times required non-standard routeings for aircraft at night when lighting in a particular area was disconnected. The contraction of the panel made space available on the eastern side of the VCR, which was put to good use. The assistant who had sat at the northern end of the 'Air' desks was relocated, with the Lamson tubes, at a new desk on the south-eastern side of the VCR, shared with the other assistant. Meanwhile, downstairs in Approach, equally important changes were taking place. Increased requests for Special VFR clearances within the Control Zone meant that provision had to be made for a dedicated Special VFR position to off-load traffic from the No.1 Director, and the introduction into service of the PAR2000 radar allowed the talk-down staff to become resident in the room instead of going out to the GCA truck when required. Intended as a replacement for the precision element of the GCA this radar, like the ACR6, had been developed to a joint civil / military requirement, and both had been intended to be air transportable (by the Blackburn Beverley). Designed by our own Tels Engineering staff it was a 3 cm equipment providing display facilities in Approach Control. The basic radar equipment (aerials, transmitters, receivers etc) was housed in a trailer known as the Airfield Vehicle, which was accurately positioned in relation to the ILS reference point of the runway in use. Radar data from this vehicle was fed over normal telephone lines to the Tels equipment room, and thence to the Approach room. The radar

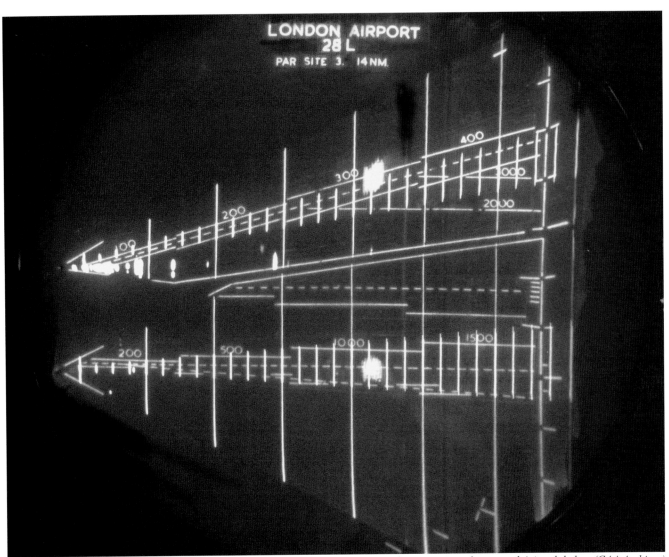

The 28L PAR 2000 picture with an aircraft 8½ miles from touchdown. Elevation information is at the top and Azimuth below (CAA Archives)

By 1963 the PAR Consoles (right) had joined the line up in Approach Control. Mobile chairs and at least some carpet had arrived too. The 'Courage Cockerel' mascot presides over operations....! (CAA Archives)

Early 1960s view of the Federal GCA Truck beside 28R with a Vickers Vanguard departing. (CAA Archives)

consoles each housed two 12 inch CRTs, one with a fourteen mile range, the other three miles, and both showed azimuth and elevation information. Controls were provided for servoeing the aerials to maintain the optimum aircraft/permanent echo responses through the approach. For obvious reasons the landing rate achieved on PAR was lower than that on ILS, and its primary use was to monitor approaches to the main runways in poor visibility although it could still become the main approach aid on occasions when the ILS was not available. Bill Woodruff, the ATCO i/c, was so enthusiastic about this new equipment that he arranged a PAR course for himself!

Another radar also came into service at about this time. Delays to departures from London Airport had been significantly reduced when the 50cm AMES Type 11 was brought into service at the Southern Centre. Prior to this, heavy clutter close in on the MEW 10 cm radar - affecting fifteen miles to the west and twenty miles to the south west - had made it impossible to provide an efficient service to outbound traffic but on the 50 cm radar departures were visible soon after take-off. Although the Type 11 had been rejected by the military, Marconi were developing their S232 (based on the Type 11) as a private venture and since the cost of this radar was half that of the ACR6 a decision was made to modify the plans for radars at London Airport. Instead of a duplicated ACR6 service this 50 cm radar would be provided as backup for the ACR6 already in use. The 232, and later the higher powered S264, were used in normal operations for the longer range planning of the approach sequence with the more precise vectoring carried out on the 10 cm radars. The target size and tangental fade were problems with the 50 cm radar but an advantage was that it was only affected by the heaviest weather. One of the delights of training on radar was the need to carry out SRAs with this equipment, which was like vectoring snow balls. A console was also installed in the VCR for general monitoring of traffic in the vicinity of the Airport. This stood on the western side of the VCR, behind the central dais.

PREFERENTIALS - AND MIXED MODE?

Continued efforts to reduce the noise disturbance caused by aircraft operations at London Airport resulted in the introduction of the Preferential System of Runway Selection on 15th February 1962. After discussion with operators it was agreed that a down wind component averaging three knots, and with a maximum not normally exceeding five knots, was acceptable for the continued use of 28R and 28L in preference to 10R and 10L. Subsidiary runways would not normally be considered for use until the cross wind on the main runways exceeded fifteen knots. Pilots could still ask for permission to use the runway into wind, both landing and taking off, but would obviously have to accept that delay might occur in accommodating their request.

Ways of increasing the Airport's landing capacity were also being considered. One possible solution was the use of mixed mode parallel operations although observations of the accuracy of turn-ons to the ILS were not promising. As a data gathering exercise a trial to determine how accurately final approach could be flown was begun on 1st October. Rather predictably, one might say, the results proved that pilots could do much better when they knew they were being watched, and this encouraged continued development of procedures aimed at an operational trial.

LEAVESDEN/GARSTON

Adjustments continued to be made to the boundaries of the London TMA and to adjacent airways to improve separation between inbound and outbound routes, and between terminal and through traffic. This particularly affected the eastern half of the TMA and resulted in a number of revisions to routes into and out of London Airport. It was also now, late in 1962, that the Leavesden VOR was brought into service replacing Watford NDB as the northern holding

The VCR early in the 1960s. The pedestal binoculars survive some 40 years later! Bill Broadmore is identifiable on the left. (CAA Archives)

facility. This was, incidentally, the first holding pattern in the TMA to be based overhead a VOR. Watford continued to be used by outbound traffic where applicable, and was also designated as the stand-by for periods when Leavesden was out of service. However, the name Leavesden was found to cause R/T confusion, and the name of the VOR was changed to Garston on 9th May 1963. Lowest holding level was 5,000 feet.

Other noteworthy events that occurred in 1962 include the change of the identification letters of the Air Light Beacon situated on the southern boundary of the Airport from VA to LH. This was done at the same time at a number of other Airports, including Manchester (from ZM to MC), Hurn (VH to HR) and Glasgow Renfrew (from ZG to RF), so that the identities could be as self evident as possible. Also out on the Airport VASIs were installed on runways 05R and 23L - the latter set at a 3.5 degree glide slope due to the gas holder 2.5 nms from touchdown - and elevated sodium lighting was fitted along the edges of the two main runways for use in snow. Being omni-directional these offered certain advantages over the other runway lights, and could be particularly useful - at any time of the year - when positioning aircraft downwind for a visual final, by offering a continuous reference. Which provides as good a link as any that may arise to one particular visual approach a few years later, recalled by Alan Carter who was the Approach Controller to Kevin Staunton as No.1 Director. It was normal for a heading of 140 degrees to be given off the northerly stack for the westerly runways (in this case 28R) but after a brief exchange in Gaelic between Kevin and the pilot of an inbound Aer Lingus Viscount Alan was told to give a heading of 170. Descent was given with Alan expecting the aircraft to be turned out onto a more easterly heading to allow a reasonable length final. However, the aircraft continued on a very tight base leg - so tight that the Air Controller, Keith Waud, rang to enquire if there was helicopter traffic operating on H9 - and turned well inside the outer marker, landing some way down the runway. Kevin now

announced that he would need to take a short break and, when asked why, admitted that he had bet the Aer Lingus pilot that he would not be able to keep the approach inside the middle marker, and would now have to settle his debt.

'CIGARETTE' FOR LIGHT AIRCRAFT

Increases in scheduled traffic using the Airport had made restrictions to non-scheduled flights inevitable and at the beginning of 1963 the period 0800 to 1000 was made unavailable for take-offs and the period 1600 to 1800 unavailable for landings by this type of traffic, although these hours were constantly subject to revision to reflect seasonal variations in traffic density. In addition the Airport was 'prior permission only' to non-scheduled flights from one week before until one week after any public holiday. Further requirements, which applied to single engined and light twin engined aircraft operating on Special VFR clearances, were introduced in February 1963. Four entry/exit points were designated - Pyrford, Redroad Hill, 1.5 nms SE of Wokingham and 1 nm NW of Marlow - with a warning that aircraft operating into and out of the Airport Special VFR should be prepared for delay due to the difficulty of fitting them into the main traffic flow. So that these aircraft could be readily distinguished it was made mandatory for the pilot to include the code word 'Cigarette' in his first call to Approach. The type of flight and type of aircraft had also to be included, so the initial transmission became, for example, 'Cigarette International Gemini G-AKHZ'.

NORTH EAST PARK AND NEW DRIs

In the VCR this was a quiet period, with construction work on the Airport to the north east and south east of the Tower providing the major interest. The taxiway through the original south east face (block 62) was closed by the construction of a pier from the southern end of the Terminal

Local Standby! Vickers Vanguard G-APEI approaches 28L one September morning in 1964 with #2 Rolls-Royce Tyne feathered. Note the vortices from the outboard engines and flaps. (Brian M Service)

building, effectively transforming this part of the parking area into a cul - de - sac with entry from the north. And a new parking apron, east of the northern end of runway 33R/15L, provided six new stands (85 to 90) in what was named the 'north east park'. New experimental DRIs also began to appear from November 1963, made necessary by the large areas of apron and taxiway that were being created. They were sited beside the stop bar on a taxiway and consisted of a set of illuminated green arrows, the appropriate arrow occulting to indicate the correct route to take. Two red lights associated with the group were lit if an aircraft was required to stop. The intention was to extend the use of this type of DRI to all areas under construction and to locations where DRI boards carried too much complicated information or presented clearance problems. Towards the end of 1964 another form of daylight route indication was also tried out experimentally in block 48(N). The existing green centre line lights were modified to provide two modes of operation, the standard green centre line lights or, for daylight and low visibility, high powered white xenon discharge lights flashing simultaneously throughout the whole block with a repetition rate of 90 flashes per minute. Pilots at this time were obviously an undisciplined bunch, having to be given several Notamed warnings of the need to follow the routes indicated by the DRIs, and not to wander off at random in different directions and then complain of 'reds ahead'.

Pilots also contributed to the failure of a trial which began on 4th June 1964, which was designed to reduce R/T communications in the period immediately after take-off. Prior to take-off pilots were instructed to call London Radar on the appropriate frequency 90 seconds after commencing the take-off run, and were required to maintain a listening watch on the Tower frequency until this time. But this latter they often failed to do, with obvious safety implications if traffic overshot from the parallel runway as they rolled, or if for any other reason the take-off had to be aborted. The period of 90 seconds, incidentally, was chosen so that the departure would check in with London Radar approximately one minute after becoming airborne enabling radar identification to be effected within three miles.

APPROACH REORGANISATION AND PARALLELS

1964 was particularly notable for two events, the publication of the Radley Report on ATCO working conditions and pay, which although it was a national issue obviously affected Heathrow ATCOs, and a full operational trial of parallel landing procedures. In April 1962 the ATCEU had been approached by Headquarters Section CP3 and asked to develop procedures and a new layout for the Approach room, suitable for parallel runway operations which, it was thought, would be necessary to cope with expected traffic demand on a more or less continuous basis during the summer peak periods of 1966. An essential feature of the re-organisation of Approach was, of course, that normal daily operations could continue while it was done. Fortunately, since Approach Control only occupied half of the available floor space on the 6th floor, the EU were able to plan a layout using the whole space of which a half, consisting of not less than the current positions, could be engineered in the vacant half while operations continued from the existing positions. ATC could then move across to continue operations as before from the new positions and leave the old half free for dismantling and re-engineering. Finally, with works completed, the entire room would be available with a layout suitable for operating parallel procedures. This layout was accepted by DCO and the winter of 1964/65 was allocated for actual re-engineering.

However, before this work was started, an operational trial of the parallel landing procedures devised by the EU was carried out. The promulgated starting date was 7th May 1964 but this had to be delayed to 1st June because of a delay in the production of revised video maps for the PAR and ACR6 radars. The trial continued until the 30th September. A number of compromises had to be made by ATC, in the existing room layout, equipment, and in the procedures devised by the EU, but this was considered acceptable. It was decided that the first exercises should take place at the beginning of afternoon watches so that the new procedures could initially be operated under relatively light traffic conditions. The first exercises for each Watch were also confined to the 28 runways to avoid the possible complication of confusion with traffic working Southern ATCC through Woodley when the 10 runways were in use. Other factors which influenced the decision to operate or cancel on a particular day were:-

(1)   weather - visibility not less than 5 nms and cloud base not below 3,500 feet.

(2)   equipment availability - the ACR6 was required for directing, the S264 for DFTI, both 28 ILS equipments and both PARs.

(3)   staff - two supervisors and fourteen ATCOs (eleven essential operating positions plus three for co-ordinating and relief duties). GMP, GMC and two Air positions were necessary in the VCR and the line up in Approach was Assistant Approach, Approach, No.1 Director, Epsom No.2, Garston No.2, Garston PAR, Epsom PAR. During trial periods the Special VFR position was occupied by the Garston No.2 with Special VFR traffic shared between the two No.2 Directors.

The procedures proposed by the ATCEU envisaged stacks at Weybridge to the south and Chalfont to the north, but Tels were unable to find suitable sites for the VORs. Epsom and Garston were expected to be unsuitable as stack positions for parallel landings since a rectangular traffic pattern was considered essential for establishing vertical separation on base leg and also to enable a shallow (20 degree) ILS intercept heading. And this proved to be the case on westerlies where Approach were confined by restrictive headings off both stacks. For the 28 runways traffic from Epsom descended to 3,000 feet and from Garston to 2,000 feet, turning base leg after passing 3,000 feet. On easterlies it was Epsom traffic that descended to the lower altitude of 2,500 feet (White Waltham circuit height 1,500 feet) so that departures to Woodley routeing south of the Airport could achieve vertical separation above the inbounds more readily. ILS intercept range would ideally have permitted a short period of straight and level flight but this could only be achieved on westerlies (11 nms) with the lower intercept altitudes, and spacing used was seven miles. Interestingly a turn on to the localiser given by ATC was found to be more accurate than either autocouple or a manual turn on by the pilot. Two new frequencies were made available, 120.1 Mcs for GCA and 121.25 Mcs for the second Air position, which gave this sequence for inbound traffic

Garston Traffic to Runway 28R/10L
119.2 Mcs	No.1 Director
118.5 Mcs	Garston No.2
119.5 Mcs	Garston PAR
118.2 Mcs	Air
121.9 Mcs	GMC

Epsom Traffic to Runway 28L/10R
119.2 Mcs	No.1 Director
120.4 Mcs	Epsom No.2
120.1 Mcs	Epsom PAR
121.25 Mcs	Air
121.9 Mcs	GMC

As a result of these trials a number of recommendations were made which, it was felt, were necessary to obtain the maximum benefit from mixed mode operations. Among these were a westward extension of controlled airspace, data links including a CCTV stack indicator and an 'Inbound Release' display between London Airport and the Southern Centre, and the implementation of the new Approach room layout. Concern was also voiced over the ability of SATCC to handle an increased departure flow.

RADLEY

While these trials were in progress a committee chaired by Sir Gordon Radley KCB, CBE, PhD, MIEE was appointed by the Minister of Aviation (on 26th June) 'to examine, and report on, the structure and conditions of service of the ATCO class and the basis on which its pay should be determined in relation to its duties'. There had been discontent in the ATCO ranks for some time and the situation had deteriorated since 1962 when the Civil Service Arbitration Tribunal made a pay award that was not only much less than had been claimed, but also broke a salary relationship with the Executive Class that ATCOs thought well established. The situation took a further turn for the worse early in 1964 when negotiations broke down on the issues of hours, and pay for shift disturbances. Eighteen units, including London, were visited by members of the Committee, who found the causes of the grievances to be both numerous and complex. These causes could be conveniently divided into two groups. Group One contained what might fairly be called the overt causes - structure, career prospects, pay, hours of work, payment for shift working and superannuation. Group Two contained a number of issues that had not been the subject of formal representations from either party but many of which appeared to present formidable difficulties for Management. These included amongst others fears over the annual medical with its threat of loss of licence, the difficulties imposed by shortfalls in recruitment and limitations of training capacity during a period of increasing demand, dissatisfaction with the limited employment of ATCOs in non-operational planning posts, and manifest shortcomings in many aspects of personnel management, particularly leadership, which exacerbated every issue and turned minor complaints into major difficulties.

The report was presented on 7th December 1964 and recognised the limitations of the ATCO grade structure. A new ATCO4 grade was recommended, to cover the period when an officer was undergoing his initial training and gaining experience of basic non-radar duties, from which promotion to ATCO3 would be automatic on radar validation. ATCO3 would continue to be the main operational grade, with a long pay scale, and ATCO2 would be the career grade of the Class (at the time of the Enquiry only 67 of the 950 ATCOs in the Class were above the rank of ATCO2). A reduction of hours worked from the then 44 hours net per week to the levels worked by the Civil Service office staff and a substantial pay rise were also advocated, the latter re-establishing the pay link with the Executive Class.

GRADE	PAY RANGE ON 15.7.64	SCALE RECOMMENDED
Chief ATCO	3385 - 3900	3385 - 3900
Deputy Director	2645 - 3325	2645 - 3325
Senior ATCO	2559 - 2795	2882
ATCO1	2117 - 2240	2582
ATCO2	1743 - 2036	2000 - 2353
ATCO3	935 - 1730	1100 - 1900
ATCO4		889 - 1497
ATCO CADET		580 - 878

The recommendations contained in the report were a welcome attempt to resolve the problems affecting the ATCO grade. Bud Aitchison and Stewart MacKinnon, who were the Unit IPCS (Institution of Professional Civil Servants) representatives at the time, worked out that the reduction of hours was equivalent to twenty eight days extra leave each year and duly presented this suggestion to the ATCO i/c Ray Kirk, who threw them out of his office. However, the ATCOs at London Airport did subsequently receive nine extra days leave per year in line with controllers at the Southern Centre.

WRONG AIRPORT!

The proximity of London Airport to Northolt and the alignment of their runways had, on a number of occasions, caused pilots to mis-identify their intended destinations. Pilots closing the centre line of Northolt's runway 26 from the right were directly in line with London's runway 23, and closing from the left for London's 23 would see Northolt's runway 26 in front of them. Further confusion resulted from the existence of gas-holders on the approach to each of these runways at approximately the same distance from touchdown. Despite monitoring of aircraft final approaches there were inevitably some that 'got away', of which perhaps the best known is the Pan American Boeing 707 N725PA en route from Frankfurt to London Airport which actually landed at Northolt on 25th October 1960. Heavy braking by Captain Warren Beall just kept the aircraft from over-running the runway, and getting it out again was pretty exciting too! On 28th April 1964 a Lufthansa 707 D-ABOT was similarly confused, but fortunately was retrieved, overshooting from low altitude. Nor was mistaken identity confined to London and Northolt. Sitting on radar less than a week after the latter incident Bob Cook transferred a Spanish Air Force C-54 to Northolt on final approach to runway 26, but feared the worst when the aircraft disappeared from radar shortly afterwards. He was in the process of alerting SATCC when he heard a faint call from the aircraft saying that it could not contact Northolt and asking for taxying instructions. It had landed at Hendon! Peter Bruce-Smith was involved in a very similar incident with an Indian Air Force Super Constellation which he positioned onto final for runway 26 three times. On each occasion the pilot called 'visual' and then made a rapid descent with the obvious intention of landing at Hendon. PBS was able, with swift intervention, to prevent the aircraft landing and when, on the fourth approach, the pilot again called 'visual' PBS quickly replied 'Negative. This time I shall tell you when you are visual'. Within two months of the Lufthansa incident the letters LH and an arrow pointing to runway 23L had been painted on the north east side of the Southall gas holder, and the letters NO and an arrow pointing to runway 26 had been similarly painted on the north east side of the gas holder at South Harrow. The letters and arrows were white and thirty feet high.

During his cadetship Peter Wilde spent some time at Heathrow, training in Aerodrome Control. One Saturday morning in 1964 he was invited by Ray Mapleson, one of the ATCAs, to accompany him to an event at Denham Flying Club which was taking place that afternoon. Although he had no transport of his own he accepted Ray's offer of a lift and spent a very pleasant afternoon at the Club, only to realise that time had passed too quickly and that he risked being late for his night shift. Somewhat embarrassed he asked if he could have an urgent lift back to Heathrow but Ray seemed unperturbed by the problem and said that there was plenty of time. A few minutes later they climbed into a Piper Tri-Pacer, got airborne in the Denham circuit and called Heathrow Approach for joining clearance, which was duly given. Having obtained clearance to cross the 28R approach behind other landing traffic they landed on 28L and taxied back to the runway caravan where Peter was met by the ATC van to be brought into the Tower in good time for his duty.

THE INNER AND OUTER ARE BORN.....

Before ownership and management of London (Heathrow) Airport - as it was by now known - were transferred to the British Airports Authority on 1st April 1966 work was undertaken to extend 28L/10R to its planned final length of 12,000 feet (3,658 metres). A similar technique to that used for the first section of the extension was used - a blast screen to protect the contractors and their equipment, and an offset localiser for 28L until the in-line localiser could be restored. Work began early in 1965 and by the end of the year the extension and its associated taxiways were ready for use. Meanwhile, in the Central Area, the block numbering system was under review and at the end of the year a decision was made to change the suffix letters from N(North) and S(South) to I(Inner) and O(Outer), to indicate the inner and outer taxiways. This, it was felt, would better describe the developing system even though it would not be completed for some years. To assist pilots to recognise the respective taxiways the block number boards would be colour coded - black figures in a white square on either a red surround for the inner, a blue surround for the outer or yellow surround for other areas. Work was also taking place at the south west end of the apron in front of the Terminal building to create the first purpose built cul - de - sac (later to be the 'Foxtrot' apron).

Apart from minor revisions to the boundaries of the Control Zone the only change to procedures worthy of note in 1965 was the introduction, towards the end of the year, of measures intended to reduce the noise nuisance caused by large aircraft flying at low level inside the Zone. Special VFR flight had been designed to enable pilots unable to comply with the instrument flight rules to penetrate IFR control zones, and in the case of the London CTR was intended for light aircraft only. However, it was not unusual to see much larger aircraft - even the VC-10 - issued with Special VFR clearances at low altitude, and this was now controlled by imposing a weight limit of 12,500 lbs. A minimum altitude of 1,500 feet was also introduced for the sector of the Zone between 020 degrees (T) and 140 degrees (T) from the Airport (except for helicopters on the published routes) due to its heavily built up nature.

STANDARD INSTRUMENT DEPARTURES

In contrast the next two or three years, during which the metamorphosis of Approach Control (per the ATCEU plan) took place, saw a number of developments in procedures and equipment which were very necessary if ATC was to keep on top of the ever-increasing demand - movements for 1965 totalled 206,336. A significant step forward was made on the 2nd June 1966 when Standard Instrument Departure Clearances (SIDs) were introduced, initially on a trial basis but later to become permanent. The advantages of the SID were seen to be threefold:-

(1)   A reduction of R/T loading for both ATC and pilots.
(2)   The streamlining of ATC procedures.
(3)   The incorporation, in tabular form, of comprehensive routeings including MNRs, intermediate TMA reporting points and altitudes, and basic ATC instructions applicable to any given direction of take-off. This would enable individual routes to be identified by a simple reference.

The content of a typical clearance was considerably reduced from (existing clearance) : 'G-AMON is cleared to Le Bourget via Airway Amber One to cross Fairoaks above 3,000 feet, Dunsfold 4,000 feet, to climb when instructed by radar to maintain flight level xxx' to (SID clearance): 'G-AMON is cleared to Le Bourget, Seaford departure, flight level xxx'. The introduction of SIDs was relatively trouble free, and the significant reduction of R/T was of real benefit to the clearance delivery position which, by now, was continuously

manned through the day. Minor problems arose when a pilot did not understand or was unaware of the new procedures, and needed the clearance read out in full, and there were instances where crews misunderstood the restrictions of the SID and climbed above the initial 4,000 feet limit without clearance. Martin Johnson, a friend of Bill McColl and a First Officer on BEA Tridents, was involved in one such incident as he returned to Heathrow one day. Approaching Epsom from the south he was 1,000 feet above and catching a British Eagle Britannia which disappeared into cloud as it neared the beacon. It's easy to imagine his concern when the Britannia shortly afterwards reported an airmiss with a Caravelle which had just climbed through his level.

Also on the 2nd June tighter restrictions were imposed on the speeds (at times excessive) flown by inbounds to Heathrow, to comply with new ICAO recommendations. Speed limit points were introduced at Biggin, Dunsfold and Woodley for Epsom and at Beacon Hill, Brookmans Park and Woodley for Garston, by which aircraft inbound to the holding areas had to have reduced to 240 knots or less unless they were capable of rapid speed reduction. Holding and intermediate approach speeds were also defined, but as yet no specific speeds were laid down for final approach, although aircraft might at times be asked to increase or decrease speed to maintain separation.

DISTANCE FROM TOUCHDOWN INDICATOR (DFTI)

New pieces of equipment started to appear. In the VCR the Distance From Touchdown Indicator (DFTI),

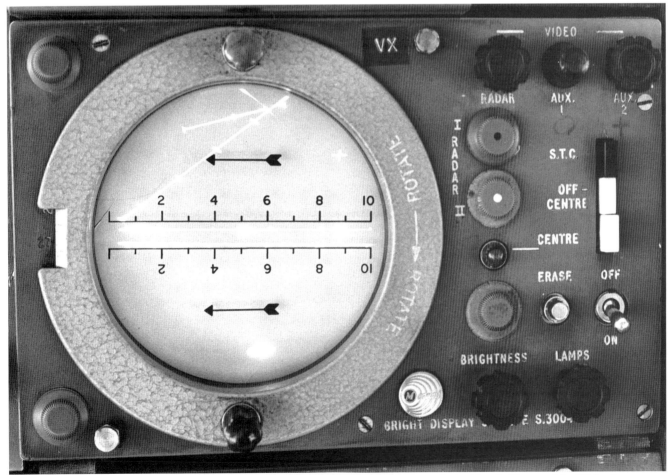

The Marconi Distance From Touchdown Indicator (DFTI) with information fed by the S264 50cm Radar. Note the blip size of the 28R landers....
(Pete Bish)

considered necessary by the ATCEU for mixed mode operations, appeared in the form of a Marconi 5 inch diameter display. The radar picture was taken from the 50cm S264 and was bright enough to be clearly visible in all ambient light levels. Although the display could be centred it was normally off-centred to show final approach out to ten miles. A graticule, calibrated in ranges to touchdown, had to be rotated to the bearing of the runway required and was not too satisfactory when a combination of main and subsidiary runways were in use. Video mapped information from the S264 was also displayed. The only slight operational disadvantage of this equipment was a tendency to 'flood', but an erase button was provided to remove this.

CLOSED CIRCUIT TELEVISION (CCTV)

At about the same time Approach saw the arrival of closed circuit television (CCTV), to display weather actuals and to provide stack information to LATCC. An interesting feature of the Met system was that the insertion of the display board in front of the camera automatically triggered a still camera to record the display for possible use at an enquiry. It also initiated a flashing alert signal at each display to draw the attention of the controller to the new information. This continued to flash until it was acknowledged. The stack display CCTV, which provided LATCC with an up to date picture of the situation at both stacks without the need for constant telephone coordination, greatly improved release procedures and was the first step towards removing the 'phones' man in Approach. Coordination now became one way with releases being passed based on what was seen to be happening in the stacks. Two cameras were used, one for each stack, with a third camera available as an immediate reserve, and these were focused on the image of the flight progress board reflected in a mirror mounted above the flight progress strips. In addition to the displays at LATCC monitors were also provided in Approach and in Telemove, for information on inbound flights. What was not known by most people was that, at some later stage, a monitor was also installed in BEA Ops, this only coming to light when one day they phoned to say how much they had enjoyed the copy of 'Playboy' magazine that the Approach controller had been reading over the display in a quiet period. For the technically minded the Met system was by EPSYLON (type CCV1) and the stack system by Vidi-aids, and both were 625 line, 50 frames interlaced.

A few months later, in the Spring of 1967, a third radar service was introduced. Provided as a backup for the ACR6 the Plessey AR1 was also a ten centimetre system, with a rotation rate of 15 rpm. One of its novel features was the facility to operate with its dual transmitters in frequency diversity for an increase in performance of between 15 and 20 per cent. A staggered PRF system gave a first blind velocity of 540 knots, as compared with the 83 knots of the ACR6. Before coming to Heathrow it had been with TEE at Gatwick, and a number of modifications needed to be made to improve its low level cover before it was accepted operationally at Heathrow.

AERODROME TERMINAL INFORMATION SERVICE (ATIS)

On 3rd July 1967 a new service was introduced for arriving traffic. The Aerodrome Terminal Information Service (ATIS) gave pilots of inbound aircraft weather information, routine ATC messages and short term AIS information and was broadcast on the Biggin and Garston VOR frequencies. This relieved the Approach controller of a rather onerous part of his duties and, of course, freed valuable R/T time. A similar service for departures was brought in early in 1969 using a discrete frequency 121.85 Mcs, and from this time both services were known as Automatic Terminal Information Service to conform with ICAO terminology. The Arrival ATIS was recorded on wall-mounted equipment close to the Approach Supervisor's desk and was provided with a hood to reduce unwanted additions to the broadcast from the room generally or from noisy passers-by as the recording was made. This hood found another use after ATIS hours. Night Watches at this time saw a large number of ATC staff on duty. Two ATCOs and an assistant were required for each half in Approach and the VCR, and in addition there was a Supervisor and two lighting operators. It was quite normal for people to take a break by visiting the other Ops room and in the early hours of the morning an order would be taken for food from the canteen resulting some time later in the distribution of various toasted delicacies (a particular favourite being the toasted sausage sandwich) amongst the staff. The canteen, incidentally, had a very cosmopolitan night-time clientele largely of Asian, African and Caribbean extraction and there was always voluble discussion, and quite often disagreement, to be listened to while waiting for the Air Traffic order to be completed. Visits to the Ops room by Tels staff to carry out equipment checks and by the cleaners all helped to maintain a certain level of noise, but one night Alan Hickman and Brian Smith were making rather more than the usual disturbance and this resulted in an irate Supervisor, Jimmy Birchall, surfacing from his office - located at the northern end of the Approach room - pyjama-clad to ask for a reduction of decibels. After this Jimmy used to remove the ATIS hood and sleep with his head inside it to reduce extraneous noise.

Development work had, by now, begun on the Cargo Area south of 28L/10R together with the associated taxiway from block 79 to block 90. Construction of the tunnel from the Central Area to the Cargo Area was also well under way. To enable the taxiway to be linked to 28L/10R and 33L/15R a number of runway closures were necessary and these affected not only these two runways but also 23R/05L which was not available for most of October and November 1967. The BAA made the most of this by using the runway for daytime parking - primarily BEA Argosies -and then returning it for use as a night time taxiway. But one night, before the runway had been handed back for use, an Egyptair flight taxiing out for departure left the green route that had been selected for him and taxied onto this uninspected area. The pilot's error was, naturally, noticed but as there was no chance to correct it the aircraft was allowed to continue to the holding point and transferred to the Air Controller. Just as the aircraft was lining up a BAA Inspection vehicle reported that the Egyptair had hit a set of steps as it taxied down 23R, so the aircraft aborted its take-off and returned to stand where the passengers were off-loaded pending a visual inspection of the aircraft for damage.

Reports were submitted by the Egyptair Captain who blamed ATC, and by the GMC controller who blamed the Egyptair Captain, but it was unfortunately not possible to refer to the R/T recording, which somehow had been erased. Three years later a letter arrived at Heathrow via the Foreign Office with a demand from the Egyptian Government for reimbursement of £42-12-00d for fourteen meals in the 'Pie in the Sky' restaurant, Terminal 3, incurred due to the negligence of the GMC controller, Mr Alan Hickman! When completed late in 1968 the Cargo Terminal provided thirty aircraft stands (300 to 329), all equipped with hydrant refuelling.

Experience gained over the eighteen months or so since their introduction had proved the value of SIDs to pilots and ATC, and so, in March 1968, they were made standard practice. By now the SID consisted of a designator followed by a number - introduced in November 1967- so that the Seaford departure became a Seaford One departure. As yet there was no element in the SID title to indicate the runway in use for take-off. A number of detail changes were made to the Heathrow SIDs at this time to reflect changes in MNRs and the operational introduction of the Detling VOR.

FULL WIDTH APPROACH ROOM

A variety of developments took place in 1968 and these included the eagerly awaited unveiling of the full width Approach room. This year also saw the arrival of the first female ATCO to achieve full Unit validation. Prior to this a number of female Cadets had passed through during their courses but they were only permitted to achieve Unit endorsements (enabling limited solo work) having not yet obtained their 'yellow perils'. Amongst those was Anna Caush, who arrived in 1966, but resigned later that year to start a family. Sue Williams, later to re-marry as Sue Clifford, was therefore a first when she validated in Aerodrome Control on 20th December, just three months after arriving at Heathrow. Her arrival from Cadet course 7 presented some problems as no provision had been made for female ATCOs to sleep on night duties - unless they were prepared to share the male ATCO dormitory on the 7th floor - but this was over-come by allocating to her the room originally planned as the GMC viewing balcony, by now known as the 'four and a half'. Sue would later take two six month breaks for pregnancy, in 1974 and 1977, so is also remarkable for having validated in Approach and Aerodrome Control three times during her record 36 years at Heathrow.

Staffing levels at this time reflected Civil Service attitude and were quite generous. A Watch list from 1967 shows one Watch with seventeen fully trained assistants with four more U/T, but there were times when all positions were manned and busy as a result of the high manual workload. However, early in 1968, the requirement was cut by four per Watch when ATC staff were withdrawn from the Runway Caravans, which had become an increasingly expensive luxury as aircrew and ATC techniques improved. For a short while, until the arrival of transmissometers, BAA staff took over the responsibility for taking RVRs but ATC were still required to move the Caravan from site to site for insurance reasons.

A new piece of equipment appeared in Flight Clearance to replace the Type 11 strip printer, a rather bulky machine that had been in use for some time. Type 11 strips for outbound flights appeared from the back of the machine and had to be guillotined off, then sent to the Tower by Lamson tube. The new 'Hermes' printer produced a strip in the VCR as well as strips at the Centre (one for the departure airfield plus others for en-route reporting points). The Type 11 was not

June 1968 view of the full width (and fully staffed) Approach Room. (CAA Archives)

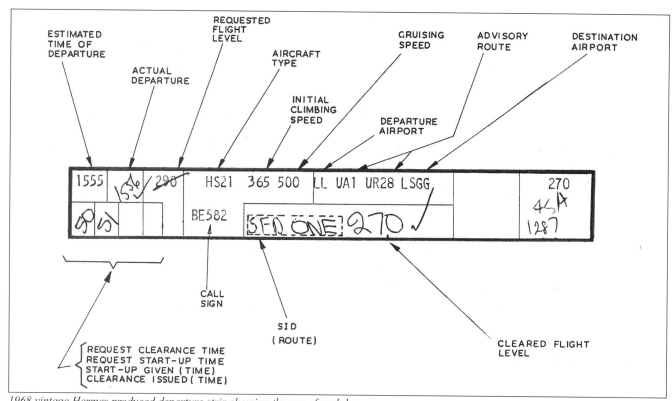

1968 vintage Hermes produced departure strip showing the use of each box.

removed, however, but retained as a backup for several years.

It was in Approach, though, that the most dramatic change occurred when the full width room was made available for use, with working positions and facilities suitable for parallel operations. The two halves of the room were mirror images of each other and, from north to south, the seating arrangement was: Asst (N), Phones, APC (N), Dir1 (N), Dir2 (N), Dir2 (S), Dir1 (S), APC (S), Asst (S). Behind them in the northern half of the room were a Special VFR and two PAR consoles while at the southern end of the room there was the

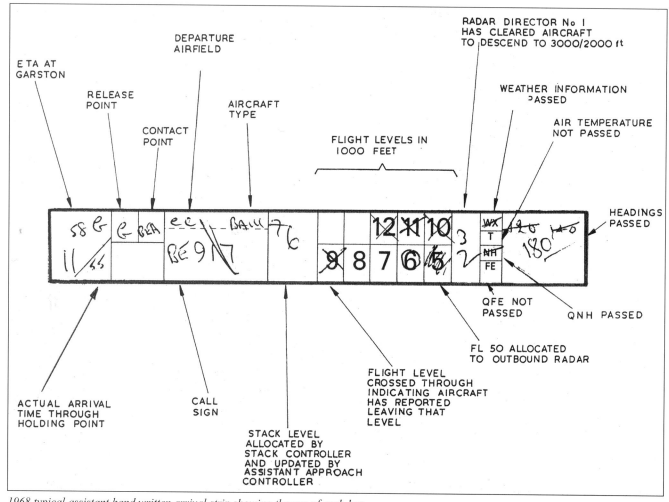

1968 typical assistant hand written arrival strip showing the use of each box.

The PAR consoles with Derrek Joyce nearest the camera. Mike Perry is believed to be in the centre and Ken McLeod on the SVFR position at the far end of the line. (CAA Archives)

Supervisor's desk raised on a dais. At the end of the desk, to the Supervisor's left, there was a radar so that he could monitor what was going on and, to this end, his desk was equipped with all VCR and Approach frequencies. In quiet periods the operation was band-boxed to the northern half of Approach and it was not long before the Special VFR controller occupied the Dir2 (S) position when trials of parallel operations (which had continued in 1966, 67 and 68) were not being conducted.

FINAL DAYS OF PAR

Although there were two PAR positions in the new Approach room the service was withdrawn nationally later in 1968, its use having diminished as the serviceability and accuracy of the ILS equipment improved. Before the PAR was removed, however, it was re-instated following the crash of an Ariana Boeing 727 on approach to Gatwick in shallow fog on 5th January 1969, questions being asked as to whether PAR monitoring might have averted the disaster. Since their validations had lapsed PAR rated ATCOs had to attend refresher courses, and other ATCOs were sent on rating courses. Among these were Brian Piket and Tony Hall-Willis who were the last two Heathrow ATCOs to validate on PAR. After the rather leisurely talkdowns during the course with a Ministry de Havilland Dove validation training at Heathrow was a more frantic affair and one of the delights of the time was to find a Convair Coronado - respected as a 'hot ship' - for a run. The validation board could also be unpredictable. Three talkdowns were necessary for this, and Brian Piket thought that the Gods must be smiling on him when his first run, with a Viscount, was perfection - a smooth turn-on, centre line and glide path all the way, even praise from the pilot on

completion. But the Board would not accept this run, maintaining that the pilot must have been using the ILS. Jack Frith, on the other hand, had to work really hard to complete one of his runs successfully. Once again the approach, with an Ambassador, had been very tidy with little correction needed until the aircraft got to about two miles when it suddenly pulled off the centre line to the right. Rapid correction brought the aircraft back to the centre line very quickly and since he was concerned at what had happened Jack asked the pilot to phone in. It transpired that the pilot had thought it was a standard training exercise and, because he thought it was going so well, had decided to 'spice it up' a little. One of the perks of being PAR valid was that when one of the two per watch was on leave at night the other automatically had a long sleep to cover both halves, as a result of which Brian Smith earned himself the nickname of 'Bedsores'. The PAR remained in use until 28th February 1974, the honour of carrying out the last talkdowns going to Bill McColl. He had asked a Cambrian Viscount if it would like to do one final talkdown and this was accepted, but an inbound Lufthansa flight overheard the conversation and asked if he, too, could make a PAR approach. A time had been set for the PAR to be withdrawn and so the Lufthansa aircraft was told to maintain its speed to beat the deadline. But, rather inevitably, this brought the aircraft onto final high and fast and the very last talkdown was a hurried, unsettled affair.

GMC had continued to experience problems with the routeing of aircraft by day, and there were further attempts to overcome the difficulty of pilots not seeing or misunderstanding the route required. The experimental flashing taxiway centre line lighting in block 48 (N) was re-positioned for further trials in blocks 22 (N) and 22 (S), and an improved larger version of the 'arrow' guidance system was installed at block 62 (N) /47 (S) from March 1966 to April 1967. Another new form of taxiway centre line light was also tried out on the inner taxiway between blocks 24 and 43 from April to November 1967. These were modified to produce a white sector with an arc of 40 degrees along the line of the taxiway, but otherwise retaining their green filter. None of these experimental forms of daylight route indication provided the solution to the problem, however, so from the 2nd May 1968 a different approach was tried. The illuminated arrow system on the inner and outer taxiways was withdrawn for a trial period, and by day when the visibility was 2 kms or more pilots received descriptive routeing instructions ie:- 'G-ARPU cleared to taxi east via the outer ring taxiway for departure 28L, follow the VC10'. At other times routeing continued to be defined by green centre line lights and red stop bars.

CONDITIONAL LANDING CLEARANCES

Shortly after the start of the GMC trial new procedures were introduced (on 25th July 1968) for the issue of landing clearance. They resulted from a Recommendation made at the ICAO 5th Air Navigation Conference and were designed to improve runway capacity. Landing clearance could now be given while the runway was still occupied provided that a number of conditions were met. The most important of these was that when the landing traffic crossed the threshold of the runway in use the runway should be clear or, if not, that the previous landing or departure should be a minimum specified distance from the threshold. There were obvious benefits, not least of which was that the Air controller could now issue landing clearance at a much earlier stage rather than having to wait for the preceding aircraft to vacate or get airborne, and it was still possible, of course, for the controller or the pilot to over-ride the landing clearance if anything went wrong. Most pilots quickly accepted this new style of landing clearance although some, notably KLM, would not land if there was traffic still on the runway, no matter how far down it was. A new R/T phraseology -'G-ARPX, after the landing/departing (type of aircraft) cleared to land' - was introduced for the procedure which initially was only used at Heathrow, although more general use was intended later.

EXTENDING 28R/10L

Development work on the Airport at this time included the western extension of 28R/10L, and the expansion of the long haul building (Terminal 3) to accommodate the introduction of the Boeing 747. The latter required the construction of a new pier, with associated taxiways and apron area, and to provide the space required runway 15R/33L was permanently withdrawn from use. This spread of passenger facilities to the west would also bring the final closure of 23R/05L two years later, leaving the Airport with just three of the six runways (seven if the original runway 16/34 is included) that had been built for it. The work to extend 28R/10L from 2,838 metres to 3,902 metres began in October 1968 and initially was west of the existing perimeter road so, apart from the non-availability of the 28R clearway, there was no change to declared runway distances. The runway was then closed for a month to allow for preparatory work, including a

blast screen at the western end of the runway, after which the work progressed through several stages until the extension and its related taxiway were brought into use on 29th April 1970. The offset localiser which had necessarily been used for 28R during this period stayed in service until 3rd November when an in-line localiser was restored.

GUINNESS

Following a meeting with a former Services friend, Colin Coomber was invited to spend some time working as a barman on the Guinness stand at the 1969 Earls Court Boat Show. Having enjoyed the experience he began to make regular appearances each year and, when extra staff were needed, he was able to arrange for others from ATC Heathrow to join him. In the early days these included Colin Ward, Ian McConnell, Doug Bush, Pete Kemp, Paddy Treacy and Eric Dallison. When the stand began to appear at other events - the Ideal Home Exhibition, the Do-It-Yourself Exhibition, Smithfield and the Cambridge Folk Festival - it had enthusiastic ATC support although by 1992 its appearances were once again limited to just the Boat Show. The events were not without incident, however, and on at least two occasions explosive devices went off close to the stand while there was ATC presence but fortunately no one was injured. On another occasion the MP Ted Heath arrived at the stand 'after hours' to sample the brew and was served by Doug Bush who handed him his drink in a sherry glass, reducing him to fits of laughter. For the staff involved the taking of leave to cover these extra mural duties became an inviolable ritual and it was a brave man who threatened their annual pilgrimage. Other regulars over the years included Chris Cosgrave, John Cant, Ian Frankeiss-Moor, George Dyer, John Siddell and Steve Hobbs, but the association sadly ended in 2003, after over thirty years of involvement, at the final Guinness Boat Show.

Later in 1969 Heathrow was visited by an American 'senior' - a lady by the name of Mrs Hart - who was attempting to fly around the World in her single engined Beechcraft Bonanza registered N9493Y. She was given vectors for a landing on runway 10R but was unable to identify the runway and had to be re-positioned. This happened again on her next approach and when she subsequently came onto final again the Air controller Chris Barrows asked her if she could see anything that looked like a runway. She replied 'affirmative' and Chris told her to land on it. Unfortunately it was not the runway but the southern taxiway outside the cargo apron. When told of her mistake she asked if landing fees would still need to be paid as she had not used a runway!

A break-time pursuit which had become quite popular was tunnel walking, and after its discovery the tunnel from the basement of the Tower to the short-haul Terminal was used by many ATC personnel, particularly when the weather was inclement. But other, more adventurous, 'tunnellers' found that there was an extensive system under the Central Area which made their return from breaks rather unpredictable at times. Among the most famous explorers were Colin Ward, Alan Hickman, Brian Smith and Ken Ibell.

The process of change continued with the introduction of a new Worthing SID (via Woodley and Midhurst) on 6th March 1969, and two new helicopter lanes, H10 and H11, on 26th June. The Midhurst SID followed on

26th May 1970, using the same route as the Worthing SID but with additional climb requirements so that traffic would clear Farnborough airspace. This was designated as the principal jet departure route to the south, although those unable to make the climb profile could still request the Seaford or Ibsley SID which remained in use for propeller driven traffic and Boeing 747s. A number of Heathrow ATCOs who lived in the Camberley area at the time attended a heated meeting in the town's Civic Hall, called to protest at the extra noise that this route would generate for local residents, but for obvious reasons did not disclose their operational interest. Taking the questions were a Ministry representative and the local MP who, to his credit, remained adamant that to spread noise was much better than to concentrate it. Many of the audience disagreed - noisily!

Aircraft movements for 1969, which for the first time went through the quarter million mark, continued a period of steady growth, which resulted in an increase of over 76% in annual rates during the decade.

Total Aircraft Movements

1960	146,506
1961	157,518
1962	156,085
1963	168,538
1964	187,784
1965	206,336
1966	224,099
1967	236,449
1968	247,498
1969	258,374

A look at the top twelve contributors for 1969 shows the dramatic changes that had occurred in less than a quarter century since the Airport opened.

(1)	Trident 1/2/3	50,632
(2)	Boeing 707/720	44,655
(3)	Vanguard	22,984
(4)	Viscount	20,315
(5)	DC-9	19,311
(6)	Boeing 727	13,599
(7)	Caravelle	12,694
(8)	VC10/Super VC10	11,765
(9)	DC-8	11,374
(10)	Boeing 737	8,739
(11)	BAC1-11	8,641
(12)	Comet	5,914

THE GATWICK SHUTTLE

In 1969 the Boeing 747 provided just 168 movements while the Britten-Norman Islander was high up the chart at 2,570 - the result of the introduction of a service linking Heathrow and Gatwick on 25th June 1969 run by Westward Airways. The aircraft operated several flights a day, flying direct at low altitude between the two Airports and then positioning visually behind nominated traffic on 28L or 10R. When 28L was in use for landing no special gap was created for it, it simply fitted into the established stream and was required to vacate the runway before, or at the same time as, the traffic it followed. This procedure would, of course, not have been possible a few years later when the dangers of wake vortices were recognised. As it was, Heathrow was just block 85 to the Islander, which made startling use of its STOL capability. Brian Smith remembers one day that 28L was in use for departure and there was traffic lined up on the threshold when the Islander reached the Airport. Unable to release the departure he obtained the agreement of both pilots involved for the Islander to land in front of the aircraft on the runway. Departures were equally impressive, particularly when there was a southerly component to the wind, when at times it took off across the block to clear the runway more quickly.

SAGITTAIR

Another interesting customer at that time was a Beechcraft 18 operated by Sagittair, which made regular night flights to Europe delivering newspapers. One night it taxied out to 28L and was cleared for take-off, but as it got airborne flames were seen coming from one of the engines. The take-off had only used a small part of the runway and the pilot was able to land again and vacate at block 79 where he was seen to exit the aircraft and beat out the flames with what appeared to be his hat. He then called for clearance back to the holding point for another try, which was an action replay of the first attempt. Before his third try Derek Jenkins initiated a 'Full Emergency' but on this occasion the aircraft finally got away without incident. Many years later Rod Metcalfe was at a BALPA/GATCO evening and related the story to a British Midland captain who, to Rod's surprise, admitted that it might well have been him as he had spent some time with Sagittair and carburettor fires were not uncommon. On another occasion the Beech landed on 28L, vacated to the south and came to a stop. It could not be contacted on either the Air or the Ground frequencies but a quick look through the Tower binoculars found that the pilot had jumped out of the aircraft and, to put it politely, was watering the grass.

G-AXWL, one of the Beech 18s of Sagittair at rest on the GA apron, block 94. (Brian Pickering-MAP)

AUTOLANDS START

Experimental work on blind landing systems began soon after the finish of World War 2, using a leader cable system which extended for a mile from the runway threshold, and along each side of the runway. Separate alternating voltages were applied to each of the two cables at audio frequencies, inducing audio currents in two simple receivers located in the wing tips of a Vickers Varsity aircraft. When the aircraft was on the centre line the induced currents were equal, but if there was a difference then this was applied to the aircraft's auto-pilot and used to control the aircraft in azimuth. This system was simple and accurate but had certain shortcomings, and lacked the international status of ILS, so it was abandoned after a few years in favour of ILS based systems. The obvious and growing need to guarantee airlines normal operations in fog, avoiding the economic penalty of disrupted schedules and inconvenience to passengers, saw Smith's Industries become involved in 1957 when they took the decision to go ahead with the development of an all-weather flight control system, in conjunction with the Blind Landing Experimental Unit (BLEU), for BEA's new fleet of Hawker Siddeley Tridents. This resulted in the certification of the Trident's duplex system for Autoflare in June 1965, and further development saw one of the fleet fitted with a triplex system which allowed it to make a number of fully automatic landings at Heathrow in November 1966 during fog which stopped all other operations. Sufficient experience had been gained by 1970 for approval to be given for aircraft to operate into Heathrow in Category 2 weather conditions, and to protect the 28L glide path radiations during Cat 2 operations a Cat 2 holding point was introduced in block 94 on the 7th September 1970, effective when the RVR fell to 800 metres or less or when the cloud base was 500 feet or less. A mid-point RVR reading was also introduced on 1st December to provide the pilot with the additional information on runway visibility he required to operate in Cat 2 conditions. This was taken by an observer sited south of block 84 and gave a simple value of either 'above' or 'below' 150 metres. Notam 935/70 makes the point that this was provided as an advisory service only, and that the service could not be guaranteed on all occasions due to (BAA) staffing difficulties. Further safeguards followed in June 1971 with the establishment of more Cat 2 holding points - at the western end of the main runways - and the introduction of ATC procedures to protect the ILS radiations during Cat 2 operations. These now became effective when the touchdown RVR dropped to 800 metres or less, or the cloud base to 200 feet or less, with the mid-point RVR being passed when the relevant touchdown RVR dropped below 600 metres. Interestingly it was thought very unlikely at this time that Cat 2 ops could be maintained on 10L/28R during construction of an hotel on the area of the recently closed North Apron (blocks 5, 6, 7 and 8).

Sitting in Approach one evening the Supervisor, Len Hobbs, became curious as to why there were so few staff around. His assistant, Clive George, told him that there was a blue movie show in one of the Control Tower rooms that evening and that most people who were not needed had gone to see it. Len, a Jehovah's Witness, thought this meant a BLEU film on all-weather operations and, despite Clive's desperate warnings, went off to see the film with predictably embarrassing results.

RUNWAY 23 OPERATIONS

Runway 23 had developed a distinct personality of its own over the years. In early days it had enjoyed regular use as ATC chased the wind, but this had become much diminished as aircraft became more tolerant of crosswinds. The provision of an ILS on this runway was, therefore, not regarded as high priority. Prior to the introduction of a localiser on 23 approaches were generally from an SRA using a 3.5 degree glide path which, of course, meant different check heights from those used on all the other runways. The runway was not normally made available for use until there was a brisk (mean 15 knots) southerly wind, and this presented problems in maintaining a regular pattern in the intermediate approach, where the strong upper winds exaggerated small vectoring errors, and on final where even if the No.2 Director was 'in the groove' movement rates suffered because of reduced ground speeds and because the minimum spacing he needed was about five miles so that he could complete one SRA before starting the next. For these reasons different control techniques came into use, one of which was for the No.1 Director to work with two No.2 Directors, feeding them alternate aircraft. This allowed three mile spacing on final even during surveillance radar approaches, and reduced the amount of traffic working the No.1 Director. Another way of improving movement rates was for the Air controller to indicate that he would accept a 'tight' three miles spacing (in practice 2.5 to 3 nms) in suitable conditions to compensate for the reduced ground speeds on the approach. Although this could look quite exciting out of the window, and on radar, it presented no problems to the Air controller because aircraft vacated early. The introduction of a localiser on runway 23 removed the need for tandem No.2 Director working, and when the glide path became operational the glide slope for all types of approach (ILS, PAR and SRA) was set at a lower 3 degrees.

One of Heathrow's rare but, as usual, extensively reported airmisses occurred on 9th January 1970 when runway 23 was in use for landings. There were inbound delays when Olympic 257, a Boeing 727, arrived at Epsom and it was just over thirty minutes before the aircraft was vectored off for a standard left hand circuit. Descent was given to 3,000 feet and, when the pilot reported established, the aircraft was transferred to the Air frequency. Meanwhile an Indian Air Force Super Constellation callsign VUQLD inbound to Northolt was also receiving vectors for a GCA to runway 26, the hand over to Northolt taking place when the aircraft was on a ten mile final descending to 1,600 feet. Northolt began to pass heading instructions and gave further descent to 1,350 feet, but when the GCA controller queried the Constellation's height the reply was 500 feet. Concerned that the aircraft would hit high ground at Harrow on the Hill the controller gave an immediate instruction to climb to 1,350 feet which was repeated shortly after. But, still not satisfied that the aircraft was complying and noticing that it appeared to be moving left of centre line, GCA then instructed the aircraft to make a left hand orbit and climb to 1,500 feet. The turn, strictly contrary to local agreements, brought the Constellation into conflict with the Olympic 727, but was immediately noticed at Heathrow and while the No.1 Director rang Northolt to try to reverse the Constellation's direction of turn the No.2 Director rang the Air controller to ascertain the height of the 727. This was confirmed as being above the

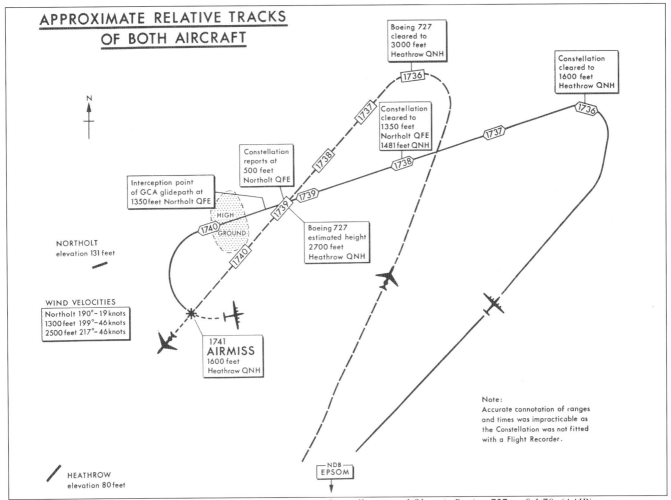

Diagram of the approximate tracks and timing of the Indian Super Constellation and Olympic Boeing 727 on 9.1.70. (AAIB)

Constellation and so the Olympic flight was instructed to climb straight ahead to 3,000 feet, and shortly afterwards the Constellation passed slightly ahead and below, sufficiently close for the Olympic crew to hear its engines. Because ot the extreme proximity of the two aircraft the investigation and report were made by the AIB, appearing as Civil Accident Report No. EW/E13/01. The Olympic flight was now very short of fuel and was given a priority second approach from which it landed, while the Constellation made three further GCAs to Northolt, descending on each approach below its cleared height, before landing. Before Approach could re-compose itself it was announced that the Olympic crew were on their way to the Control Tower to discuss the incident, and moments later they appeared in the room, taking charge of the Supervisor's desk while the ATC staff took refuge on the other side. This was not a good tactical move by ATC, although to be fair they had no option, since it gave the Olympic crew the advantage of the additional height offered by the dais on which the desk stood, and made them look impressively tall.

SOVIET ANTONOVS

26th July 1970. Although it was summer the weather was miserable and low stratus covered much of southern England. Two Soviet Antonov AN-12s (CCCP-11110 and CCCP-11719) were on their way to Bristol to pick up the aircraft and pilots of the Soviet aerobatic team who had been competing in the World Aerobatic Championships at Hullavington but, because of the weather at Bristol, were forced to divert to Heathrow. The first was vectored around for

28R but never found the ILS and eventually overflew Heathrow in cloud to be repositioned. Much the same happened with the second, the crews of both seemingly unable to understand even the most basic ATC instructions. Ian Culley, who was working GMP at the time, had time to monitor the Approach frequency and remembers hearing Approach ask one of the pilots 'confirm you have ILS frequency 109.5 selected' to which a gutteral Soviet voice replied 'OK. 109.5. Good day'. It was several minutes before two-way communication was re-established and meantime Heathrow had been reduced to a shambles. Departures had been stopped and inbounds had to be held because the Antonovs were effectively doing their own thing. Despite all Approach's efforts it was impossible to get them to follow any instructions and this resulted in the aircraft overflying the Airport several times more, either totally in cloud or in and out of the base. Desperate measures were required and a call was made to BEA Ops to ask if there was anyone on duty who spoke Russian. A request was also broadcast in Terminal 2 and this resulted in someone from BEA being rushed across to the Tower and seated, with a headset, in front of one of the PARs. Although initially very nervous he was able to translate all the Approach instructions into language that appeared to be understood by the crews of the Antonovs and they both eventually landed safely on 28L.

HELICOPTER ROUTES

It was about now that the Approach 'phones' position was finally dropped, with the Approach controller assuming what remained of his co-ordination responsibilities. Special VFR traffic was increasing, and an extensive review of helicopter operations inside the Control Zone produced a number of amendments to procedures which took effect on 1st September 1970. These included revisions to routes, nominated reporting and holding points, special procedures

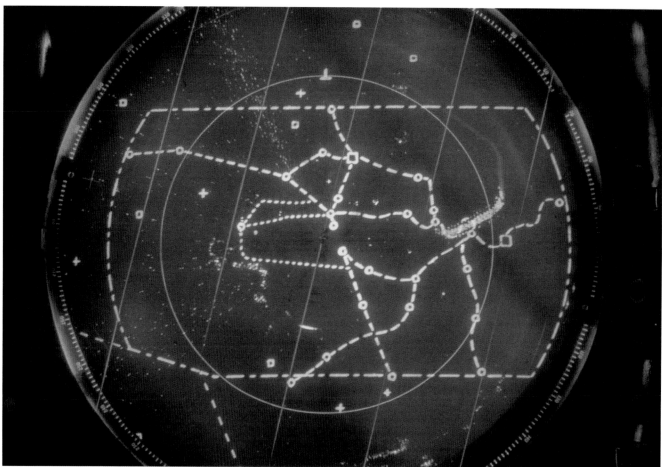

Time exposure of the ACR 6 picture during a quiet spell in 1975, showing the Special VFR video map with Helicopter Routes, including those to and from Windsor Castle. (Pete Bish)

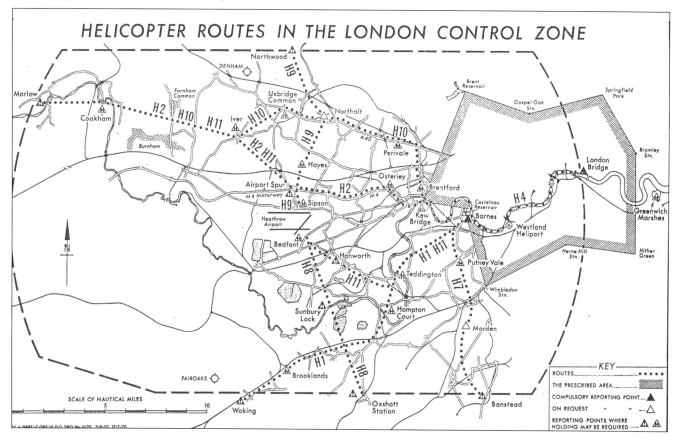

for reduced separation and new weather minima for helicopters overlying or landing at Heathrow. To operate inside the Control Zone a flight visibility of at least one kilometre was required, except when operating into or across Heathrow when three kilometres was the minimum. However, greater flexibility was allowed on the routes with the introduction of special procedures whereby separation could be reduced using visual separation provided that certain conditions were satisfied. As long as the pilots concerned agreed, and appropriate traffic information was passed, then separation could be reduced if there was a reported visibility at Heathrow and an in-flight visibility of at least 6 kms, provided that the current route structure and altitudes were followed.

The dormitory on the seventh floor, which contained seven beds, was used by most of the male ATCOs on night duties, but could get very stuffy. Nor was an uninterrupted rest guaranteed for the second half staff who generally started to get their heads down around 11pm. Late arrivals, particularly if they had not made up their beds earlier, and the comings and goings of the lift just outside, both created disturbances which were difficult to ignore. The room was very dark and finding the right people to wake at change-over time was something of a hit or miss affair, although Dave Graves was able to find a solution to this. Being a smoker he would use his gas lighter to check that he had found the correct person, but this could be disconcerting. Chris Harris woke one night to find the flame at maximum strength just beside him and remembers thinking that he had died and gone to Hell!

MEDIATOR

The introduction into commercial service of large numbers of jet aircraft in the early 1960s, operating above 25,000 feet, affected military freedom in the upper airspace and brought recommendations in the Patch Report (1961) for a joint military / civil radar based area concept. At the time there existed two separate plans, one for Air Defence and one for Air Traffic Control over the United Kingdom, but the radar coverage requirements and data processing proposals for both plans were considered to be sufficiently similar to warrant integration. Moreover, significant technical and operational benefits were envisaged with a reduction of overall costs. Approval was given in 1962, therefore, for the development of an integrated system under the code name Linesman Mediator, where Linesman referred to the Air Defence facilities and Mediator to the facilities provided for the joint civil/military ATC. By May 1964, however, it had become evident that difficulties being encountered in the definition of the Mediator element were seriously affecting provision of radar data processing systems (RDPS) for Air Defence and later that year a decision was made to proceed with Linesman and Mediator separately. By the end of the decade Mediator Stage 1 was approaching implementation and recognised that radar was now the prime controlling agent with a procedural back-up, rather than the reverse which had until now been the case. New techniques for streaming inbound traffic into Heathrow's intermediate approach and for the release of departures had been evaluated at the ATCEU, with Heathrow participation. Original proposals envisaged the use of en-route speed control to maintain an even flow of traffic into four Area controlled stacks. Only when an aircraft left a stack would it be transferred to Approach, but this was found to have two major disadvantages:-

(1)   Inefficient sequencing resulted from coarse control of the rate at which aircraft were handed over to Approach.

(2)   Half of the No.1 Director's work would be carried out by the Centre, limiting the approach sequencing teamwork between the No.1 and No.2 Directors, thereby reducing runway capacity.

Mediator also favoured the parallel approach concept, which had still not been adopted for various reasons - limited operational experience (due to weather, lack of traffic, staff shortages, single runway ops etc.), general dislike by ATCOs, and uneven traffic distribution between the north and south which reduced capacity. So by the time Mediator Stage 1 was introduced in February 1971 the bottom two levels of each stack had been re-assigned to Approach. To provide the facilities necessary a number of changes took place in the TMA. Two new stacks were needed and the first of these, an NDB at Ongar, was brought into service on 2nd May 1969 and was used initially at ATC discretion for traffic inbound from the east and north east. The lowest flight level available was normally FL60 since there was an aerobatic area situated below the holding area with an upper limit of FL50. The next year, on 12th November 1970, Garston was replaced by Bovingdon as the northerly stack, and then on 1st February 1971 the Biggin VOR was introduced as the fourth stack, accommodating traffic from the south east. The standard routeing for aircraft inbound from the west via Airway Green One also needed to be changed as Woodley lay in TMA South airspace, so this became Woodley - Chertsey - Epsom, and the optional left turn out for easterly runway departures to Woodley was withdrawn. Early experience of Mediator procedures showed that the TMA controllers could not keep pace with descents in the stacks to provide Approach with continuous traffic and so further levels in each stack were given back to Approach, which meant that there was little noticeable change from pre-Mediator days. But, of course, this also meant that the TMA controllers were dependant on the rate at which Approach accepted aircraft and consequently there was less need for effective en-route speed control, originally an important Mediator concept, to maintain an even traffic flow.

If anything Aerodrome Control benefitted more from Mediator than Approach. Instead of having to obtain individual releases for departures the Air controller now only needed to pass the departure order and SID to the relevant sector before despatching aircraft with a minimum two minutes or five miles separation (if on the same route), increased where necessary when a fast aircraft followed a slower type. Aircraft were placed in one of four speed groups, and one minute added to the basic separation for each change of group:-

(1)   piston with two engines.
(2)   piston with four engines.
(3)   turbo-prop with two or four engines.
(4)   jet.

After a little experience had been gained of these new procedures the requirement to inform the sector of the departure sequence was also removed, relieving the Air controller of a significant amount of co-ordination.

SECONDARY RADAR ARRIVES

Secondary surveillance radar (SSR) began to see use in civil ATC in June 1963, but was restricted to a small number of Area radar units, and it was not until the end of the sixties that it was introduced at Heathrow. Initially the response from a transponding aircraft was shown on the radar as two slashes coincident with the primary echo. A third slash appeared when an aircraft was asked to squawk 'ident'. No legislation existed regarding the carriage of transponders below flight level 250 until January 1972, when the fitting of 4096 code transponders became mandatory above flight level 100 within controlled airspace, but when the Area radar controllers moved from the North Side radar unit to West Drayton with the implementation of Mediator Stage One (to join the procedural side who had moved five years earlier with Mediator Stage Half) their radar was able to display a four figure identity code and a three figure altitude read out. At this stage the first two digits of the code denoted a particular route or function, the 3rd and 4th individual aircraft identity, and the squawks were issued from the wing positions at the Centre as estimates were received. For Heathrow inbounds the squawks allocated were A11xx from the north, and A30xx from the south. Departures were given codes from the blocks A03xx and A66xx. This type of display did not become available in Approach until the end of 1972 when it was welcomed as a major step forward in identifying and maintaining the identity of traffic working Heathrow.

COW OR BIRD?

One day a TWA Boeing 707 was told to give way to an Air France Breguet Deux Ponts before taxying, but when he saw the aircraft he asked 'You mean this fat cow?' The Air France pilot, rightly upset by this comment, replied 'It may look like a cow but it flies like a bird!'

These Air France Breguets, which were regular night time visitors, showed a marked disinclination to descend and could only manage a straight-in approach from Biggin if they had already by then started descent from minimum stack level.

The outbounds were equally ponderous as were Tridents which earned themselves the nickname 'Grippers' because of their poor climb rates. The Trident, however, compensated for this with a startling descent capability in an emergency, using reverse thrust on its centre engine. It was maintained that from Henton cruising at flight level 310 it could come south on a base leg and achieve a landing on 10L without going through the extended centre line.

POLARS AND INERTIAL NAVIGATION

Another type which had certain problems in its early days was the Boeing 747 and this resulted in the introduction of a new SID. Flights taking off from 10R and using the North Atlantic Polar routeing for destinations on the west coast of the United States were sometimes too heavy to comply with the minimum noise and climb requirements of the Daventry SID and so an alternative 'Polar' SID was created. This was not made generally available and could only be used by a small number of airlines who had applied for and been given permission to use it. These included BOAC, TWA, Pan Am, Japan Air Lines and Air Canada. Initially the SID route was via Epsom at 2,000 feet or above, Biggin and Brookmans Park at 4,000 feet but this later became Bromley, Hornchurch and Brookmans Park at 4,000 feet. In both cases it was made subject to release by TMA(S). The 'Polar' SID was eventually withdrawn when requests for its use declined.

The Boeing 747, which would influence air travel so dramatically, was remarkable for its size but also carried important new navigational equipment, the Inertial Navigation System (INS), which deserves brief mention even though it had little application at Heathrow. Its accuracy and the fact that it was not reliant on ground-based aids would offer major benefits in North Atlantic airspace. The system uses giro-stabilised accelerometers feeding information to a computer on changes of the aircraft's position in the lateral, longitudinal and vertical planes. Provided that the aircraft's position is input accurately at the start of a flight then its position can always be rapidly established at any later stage. A trial INS procedure for suitably equipped flights began in April 1971

The French have always had a flair for designing 'different' aircraft - the Breguet Deux Ponts was no exception! Here at a press demonstration in April 1965 two Air France double deckers (F-BASQ and RT2209) come together at Heathrow. (Brian M Service)

for traffic routeing out of Heathrow on Green One (West), using a Waypoint at Woodley North, although this was re-positioned in July to Lyneham West to simplify the traffic situation around Woodley, and new northbound routes were introduced. ATC Heathrow benefited through the ability of INS equipped aircraft to provide upper wind velocities - a by-product of the system - which assisted vectoring and gave support to decisions on whether or not to make a runway change. Indeed, at times, an aircraft's report of the upper wind could be the first indication that a runway change might be necessary.

STORED FLIGHT PLANS

Changes were also taking place for the assistants, in general reducing the amount of written work required to perform their task. The sending of arrival signals for Oceanic flights had been discontinued on 22nd August 1968, and from 1972 departure signals would also be progressively phased out. But an important step forward was the introduction on 24th June 1971 of the ICAO Recommended Practice of Stored Flight Plans, a pilot scheme for which had been operating successfully since December of the previous year. The procedures were designed to avoid repetitive filing of flight plans and repetitive transmission of flight plans and related messages, and applied to flights which operated regularly at least once a week and which would take place on at least six occasions, but not to North Atlantic flights. In charge of introducing the scheme at Heathrow was Brian Buckingham, who ran the Stored Flight Plan Reception Unit, and because of the size of the task the scheme was introduced in phases. Details from the flight plans submitted by the operators were

transferred to file cards, along the top of which a series of holes was punched relating to the days of the week on which the service would operate. These were then stored in a box in Flight Clearance and at the beginning of each day a needle was pushed through the appropriate hole enabling the flights for that day to be lifted out for activation at the appropriate time by the teleprinter operator. Other plans, for flights not yet in the scheme, continued to arrive by traditional methods, and of course required full manual processing, but it was inevitable that a reduction of the complement in Clearance would result as the Stored Flight Plan scheme became more universally adopted.

A Cessna 310 was having undercarriage problems and a Full Emergency was put on for runway 10L. Harry Richardson, supervising in the VCR, told the Air controller that he would inform the AFS when the aircraft was next to land and that they would follow it down the runway. Seeing it on final Harry rang the AFS, but he had not been told that a fly-by had been arranged with Approach so as the aircraft flew down the runway and then climbed away he was as bemused as the crews of the AFS vehicles that were in hot pursuit.

Out on the Airport the BAA engineers had been busy replacing the amber caution zone edge lighting on the main runways with coded centre line lighting. Red filters were fitted so that from 914 metres to 305 metres from the end of the runway the lights were alternate red and white, and then all red for the last 305 metres. Two further experiments in taxiway lighting were also removed after periods on trial - white occulting lights in block 83 and high intensity fittings in block 21. But the engineers' activity in the VCR was of greater interest to ATC as they progressed with the upgrading of the lighting panel to its third form in the Tower, which replaced

Flight Clearance remained in the Queens Building until 1981. Here in 1975 ATCA 2 Martin Adams receives a Flight Plan from one of Shell's HS-125 Captains. (Pete Bish)

the flush route selection buttons with raised buttons. The lighting operators themselves were trying out a new lightweight and cordless headset. This enabled them to move away from the panel, but it had limited range since the R/T was received from a unit in the ceiling. It also suffered from a fair degree of interference so was only used operationally for a short period before being removed.

Although trials of mixed mode parallels had continued there was still concern over how to provide satisfactory monitoring of approaches during parallel ops, and during 1971 the EU were asked to evaluate the effectiveness of the AR1 radar in this role. Flight trials took place from the 5th to the 10th December using the CAFU HS-748 and Dove, but the conclusion reached was that the discrimination of the radar together with the closeness of the runways made it unacceptable for this purpose. This was followed in October 1972 by a decision to suspend parallel trials indefinitely.

A NEW APPROACH TO RUNWAY 23

A number of controllers had begun to experiment with a new technique for vectoring aircraft from the northerly stack onto runway 23. Until now it had been standard practice to bring aircraft off the stack on what was virtually a base leg heading (120 degrees) and then, if extra track distance was required, to run through the centre line and turn right to re-join from the left. An early descent could be achieved with the cooperation of the Area controller who would take his traffic bound for Brookmans Park on a scenic route well north of track and therefore no confliction with the Heathrow inbound. The new technique involved bringing the aircraft off the stack on a much more southerly heading i.e 160 degrees and then turning left over the centre line to join the traffic from the southerly stacks running downwind. Although this needed tight control of the hand-off heading to the No.2 Director it became increasingly popular and was eventually accepted as standard practice.

Runway 23 was also the first to receive a modified VASI system designed to assist pilots of the Boeing 747. Because of the large vertical distance between the pilot's eyes and the main landing gear a third bar was added to the system to provide a safe wheel clearance over the runway threshold. This came into operational use early in 1972 and when using these VASIs pilots of aircraft with large 'eye/wheel' dimensions used the upwind and middle bars to obtain their glide slope, and ignored the downwind bar, while the pilots of other aircraft used the middle and downwind bar, ignoring the upwind bar.

THE MARCONI S650

A new radar arrived at Heathrow for evaluation by the ATCEU. The Marconi S650 was a solid state 50cm radar intended for Approach and Centre use and was installed on the roof of the BOAC multi-storey car park and office block, some 145 feet above ground level. Here it had an unobstructed view of the surrounding area and would be unaffected by new building development in its vicinity, but this was not an ideal location as the design of the antenna relied on proximity to the ground to enhance its performance. The SSR antenna fitted to this radar was deliberately 'squinted' to allow for the extra return time of the secondary

The Marconi S650 radar on the roof of the BOAC multi-storey car park (CAA Archives)

response but this led to frequent reports from passers-by that a part of the radar was falling off. Flight trials, using HS-125s and Doves as targets, took place between the 6th and 22nd March 1972 but results were disappointing. A number of modifications were made to the radar, including the installation of a new digital processor and reduction of the PRF, and then a further series of trials were carried out a year later between 19th and 30th March 1973. Although improvements were observed there were still major problems, principally attributable to the siting of the radar which had a significant and adverse effect on its radiation pattern. And if this was not enough there were numerous complaints from local residents that the radar was affecting their television reception, which necessitated the fitting of expensive filters. A decision not to order the radar followed and it quietly disappeared, although the site would be used again some time later.

THE CIVIL AVIATION AUTHORITY

Some years earlier, in 1967, the President of the Board of Trade had appointed the Edwards Committee (named after its Chairman) to examine the British civil aviation industry and propose changes to enable it to make a full contribution to the economy, and to the service and safety of the travelling public. It found that the economic, airworthiness and operational aspects of aviation should be combined as one organisation, which should also be responsible for air navigation services in conjunction with the Ministry of Defence. Prior to this responsibility for safety regulation had been split between the Board of Trade (operational safety) and the Air Registration Board (airworthiness), economic regulation had been the responsibility of the Air Transport Licensing Board, and the provision of air navigation services rested with the Board of Trade and the Ministry of Defence. Their recommendations were accepted in a White Paper published in 1969, but it was stressed that policy would still be formulated by Ministers, although it would be executed by the new authority which would be named the Civil Aviation Authority. The CAA was established by the Civil Aviation Act of 1971, and took over responsibility for the regulation of the British civil aviation industry on 1st April 1972 under the Chairmanship of John Boyd-Carpenter. National Air Traffic Services (NATS), therefore, now became responsible to the CAA, who replaced the Board of Trade, and the Ministry of Defence jointly for the provision of air navigation services.

After a late evening arrival the Captain of a Northeast Viscount called GMC, full of apologies, to say that his First Officer believed he had seen a body on block 83 as they vacated 28L. Investigation by 'Checker' revealed that he was not mistaken. An ethnic gentleman was found laying on the side of the runway, apparently having been hit by an aircraft, and was taken to hospital where he later died. Something of an unusual log entry for the Supervisor, John Davis.

SPEED LIMITS AND STACK CHANGES

Further changes were taking place in and around the TMA, which had a significance to the operation at Heathrow. Increasing numbers of aircraft were being fitted with DME and so the inbound speed limit points, which had previously been three minutes flight time from the holding facility, were now alternatively described by a DME range although, at this stage, only Bovingdon had a DME capability. For the other stacks a range taken from the London DME was used. From 25th May 1972 a speed limit of 250 knots was also imposed on departures up to flight level 100 to improve the departure flow and at the same time ensure separation, particularly between aircraft following the same route for the first twenty or thirty miles. Pilots could, of course, request a higher speed limit if circumstances required. Upgrading of the holding facilities saw a VOR introduced at Wisley on 9th December 1971 to replace the Epsom NDB, which was retained as the standby for periods when Wisley was out of service. However, R/T confusion resulted from the similarity of the names Wisley and Ibsley, so on 27th April 1972 the VOR was renamed Ockham. The NDB at Ongar was also replaced by a VOR on 30th March 1972, completing the set. Later in the year, following a change in the transition altitude from 4,000 feet to 5,000 feet, the minimum level available at each of the stacks was raised to 6,000 feet.

RUNWAY ALTERNATION

In 1972 a system involving daytime alternation of the landing (and departure) runway was introduced for those times when the westerly runways 28L and 28R were in use. No longer was 28L the automatic choice as landing runway, concentrating the noise of landing traffic under just one approach. Instead one runway would be used for landing from 0700 to 1500 and then the other would take over from 1500 to 2300. This would apply for a week after which the periods of usage would be reversed. The rotation was laid down for a full year and was not affected by occasions when easterly operations were necessary. Residents living under the two approaches could be sure of when they would have relative peace and could plan accordingly. For operational safety and convenience certain exceptions were made to the procedure. If, for instance, a pilot had a valid technical reason for requesting to use the inappropriate runway - perhaps for a better IRVR or because of ILS serviceability - then it could be allowed and when separation had reduced between two aircraft on final approach to the extent that a go-around was possible then the second aircraft could be switched. Single and light twin propeller aircraft, which were considered to be a minimal nuisance, could use the departure runway for landing provided that it was operationally advantageous and did not delay any departures, and finally Royal and VVIP flights were exempted. From 2300 to 0700 runway 28L continued to be the normal choice as landing runway unless, for any reason, it was not available.

Measures were also introduced to reduce the noise nuisance of night-time operations at Heathrow. Exercising powers conferred by the Civil Aviation Act 1971 the Government restricted night time turbo jet and turbo fan departures to a total of 140 for the period 1st April to 31st October. These movements were allocated to thirteen airlines.

(1) BEA	31	(8) Air France	8
(2) Lufthansa	14	(9) Pan Am	8
(3) Swissair	13	(10) KLM	6
(4) Aer Lingus	12	(11) Seaboard World	5
(5) Alitalia	12	(12) TWA	5
(6) Iberia	12	(13) Nigeria Airways	5
(7) BOAC	9		

Other operators were also permitted one take-off each during the curfew period (2330 to 0600) which would be disregarded, but if subsequently they could prove that the departure concerned was a delayed schedule then they were allowed a further out-of-hours take-off with the same conditions. The BAA could also ask for exemptions if there was severe congestion at the Airport for any reason.

Helicopters, on the other hand, were given slightly more freedom for their operations at Heathrow when the weather minimum for crossing over, taking off from or landing at the Airport was reduced from 3 kms to 2 kms. A new helicopter landing area also became available north of block 14 in addition to the one already in use in block 94. No ground staff were provided so the pilot was responsible for ensuring that the pad was free of obstructions before landing or taking off, and had to stay with the helicopter while it was on the ground. In fact use of the alighting area was limited to just picking up or setting down passengers, and if the pilot wished to leave the helicopter or stay longer than thirty minutes then he had to use block 94.

INSTRUMENTED RUNWAY VISUAL RANGE (IRVR)

On 25th May 1972 28L was declared available for Cat 3a operations. For ATC this meant the safeguarding of an area 135 metres either side of the runway centre line during Cat 3 ops to comply with obstacle clearance requirements and to avoid interference with the localiser signal. Landing aircraft were expected to vacate the runway at block 79 where occulting white lights were provided at the edge of the protected area, and crossing traffic was routed to block 85. Towards the end of the year further facilities for low visibility operations appeared in the form of transmissometers, which replaced human observers taking runway visual ranges. Each of the main runways was provided with a bi-directional IRVR capability using three units sited at the touchdown, mid-point and stop end of the runway and from 12th October readings were given using these systems. The operational range of the IRVR system was from zero to a maximum of 1,500 metres in incremental steps of 30 metres up to 210 metres, 60 metres between 210 and 810 (rounded down to 800), and 100 metres above 800 to the maximum. Only the touchdown zone value was passed unless one or both of the others was below the touchdown value and less than 800 metres.

One of 3 pairs of Transmissometers (often dubbed 'Daleks') placed alongside each of the 2 main runways in 1972 to allow Instrumented RVRs (IRVRs) to be taken. (Pete Bish)

TEA BREAKS

There was a small room where you could make tea and coffee in the south east corner of the Approach room. ATC staff on a break from Approach or Aerodrome Control, who wanted nothing more than a drink, would drift in and engage in social chit-chat or discuss events of interest that had occurred during the duty. They would often spill out of the room into Approach and, because of the tea room's proximity

to the Supervisor's desk, the Supervisor would also become involved in dispensing pearls of wisdom. On 'D' Watch the Supervisor/Deputy Supervisor team of Jack Hollis and Les West - yes, the same Les West who was at Heathrow in 1950 back on a second tour - developed this into an often hilarious routine and on one occasion Jack was persuaded to come from behind the desk to demonstrate his version of John Cleese's 'Ministry of Silly Walks' sketch. It was all going very well, his long legs suiting the routine admirably, until he realised that the viewing gallery had filled up with visitors looking on with interest! At times when spacing on final had become exciting, particularly if 28L was in use for landing, the people in and outside the tea room would make an enthusiastic audience, looking through the blinds (which were always drawn during the day to reduce light levels), eager to let the No.2 Director know - with an embarrassing cheer - if he would be talking to one of his recent customers again. Such instances came to be known as 'window jobs'. For the more energetic, or those wanting a snack, there was now an alternative to the ground floor canteen on the roof of Terminal 2. Of rather flimsy construction and extensively glazed it afforded a good view of the Foxtrot apron, and access was by way of the Terminal's central staircase and an office corridor. It was popular with airline and other Terminal staff, but the atmosphere could be oppressive - a mix of moisture from the kettles, cigarette smoke and JP4 fumes if there happened to be a Caravelle, DC-9 or 727 pushing back outside. On windy days the entrance door would close with a crash after each customer's exit or arrival and light foil ashtrays, with their contents, would become airborne. Despite its popularity this tea bar was shut down some time before the ground floor canteen in the Tower, which managed to survive until the end of the decade.

NORTH RUNWAY MISSED APPROACHES

Returning to the subject of missed approaches the Airlines had for some time been expressing concern about the Heathrow missed approach procedures, which took aircraft to Epsom at 2,000 feet from all runways. While this was considered satisfactory for 28L, 10R and 23L where traffic turned away from the departure runway, it was argued that it did not safely meet the needs of 28R and 10L where a procedure to the north was really required. Northolt traffic was an obvious problem and a solution would need to protect movements there. The result was the introduction on 12th October 1972 of a new missed approach procedure for Heathrow's north main runway to the Chiltern NDB at 4,000 feet, with an initial climb straight ahead to 3,000 feet to provide the separation from Northolt. The Air controller was provided with an alarm button to be used whenever there was a missed approach from that runway to give a visual and aural warning to interested parties (Northolt, LATCC and Approach).

FIVE WATCH SYSTEM

During the early seventies, as a rather belated result of recommendations made in the Radley Report of 1964, important changes took place affecting rosters and the ATCO grade structure. A Joint Study Group established in November 1966 had failed to rule on the acceptability of the split-day working pattern, which by then had become a major safety concern of the controllers' Trades Union, and another two years elapsed before negotiations began between NATS Management and IPCS regarding possible changes to ATCO rosters and shift patterns. One of the proposals that emerged was for a change to a five Watch roster system based on a ten day repeating work pattern, either MMAANNSOOO or AAOMMNNSOO. Controllers at LATCC favoured the latter pattern and it was duly implemented there in 1971 with the necessary increase in staff to form the fifth Watch. However this was not the case at Heathrow where day duties had been introduced on the four Watch system, using surplus night staff to enhance the day time attendance. This gave a work pattern of AMDO, but was unpopular and received attention in the national press where concern was raised over the possibility of fatigue related errors. A series of meetings between the local IPCS representatives and Heathrow Management began early in 1972, but the simultaneous imposition of an annual leave restriction by the ATCO i/c Basil Turner created a mood for militant action which was recommended to the IPCS National Executive Committee in May for endorsement. As a result of this the leave restriction was lifted and negotiations continued to a successful conclusion, with a five Watch system being introduced for ATCOs on 1st November 1972. The assistants followed some months later in mid-March 1973, both grades (unlike LATCC) preferring the shift pattern of MMAANNSOOO. Day duties formed part of this new agreement, and these were worked to a pattern of MMAADDOOOO. For the assistants there was simply a Dl duty (0800-1800), but for the controllers there were two alternatives - a Dl (0800-1700) or a D2 (1000-1900). These were worked as a three day coordinating duty D2 D2 Dl or D2 D2 O Dl, which permitted an early finish on the last day worked but this started to produce minor incidents and increased sick absence. Although this duty existed at other stations it became known that only at Heathrow was it being worked and within a couple of years it was dropped. 1977 saw

the introduction of a later day duty - a D3 working 1430-2230. In 1978, however, this was changed to 1230-2030 when a further slip shift, the D4, was added, covering the period 1500-2230.

Jimmy Birchall chose staff for the new 'E' Watch by taking every fifth name down the seniority list, although some changes were permitted, However, most saw the creation of a new Watch as an exciting challenge. Norman Whitelock was chosen to be the first Supervisor of the Watch and the ATCO line up was :- Ted Lawson, Paddy Haycock, John Kiernan, Mike Heffer, Pete Waterfield, Terry Quantrill, Alan Hickman, Colin Ward, Alan Carter, Rod Metcalfe, John MacDermot, Ian Finlay, Jim Coulter, Phil Griffith, Alan Haines and Judith Chisholm. The ATCAs were :- Pete Moss, Eric Dallison, Paddy Treacy, Alan Wright, Liz Milliner, Rod Watts, Sue Green, Neil Waller, John Harborne, John Warren, Jane Haines, Pete Richardson, Val Smith, Paul Gardner, Andy Anderson, Anne Caddington and Alison Fisher.

A mini Watch of four ATCOs, not attached to a particular Watch, was also established to cover the Assistant Watch Supervisor duties during the morning and afternoon shifts. Chris Barrows, John Kiernan, Jim Kerr, Brian Smith, Bill McGregor, John Davis, Dennis Cliffe and Dennis Berriman were among those seconded to this elite team for periods, but the work pattern of AAMMOO was not attractive compared with the main shift pattern and after a relatively short period the mini-Watch was disbanded and its duties absorbed by the Watches.

The main ATCA Watch roster which follows was published just a few months after they joined the ATCOs on a five Watch system and contains 84 names of whom a surprising 28 (highlighted) left Heathrow for various reasons within the following two years. Perhaps even more surprising is that, in the same period, there were 38 new arrivals bringing the total on the station to 94 - 89 on Watches and 5 non-operational staff.

1974 view of the VCR with (L to R) Dennis Berriman (GMP), Celia Redhead (now Kunert) (ATCA), Dick Dawson (GMC), Tony Paintin (listening in), Howard Thomas (Air Controller) and (behind) a camera-shy Geoff Bullock (Tower supervisor) (via Dennis Berriman)

ATCA MAIN ROSTER SEPTEMBER 1973

A	B	C	D	E
C.J.Warner	J.C.Wood	J.B.MacPherson	R.V.Cook	D.J.Moss
T.E.Tapsall	E.W.Percival	M.E.Davies	C.E.George	E.N.Dallison
C.W.Cleminson	R.Kunert	G.P.Kemp	B.A.Buckingham	D.P.J.Treacy
				A.J.Wright (u/t)
Miss M.I.Gibbons	Miss M.S.Price	Miss G.M.Holyoak	Miss R.Wallace	Miss S.E.Milliner
N.B.L.Knife	F.Karai	C.H.George	H.Robbins	R.K.Watts
Miss C.Redhead	Miss J.S.Roberts	P.L.Burgess	Mrs A.E.Harris	N.C.Waller
T.P.O'Connell	P.A.Hayes	B.E.Dugan	J.N.Reynolds	J.L.Harborne
V.A.Annett	T.R.Singfield	C.M.Lawson	S.R.Hughes	J.M.Warren
N.A.Rolfe	Mrs Y.D.F.Chandler	J.P.Mosses	Miss Y.Selley	Mrs J.I.Haines
Miss S.R.S.Hay	P.K.Leather	K.P.Baker	Miss M.O'Donnell	R.E.Anderson
P.Garratt	P.N.Lloyd	Mrs I.R.Daly		N.Richardson
R.Curtis	Miss C.E.Looby	Mrs L.P.Miller		Miss V.M.Smith
G.C.Crampton (AIS)	A.J.McGregor	B.Datta		Miss A.L.Fisher
		N.B.Thorne (u/t)		Mrs E.Smith
Miss K.Laurence	S.P.Batham	A.V.Norris (u/t)	Miss S.L.Makein	Miss M.A.Addiscott (u/t)
Miss L.A.Kirby	M.C.Boyd (u/t)	Miss M.Lawson (u/t)	Miss H.L.Elliott	Miss S.R.C.F.Ferguson (u/t)
M.D.Swann (u/t)			S.F.Guilbride	
			Miss A.C.Michelle (u/t)	
			Miss A.McClean (u/t)	
			G.C.Riches (u/t)	
			P.Blanchard (u/t)	

Reliefs : I.J.M.Saunders
M.Cleary
B.D.Proudfoot

At about the same time as these changes were taking place a national agreement was reached merging the ATCO 3 and ATCO 2 grades. Until now promotion to ATCO 2 had meant sitting a formal interview, and for the successful Heathrow applicants it inevitably also resulted in a posting to LATCC to validate the promotion. This new agreement removed the interview barrier and provided an ATCO satisfied the requirements of a Performance and Progression Review (PPR) - seven years experience (later reduced to five) and no adverse comments on his/her personal file - progression to the higher grade was automatic. Henceforth a posting out was not necessary with the result that tours of duty became more extended, with some staff later achieving over thirty years.

RUNWAY RESURFACING

The next two or three years saw work take place to improve the surface and facilities of the two main runways. First to receive attention was 28L/ 10R, on which resurfacing work began in May 1973. Traffic was light enough for the runway to be closed each night at 2000 and returned to service the next morning at 0700, with work areas feathered off. As might be expected the work lasted several months and required the closure of 23/05 when block 85 was receiving attention. Cat 2 operations on 28L and 10R and Cat 3 ops on 28L were suspended for the duration of the work. Resurfacing of 28R/10L followed, starting in May 1974, with a slightly earlier return to service in the morning at 0630. This also involved a short closure of 23/05 for work to be completed on the threshold of 28R. In the brief interval between these two periods of resurfacing runway 10L was brought up to Cat 3a status in February 1974, followed later by 10R in October 1975. The last of the main runways to achieve Cat 3 status was 28R in September 1976. With increasing numbers of aircraft

able to operate in very low visibilities it was also necessary now to restrict the number of aircraft calling for start when the RVR was well below their minimum. From 1st February 1973 no request for push back or taxi could be made until certain RVR - minima requirements were met, so that the holding points did not become cluttered by aircraft unable to depart.

ALDIS LAMPS DISAPPEAR

No one sitting in the Tower at this time could have envisaged the radical surgery that would be performed on the VCR three years later as they watched it receive one of its periodic facials, which involved, amongst other things, taking the Aldis lamps down from their ceiling mounted brackets. How did the Aldis lamps manage to survive so long in the VCR? Be realistic - you would not have expected to find a signals square at Heathrow in the 1970s. But linger on they did. Imagine this scene. A 747 taxies out, destination New York, but has radio failure at the holding point. No problem! He gets a steady green from the Aldis and takes off. Everybody STORCAL(E)S and CATCUMS in the approved fashion and he arrives at New York only to get a flashing red - don't want you, go away!

Apart from one or two occasions when a green was given to reinforce a landing clearance the only use they saw was with Brian Smith on night duties. He would delight in finding some innocent soul walking across from the Queens Building or Terminal 2 towards the bus park and would follow them (completely oblivious to their company) with the Aldis spot light. Great fun for the watchers aloft. One day, while the work was progressing, Alastair McLean remarked that they would make very acceptable domestic lamps, so Derek Harrlss gave them to him as a present.

Following the failure of the previous attempt in 1964 to reduce flight deck R/T workload in the immediate post take-off phase a further trial was introduced on 4th January 1973, with the first LATCC frequency being given at start up by the Ground Movement Planner (GMP) at the same time as the SID and SSR code:- 'G-APMC - cleared to Paris Orly, Standard Seaford One departure, squawk Alpha 0302. The London Control frequency will be 132.05 when instructed'. This was still not completely satisfactory, and only when the frequency was added to the published SID information over two years later, on 6th November 1975, was this problem finally resolved.

The extra day cover now provided brought corresponding reductions in night duty staffing which meant that less space was required to cater for those taking horizontal rest and enabled the various separate facilities currently in existence to be combined. A new dormitory was opened on the seventh floor containing eight cubicles, for use by both male and female staff, and this enabled the former male dormitory to be re-designated as a rest room. The female dormitory on the fourth floor was converted into additional space for the training section.

ATCA SALARIES AND LHG

Towards the end of what was otherwise a quiet year, in which only the installation of a DME facility on 10R and 28L for operational trials merits comment, the assistants received a pay rise. Their Union, the Civil and Public Services Association, had been involved in protracted negotiations and a certain amount of industrial action by CPSA members in general had been necessary to achieve a settlement. The new scales were as follows :-

In his notification of these latter scales the Union secretary apologises for having failed to increase the consolidated maxima of the women's scales by £5.00, but points out that the new rates are considerably higher than previously and that there will be substantial amounts of back pay

The new salaries had hardly begun to be paid when the ATCAs had further reason to celebrate, finding that they were eligible along with the ATCOs to receive a salary supplement known as Long Hours Gratuity (LHG). This related to excess hours worked over a six week period and had to be claimed, giving details of duties that had been worked. Factors affecting the amount of the payment included leave taken, weekend and public holiday working, as well as the standard rostered hours, and a number of people became expert at maximising this extra income. Among their number were Keith Waud, Tony Watkins and Bob Neville, and others would often approach them for advice on how to improve their payments. One obvious effect was that it made staff more aware of when they took leave, particularly over Bank holidays, and overnight the scene changed from one where people were fighting to be off duty at Christmas to one where everyone wanted to work. Very sociable but the excess staff were not required for the much reduced movement rates over the holiday period, and the cost in LHG was high so, at times, staff had to be directed to take leave against their wishes. As a by-product of LHG the assistant Watch supervisors assumed the burden of checking all the LHG claim forms submitted by ATCOs on the Watch to ensure that they were accurately completed, and of countersigning the ATCA forms. There were a surprising number of errors, not always in the claimant's favour. LHG lasted until 1984, when it was absorbed into the salary as SLP/UHP.

ATCA 1 Scale (7.11.73)		ATCA 2 Scale (7.11.73)			ATCA 3 Scale (7.11.73)	
	Shift element		Shift element	Age		Shift element
1930	270	1243	199	17	960	180
2042	286	1297	208	18	1038	187
2154	302	1353	216	19	1120	202
2266	317	1423	228	20	1197	215
2407	337	1493	239	21	1256	226
2548	357	1563	250	Main scale -	1326	239
		1633	261		1383	249
		1703	272		1440	259
		1750	280		1497	269
		1797	288		1554	280
					1614	291

It is amusing to compare these rates with the scales that existed some twenty years earlier where, as you can see, a distinction is made between the male and female staff.

ATCA 1 Scale (1.1.53)	ATCA 2 Scale Consolidated from 1.1.53		ATCA 3 Scale Consolidated from 1.1.53	
As for ATCA 2 plus £50 (male and female)	Male	Female	Male	Female
	310	310	235	235
	330	330	255	255
	350	315	295	295
	370	360	320	315
	390	370	345	330
	410	380	365	340
	430	395	385	350
	450	410	400	360
	470	425	415	370
	490	435	430	385
	510	445	445	400
	525	455	465	405
	540	460	485	
	555		500	
	570			

VORTEX SPACING

Wake vortices had not really caused any concern until the larger aircraft types such as the Boeing 747 and Concorde started to appear. There had been one accident at Heathrow in 1952 when a Rapide landing on runway 23 had been thrown out of control as it encountered the wash of a Stratocruiser that had just landed on 28R (see annex) but spacing was still considered to be very much at the discretion of the individual pilot. However there was a growing awareness that these much heavier aircraft could produce potentially disastrous vortices and, as they came into service, large separation minima were initially imposed to protect smaller aircraft operating in their vicinity. These were then reduced as operational experience was gained but it is interesting to record that, when Concorde began test flying, these were some of the required separation minima.

1) A minimum of four minutes between a landing Concorde and a succeeding landing aircraft.

(2) A minimum of four minutes between a departing Concorde and aircraft departing from the same runway or a crossing runway or a parallel runway separated by less than 3,500 feet. This was increased to five minutes if the succeeding aircraft was departing from an intersection on the same runway.

(3) No aircraft at the same height, or less than 2,000 feet below, to be vectored into the airspace behind a Concorde contained in the segment of a circle 10nm radius centred on the centre of the Concorde radar target and extending 60 degrees either side of the track made good by the Concorde.

By 1974 knowledge of the cause, nature and effects of the phenomenon had increased sufficiently for ICAO to formulate new wake vortex separation minima applicable to aircraft on approach, and these had a significant effect when introduced at Heathrow. The new minima were based on Maximum Take Off Weight Authorised (MTWA) and placed every aircraft into one of four weight groups - Heavy, Medium, Small and Light - spacing on final approach being determined by an aircraft's weight group in relation to that of the preceding traffic rather than by simple radar separation. The required minima were:-

Lead aircraft	Following aircraft	Spacing reqd
Heavy	Heavy	4nm
Heavy	Medium	5nm
Heavy	Small	6nm
Heavy	Light	8nm
Medium	Heavy	*
Medium	Medium	3nm
Medium	Small	4nm
Medium	Light	6nm
Small	Heavy	*
Small	Medium/Small	3nm
Small	Light	4nm
Light	Heavy/Medium/Small/Light	*

* Where spacing is shown by an asterisk wake vortex separation was not required

Typical examples of each group were the Boeing 747 = Heavy, Trident = Medium, Viscount = Small, and DH-125 = Light. With the introduction of these new minima not only did the No.2 Director find that he had a more complex spacing task but the No.1 Directors also had to consider the sequence of traffic leaving the stacks to ensure that the best combinations of aircraft were achieved, even if some judicious juggling of traffic was necessary. Speed control to maintain these final approach separations was applied only as far as the outer marker, not strictly in accordance with Manual Part 1 procedures, and there was an inevitable reduction of the spacing after that point for which there was no obvious solution. The new minima also meant that as the proportion of Heavy aircraft increased so the Airport's capacity would be reduced.

Also in 1974, with scheduled traffic constantly on the increase, the BAA was finally forced to make the Airport PPO to non-scheduled flights - commercial, executive and private - for the whole of the congested morning period of 0700 to 1300. Traffic using the services of Special VFR was also rising and, in readiness for the Farnborough Air Show, procedures were introduced to regulate the associated high helicopter activity by making routes H1 and H7 uni-directional for the Show week. Until 1400 daily helicopters were routed on H1 from Barnes to Woking only and on H7 from Banstead to Barnes only, after which the direction was reversed. In subsequent years similar procedures would become necessary to safeguard the operation of helicopters into Ascot racecourse during Royal Ascot week, and into Epsom racecourse for the Derby meeting.

By now the method of controlling taxying and towing movements by either descriptive routeings by day in good visibility, or by use of the green centre line lights and red stop bars at other times, was accepted as the most effective solution to the GMC problem and the redundant DRI boards had passed into ATC history. With increasing numbers of BAA staff able to carry out airfield inspections - trained by Eric Percival and Paddy Fennell in the ATC training office - the need for lighting operators to leave the VCR for long periods also disappeared. Information derived from the ASMI was used to support operations in low visibility and, if this occurred during daylight hours, a hood could be fitted around the radar screen to improve the picture quality. The controller's or lighting operator's face pressed against this completed the light exclusion process, but it was easy to become absorbed in this miniature world only to realise when you next surfaced from your docking bay that the fog had thinned and aircraft were again visible outside. Occasionally, at the request of either the Fire Service or a sadistic ATC Watch Supervisor, an ASMI exercise would be arranged using a number of AFS vehicles, to allow both parties experience of operation to an incident site in low visibility, and information such as current position (by block numbers) or approaching turns might be passed. The vehicles would often split into two groups and more than one ATCO found that chaos could result if he or the AFS transposed the respective group call signs. Towards the end of 1974 another item of Airport furniture was also retired. Heathrow had once possessed two light beacons, a white and green aerodrome beacon situated 2.5 nms ENE of the Airport which was permanently withdrawn from use on 1st July 1957, and the green ident beacon now coding 'LH' situated south of block 96, which was switched on and off for the last time on the night of 31st October/1st November 1974.

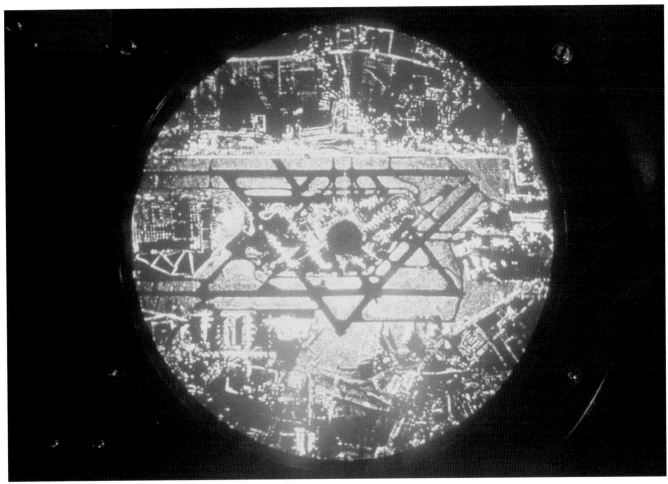

The ASMI as seen peering into the hood in 1975. (Pete Bish)

COMPUTER ASSISTED APPROACH SEQUENCING (CAAS)

Research at RRE Malvern indicated that, using computer derived information, controllers could achieve more accurate spacing and thereby improve runway capacity. Results from similar work carried out at New York JFK in 1967 using an FAA system showed that a possible improvement of 5 to 10 per cent in runway capacity could result, and additionally controller workload could be reduced by Computer Assisted Approach Sequencing (CAAS) performing the simple mental calculations and presenting the information in book keeping form on a touch-wire display. Initial trials took place at the ATCEU in 1971 and 1972, firstly using ATCOs from Scotland, prior to a number of Heathrow ATCOs (including Dick Smith, Alastair McLean and John Pemberton) taking the concept one step further. In turn this lead to a much larger evaluation of the system during October and November 1974 conducted on the Heathrow simulator. 'D' Watch were chosen to provide the Heathrow 'guinea pigs' and a total of seventeen ATCOs took part. The system used two computers, an Elliott 920B and a Ferranti Argus 500, and each ATCO was given about thirty hours training spread over six days to familiarise himself with the new equipment which included electronic data displays (EDDs), touchwire displays (TWDs) and rolling balls. Using CAAS the Director would 'acquire' an aircraft as it left the stack by using the rolling ball, after which the system issued headings and speeds, supported by track prediction lines, to achieve a target threshold time based on the preceding aircraft. CAAS ignored the possibility of vertical separation, using only the minimum three miles horizontal radar separation to

produce four mile final approach spacing. Inbounds to other airfields such as Northolt and Leavesden were not included in the program and had to be dealt with manually. Results of the trials were, however, very disappointing, part of the blame being attributed to the fact that ATCOs had been given little opportunity to contribute to the development of the software. Although certain parts of the system such as the EDDs and TWDs were considered worthy of further investigation, CAAS itself was considered unsafe in heavy traffic and often increased the ATCO's workload rather than reducing it. Headings issued were found, at times, to generate a confliction requiring intervention, and other headings took aircraft outside the vectoring area available to Approach. The slowness of the computer could raise doubts in the ATCO's mind as to how to proceed, and the system would also produce unusual solutions to a situation which would not have readily occurred to a controller. The spacing achieved was far from satisfactory, varying over three exercises from 3.1 nms to 7.6 nms, and so operational trials were deferred. However the concept of some of these (then) advanced pieces of equipment would surface again much later. The metering device which indicated when to start traffic from the stacks onto intermediate approach was developed into the much improved EAT machine in use at LATCC two decades later, and the prediction and vectoring device was also refined and re-appeared during 1998 as part of the FAST trial at Bournemouth although once again it was rejected.

HI-JACKS

Prior to 1968 it was unusual to hear that an aircraft had been hi-jacked and only once, in 1961, had the annual total worldwide reached double figures. But the popularity of this type of 'unlawful act' really took off - please excuse the pun - in 1968, particularly involving Cuba which had a rather benevolent attitude to offenders. However the rest of the World also recorded substantially higher returns, pushing totals to over eighty per year in 1969 and 1970 before they began to fall again. Heathrow had first been introduced to this form of aerial piracy in September 1970 when two Palestinian guerrillas attempted, fortunately unsuccessfully, to hi-jack an El Al Boeing 707 inbound from Amsterdam. A male hi-jacker was attacked by a steward and fatally wounded in the ensuing struggle, while a female was overcome by a number of passengers. This woman, Leila Khaled, was carrying a hand grenade which she dropped on the floor of the flight deck with its pin pulled but a faulty spring prevented it from exploding. Perhaps not surprisingly the aircraft burst a number of tyres when it landed on 28R and the runway was closed for some time while the security forces dealt with the situation. The Air controller, incidentally, was John Davis (again!) - it was he who had been working the position when the 'Double Echo' and 'Whisky Echo' tragedies occurred. The El Al jet would have been a major prize but was just part of a massive operation which resulted in the seizure of four other aircraft which were later destroyed on the ground - Pan Am Boeing 747 N752PA in Egypt, and TWA Boeing 707 N8715T, Swissair DC-8 HB-IDD and BOAC Super VC10 G-ASGN in Jordan.

Then, on 7th January 1975, Heathrow once again found itself involved, this time with a British registered aircraft, when a British Airways BAC 1-11 G-AVMP landed on 28R and was routed to block 115. It had taken off from Manchester as Speedbird 4069 to Heathrow with 52 on board, but en route a hi-jacker armed with a pistol and a grenade (both of which turned out to be fakes) demanded payment of £100,000 and a flight to Paris. The negotiations that followed were still in progress when Alan Carter arrived for his night shift. Surprised to discover all positions still open, and having not seen the news that day, he chose to take over the planning position, only to find himself very much involved in the incident as the frequency had been set aside for the exclusive use of Mike Papa. Some time later, when Mike Papa began to talk about departure, there was obviously a fair amount of co-ordination to be effected but eventually Alan was able to issue line up clearance. However cables had been laid across the runway in association with the incident and when Mike Papa called for take off clearance Alan had initially to decline and tell him of the obstruction but Mike Papa was adamant that he had to go. So Alan quickly worked out the available distance before the aircraft reached the cables, informed the pilot and gave him 'at your discretion cleared take off', which he did. Although it was supposedly bound for Paris everyone, including the media, seemed to know that its destination was Stansted. Fortunately the hi-jacker himself did not appear to realise this until well into the flight and he was arrested while trying to escape with an hostage, one of the cabin crew, later being sentenced to seven years imprisonment. The passengers on the flight were disembarked at an early stage, and the only casualty of the hi-jacking was the steward taken along as a hostage who was bitten by a police dog in the chase but not seriously hurt.

The ANK in the VCR being used to input departure messages. (Geoff Bullock)

IBM9020D

A major advance in flight plan data processing came later in the year when the IBM9020D entered service. Ordered in 1972 at a cost of £25 million it comprised a triplex operational system together with a developmental system in the LATCC equipment room. The operational system had a computer complex containing three modified IBM 360/65 computers, and also included three modified IBM 360/50 computers to organise the flow of flight data into and out of the central processing complex. Peripheral devices were provided at LATCC, the Manchester Sub-Centre, Gatwick and Heathrow for the input of initial flight data, the activation and update of this data and the presentation of printed information in the form of flight strips. Stored flight plans were automatically processed as if they had been entered at one of the input devices, and an SSR code was allocated to every flight plan entered into the FDPS in accordance with programmed criteria. At Heathrow the peripheral equipment comprised:-

(1)   In Flight Clearance a teleprinter connected to the 9020D and manned by a specialist teleprinter operator (STPO), for the input of data on flights not held in the store. Pro-formae had to be completed by the assistants in strict format and handed to the STPO for transmission.

(2)   In Approach Control a flight strip printer (FSP) for the printing of strips on inbound flights. If for any reason a strip was not printed a phone call to the VCR was necessary to request the required data, as there was no input device in Approach.

(3)   In Aerodrome Control an Alpha Numeric Keyboard (ANK) and two FSPs. The ANK and one of the FSPs were used for the input of departure messages and amendments to, or requests for, information held in the computer while the other FSP printed arrival and departure strips. If either of the FSPs failed its service could be transferred to the other.

Details of departures were printed out forty minutes before the ETD (or P time) and retained until four hours after the ETD when the flight was automatically deleted unless an update had been entered.

It was the assistants, obviously, who were most affected by the introduction of this new equipment, needing to learn the computer's rules for input (formats), and the content of each of the flight plan's ten fields (groups of characters). Field 01, for example, was the message type and was one of seven two letter codes :- FP = flight plan, AM = amendment, DM = activation, HM = hold or cancel hold, SR = strip request, RS = remove strips and PR = progress report. Provision was made for those times when traffic in general was being extensively delayed, for whatever reason, by the input of a message to the computer which would delay the printing of all departure strips by an agreed amount of time, thereby avoiding a mountain of strips building up in front of the GMP controller. And for those hopefully rare occasions when the computer failed a printed copy of all the stored flight plans was available so that strips could be produced manually.

When the IBM9020D entered service in 1975 it was only able to provide printed data but the intention was that it would be developed for radar data processing as well. The original computers remained in service until 1989 when a major upgrade was performed.

CODE-CALLSIGN CONVERSION ARRIVES

The requirement for aircraft to carry SSR transponders with Mode A (4096 codes) and Mode C (automatic height reporting) capability had progressively been extended until it now applied to the majority of UK controlled airspace, and on the ground improved processors led to rapid improvements in the information displayed on the radar screen. The primitive slashes were replaced by a 64 code and then a 4096 code presentation, to which was added a second line with level information. Finally, with the advent of code - callsign conversion, the data block displayed the aircraft's radio callsign (flight number or registration), its level and an indication of its route. This latter was either a two letter code taken from the ICAO location indicator for its destination Airport if landing in the UK eg:- LL for Heathrow, or a single letter to denote its UK exit point eg:- D = Dover. On the aircraft's flight plan there was a section where the different types of transponder carried were identified by a single letter code and one day Pan American's flight Clipper 106 was asked to confirm whether it had a 64 or 4096 code transponder. After a pause where the crew were obviously doing some counting the reply came back 'We reckon it's 63'. The increased information was very welcome, making the process of identification considerably easier and reducing requests for level checks significantly, but nevertheless had its

SVFR occupied the console in Approach originally designed for the second No 2 position in the parallel configuration. This view shows the usual mode of operation with 10cm radar selected on the lower tube, 50cm above and self contained strip display. Equipment to the Controller's left (top to bottom) are; Anemometer reading, SSR selector/filter buttons, D/F, Telephones and R/T selectors. Vortex spacing crib sheet appears left of the ATCO's arm and tell-tale ash tray dates this picture to a by gone age! (Geoff Bullock)

drawbacks. With so many labels on the screen it was at times difficult to pick out Heathrow traffic, and in 1979 ORCAM (Originating Region Callsign Allocation Method) would further complicate the situation as there would no longer be specific codes allocated to Heathrow from the A11xx and A30xx blocks. Instead aircraft would retain the code allocated on departure. Chris Harris, who was in the ATC Ops section at this time, and Rod Metcalfe were tasked with finding a solution to this problem and hit on the idea of filtering by the two letter destination code. Those pertinent to Heathrow were identified and isolated on a radar thumb-wheel as Mode D, with additional selections made as necessary on other wheels to suit each individual's taste. Typical selections would be the inbounds together with the altitude only of departures, unless they were from Heathrow's easterly runways to Woodley when full information would be required.

SUBSIDARY AIRFIELDS TRAFFIC

For a while in the 1970s Heathrow Approach provided an expanded service, handling inbounds to and departures from Luton, and also departures from Leavesden, Elstree and Northolt, as well as fulfilling its normal responsibilities towards Heathrow's inbounds and easterly departures on Brecon SIDs, and to the occasional Leavesden, Elstree or Northolt arrival from the Airways system.

Luton inbounds via Bovingdon:
Luton inbounds routed to Ongar (Lambourne) remained under the control of TMA (N) until transferred to Luton Approach, and were cleared to the Luton NDB via Brookmans Park. Procedures existed to protect Heathrow inbounds vertically. Inbounds to Bovingdon, however, were transferred to Heathrow Approach as though they were Heathrow inbounds. Heathrow then passed the details to Luton and co-ordinated an inbound release. The aircraft was descended in the Bovingdon holding pattern, and when Heathrow was on westerlies it would be cleared to set course for the Luton NDB when it reached minimum stack level and could be cleared to descend en route to 4,000 feet or lower. When Heathrow was on easterlies the aircraft descended in the Bovingdon holding pattern to 4,000 feet before transfer to Luton Approach who would continue the descent in the holding pattern to 3,500 feet before clearing the aircraft from overhead Bovingdon to the Luton NDB. There were times, of course, when Luton traffic entered the stack at high level due to delays at Heathrow and had to accept the Heathrow delay although there was none at Luton - not the best way to impress the customer with the service, and leading to some irate comments from crews about the system.

Luton departures to Woodley - Heathrow on easterlies:
Although there was no problem when Heathrow was on westerlies Luton departures to Woodley when Heathrow was on easterlies were required for a time to work Heathrow Approach due to the interaction with Heathrow's inbound stream from both the northerly stacks. The departure routeing was via Beacon Hill (Henton) at 4,000 feet to Woodley at flight level 70 but the aircraft could be turned towards Woodley after it had passed the Bovingdon 329 radial and 3,000 feet. It was the responsibility of TMA (N) to separate the departures against Luton's inbounds through Bovingdon, which was achieved by restricting the outbound aircraft to

Beacon Hill (Henton) at 3,000 feet, and he was also responsible for the application of take-off restrictions to achieve a longitudinal separation of five minutes at Woodley. This was quite essential due to the mix of traffic using Luton at that time which, even if the executive types were excluded, ranged from Heralds, Viscounts and Britannias to BAC1-11s and TriStars. The latter two types figured in the fleet of Court Line who, to reflect their involvement in the holiday sector, had their aircraft painted in distinctive colour schemes, each aircraft in a different pastel shade of blue, green, pink etc. This, of course, gave rise to such comments as 'what's the flavour of the day' which must have become quite tedious to the crews after a time. The performance of many of these aircraft meant that to leave them at flight level 70 to Woodley was very restrictive, so most were the subject of a request for further climb to the relevant TMA controller, and a modest competition existed to see who could achieve the highest flight level at Woodley. These procedures remained in force until the departure route was moved further west (through Norry).

Leavesden, Elstree, Northolt departures to Woodley - Heathrow on easterlies:
Departures from these three airfields to Woodley when Heathrow was on easterlies were also made subject to release by Heathrow Approach, for the same reasons as the Luton departures above. Heathrow assumed responsibility, too, for the positioning and descent of Leavesden and Elstree traffic inbound via the Airways system, in addition to the service provided to Northolt's Airways inbounds. Having left the stacks they were descended (eventually) to 1,500 feet, appropriately coordinated with Northolt, and given a heading for their intended destination. Following the TMA changes recorded below this procedure needed to be amended to keep such flights in controlled airspace and resulted in them being directed to Chiltern at 2,500 feet whence they made their own way to their intended destination.

The final change of identity for a Heathrow holding facility, at least for the period of this book, took place at midnight on 27th/28th March 1974, when Ongar was re-named Lambourne. This established the set as Bovingdon and Lambourne to the north and Ockham and Biggin to the south. Changes to the TMA were also in the pipeline, to update the airspace and enable it to accommodate the higher performance aircraft which were entering service in increasing numbers. From 24th April 1975 there was a contraction of the eastern boundary of the old TMA, and an extension to the northeast over Luton and Stansted. More pertinent, from Heathrow's point of view, was the lowering of the upper limit of the London Control Zone (from flight level 110) to 2,500 feet - the new base of the TMA. Finally the transition altitude within the TMA was raised to 6,000 feet. As a result of these changes there were necessary amendments to the SIDs, and the opportunity was taken to renumber them (except the 'Worthing One' which was withdrawn on 5th December 1974) to better identify the runway used for departure.

28R = 20	28L = 22	23 = 24
10R = 31	10L = 33	05 = 35

There were now six SID exit points in use on easterlies - Brecon, Clacton, Daventry, Dover, Ibsley and Seaford with the additional Midhurst SID on westerlies.

RAFFLES ONE

1975 saw the end of an era when one of ATC's favourite customers made his last flight after ten years of operations from the Airport. From early in 1965 Eric Raffles, the Jewish owner of a textile manufacturing company, had based his Beechcraft Travel Air (initially registered OY-AOP and then later G-ASZC) at Heathrow, using the Fields apron in block 94 on the southside. This he used on virtually a daily basis to commute to Manchester, leaving Heathrow soon after 0730 in the morning and returning at tea time. Occasionally he would stop off at Hawarden (Chester) on his way north. It was always a pleasure to work the aircraft and Mr. Raffles built quite a rapport with ATC, generously offering lifts to anyone needing to get to, or back from, Manchester. His reward was to be accommodated almost always - for take off or landing - on 28L/10R, and to be able to phone only the briefest details of his flight to Flight Clearance to make up what became Heathrow's first 'stored flight plan'. He was also probably the first private owner to be allowed a personalised R/T callsign 'Raffles One', shown on the flight progress strips as RZ 1. Despite the attempt by ATC to write off his aircraft on New Year's Eve 1965 (see accident section) Mr. Raffles continued his long distance commute, changing aeroplanes late in 1969 to a Beechcraft Baron with Swedish marks SE-EXK. When the time came to register it in Britain (mid 1970) he was offered the letters G-AYIA but requested the more appropriate G-AYID from the ARB 'for a bit of fun'. Having no minima for bad weather operations his slow final approach speeds allowed him to land with RVRs down to 150/200 metres, making diversions rare. Quite suddenly, in 1975, and after some 2,000 return trips, Mr.Raffles sold his business, re-married and bought a farm in Somerset. When Pete Bish visited him in 2000 he was still the perfect gentleman - as everyone remembered him - but had done very little flying in the meantime. One of his favourite memories of Heathrow relates to vacating 28L at block 85 one night for the southside and asking if he should change to the ground frequency. The reply, from the female ATCO working the Air position was 'No, Mr. Raffles. You can stay with me tonight'.
He liked that …..!

'Raffles One' at rest on the Block 94 apron in 1970. (Pete Bish)

TAXIWAY DEVELOPMENT

Work on the Airport around this time provided additional parking for peak period use, and development of the 'L' and 'M' aprons together with extensions to the taxiway system north west of the Tower. From 1st June 1975 stands, which effectively extended the 'E' and 'F' aprons, could be activated by the BAA when there was heavy demand, provided that ATC could approve their use. Situated at the north east end of block 61(I) and the south west end of 62(I) their periods of use were indicated by a sign, covered when they were not active, situated beside the taxiway leading into the park from block 72(I). Work went ahead to install stop bars at both ends of this parking area, creating a new block 77 between 61(I) and 62(I). Around the north west corner of the Central Terminal Area new taxiways were under construction, to extend the encirclement of the central aprons by an inner and outer taxiway. New routes joining block 37(I) to block 36, and the north - south section of the inner taxiway between 37(I) and 52(I) became available, as did the new outer taxiway from block 36 to 52(0). But, in addition, unexpected and comprehensive attention had to be given to measurement of wing tip clearances on taxiways and in holding areas following two collisions which occurred in May and June 1975, in both cases caused by a Boeing 747 striking a smaller aircraft waiting for an intersection departure (see Appendix). These followed two previous incidents, which also involved Boeing 747s, and resulted in the introduction of a number of taxying restrictions.

GRAHAM HILL

29th November 1975. The last hour of an afternoon duty. John Rymill (No.1 Director) and John Cant (Approach) looking after the traffic. Although fog had been forecast it was thicker than expected and at 2020 the visibility at Heathrow, Gatwick and Southend was 100 metres, at Stansted 400 metres, and at Luton it was 2,500 metres but this would fall to 800 metres at 2050. A Lambourne release had been given for a Piper Aztec N6645Y inbound to Elstree from Marseille, and its first contact with Approach was at 2119 when the aircraft was eight miles south of Lambourne on descent to 4,000 feet. The aircraft was turned on to a radar heading of 290 degrees direct to Elstree and at 2121 was informed of a deterioration of the Elstree visibility to 800 metres. At 2122 the aircraft was given a course correction of ten degrees left (280) and cleared to descend to 1500 feet on the London QNH setting. At 2127 the pilot reported at 1,500 feet and was advised that his range from Elstree was four miles. He then requested further descent clearance, and was advised that further descent was at his own discretion. Shortly afterwards the pilot was heard to say 'Elstree' on the Heathrow Approach frequency, suggesting that he believed himself to be in contact with Elstree, although he had not been given a frequency change. No reply was received to Approach's next transmission (three miles to run) and when the aircraft was two and a half miles from Elstree the primary and secondary returns from the aircraft both disappeared. The pilot, as supposed, had made contact with Elstree calling '45 Yankee finals', but shortly afterwards the aircraft collided with trees and crashed on Arkley golf course, killing all six on board.The accident made front page headlines as the pilot was Graham Hill, a well known Formula One racing driver, who had been in France to oversee final

Following the merger of BOAC and BEA into British Airways, many aircraft flew in their old livery but with new titles for a considerable time. The HS.121 Trident was the mainstay of the Domestic and European BA fleet for most of the 1970s and topped Heathrow's movements chart by type. Trident 3 G-AYVF is seen here in the TriStar pen - or 'Biscuit Tin' - at the eastern end of blocks 50/51 in November 1978. (Pete Bish)

adjustments that were being made to a prototype racing car, though he did not drive the car himself. Failure to renew various sections of his licence meant that at the time of the accident he held only a United Kingdom PPL containing Group A and B ratings and a night rating, but his certificate of experience and medical certificate were current and valid. In addition the aircraft was unregistered and stateless, resulting from the cancellation of its American registration when it was sold to Grand Prix (Bahamas) Limited of Nassau and not subsequently re-registered by them elsewhere. The aircraft continued, however, to display its former US registration marks. The accident report concluded that the pilot attempted to land in conditions of low visibility at an airfield not equipped with the appropriate precision landing aids. The precise reason for the aircraft hitting the ground short of the runway could not be established but the possibility that the pilot underestimated his distance from the aerodrome and descended prematurely was not excluded.

CONCORDE

British Overseas Airways Corporation and British European Airways had been merged on 1st April 1974 to form the new British Airways, which for a while gave Air controllers the opportunity to say to a Trident 'after the departing Company 747', or similar, before the identities of the two constituents were lost beneath a new colour scheme. The airline was also preparing to accept deliveries of an aircraft which had been flying since 2nd March 1969, and which would still turn heads thirty years later. Already familiar to millions due to its shape and noise the Concorde, although it had landed at Heathrow before, found that its first official visit would not go to plan. Following a landing on 28R the aircraft (G-BSST) was routed west of the Tower on the inner taxiway for its stand in the 'Hotel' apron, where a military band and large reception party were waiting. As the aircraft approached the entrance to the cul-de-sac the band struck up, only to see the aircraft taxy past and not re-appear for five minutes while a suitable route back was found for it. In anticipation of its entry into commercial service new SST

routes and procedures were promulgated for implementation on 14th August 1975.

These were designed to permit early acceleration to supersonic speeds without the production of a sonic boom over land and covered the Oceanic operations of both Air France from Paris and British Airways from Heathrow. Track SMB was established for Heathrow departures, with a routeing Heathrow - Lyneham - Merlin (51.20N 05.00W) - 50.30N 12.00W, and this would also initially be used by the return flights pending the introduction of a further Track SNL for their specific use at a later stage. Unlike other Oceanic flights the Oceanic clearance would be obtained before start-up, and squawks A6204 (for Track SMB) and A6205 (for Track SNL) were reserved for SST movements. Staff attending Technical Staff Courses around this time were told, amongst other things, that Concorde had a supplementary fuel tank to cover its taxying from stand to line up, and that because of this the aircraft would need to be airborne no later than ten minutes from engine start. Also that the crews of inbound flights would prefer to absorb inbound delays through linear holding - reducing speed from Mach 2 at an earlier stage than normal - rather than holding over a beacon. But in practice neither of these requirements was obvious and the few movements in a day presented no special handling problems although its high intermediate and final approach speeds - downwind 250 knots, base leg 210 knots and on final 190 knots - did make precise spacing difficult to achieve, both in front of it and behind. On easterlies approval was frequently sought for the aircraft to land on 10R, which not only reduced its taxying distance but also benefited the No.2 Director. The fact that Joe Hanbury was able to organise over ninety trans Atlantic familiarisation flights on the aircraft for ATC personnel had nothing to do with the success rate of such requests, of course! With the outbounds it was found that early removal of the speed limit on 10R departures to Woodley only served to increase the radius of turn, never exactly on a sixpence, which could find it struggling to stay inside controlled airspace as it came round to its westerly heading. The aircraft received its Aircraft Type Certificate on 5th November 1975, and began commercial services on 21st

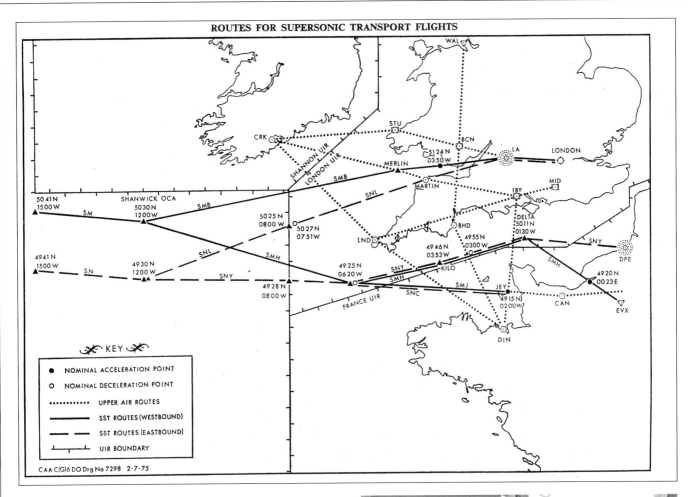

KEY

- ● NOMINAL ACCELERATION POINT
- ○ NOMINAL DECELERATION POINT
- •••••• UPPER AIR ROUTES
- —— SST ROUTES (WESTBOUND)
- – – – SST ROUTES (EASTBOUND)
- ⊢—⊣ UIR BOUNDARY

CAA C(G)6 DO Drg No 7298 2·7·75

January 1976 as BA300 to Bahrain. The Air France Concorde took off at the same time (1140), operating as AF025 to Dakar en route to Rio de Janeiro.

SPLIT AIR

As traffic increased so the services of a 'phones' man were needed more often by the Air controller to carry out his essential co-ordination. Finally it was agreed that a new position of Air Movement Planning (AMP) would be created to formalise what until now had been an informal service. His remit was to carry out requested co-ordination, to organise the departure sequence for the Air controller, and to pass aircraft their clearances using a discrete frequency (118.5 Mhz), and provision was made for the position to be manned for ten hours a day (0830 to 1830). After a little experience had been gained it was decided that the passing of clearances would revert to GMP but it was also evident that quite a few of the Air controllers resented having their departure sequence set up for them although they accepted that the position had become too busy to be handled efficiently by just one person. A decision followed to split the Air position into two, Air Arrivals and Air Departures, which proved to be the solution to the problem. During normal operations this gave each of the controllers responsibility for the movements on just one runway, and freed up planning and coordination time. Expedition also benefited with aircraft and ATC transmissions being shared between the two frequencies - no longer would the Air controller be about to press the transmit switch to give a take-off clearance only to be frustrated by another aircraft checking in with a lengthy 'established' call. There were, of course, deep reservations amongst the ATCOs about the

Alan Wright at the restyled Lighting Panel in 1976 as part of the peripheral layout. Alan went on to be one of the longest serving ATCA/ATSAs (35 years at Heathrow), retiring in 1998. (CAA Archives)

problems that might arise in the event of go-arounds but experience would show that these were easily resolved provided there was effective co-ordination - not difficult as the two Air controllers sat next to each other.

Notam 839/76, which warned of the testing of large sections of taxiway lighting, and 1109/76, which announced the completion of this work, bracketed the introduction of a further upgrade of the lighting panel which took place in the second half of 1976. The panel was again re-styled, being replaced by a smaller unit which allowed the surface to be flat although it was mounted with a slight tilt upwards towards the rear to improve the presentation and ease of selection. Joy Legge, who was posted into Heathrow in 1976 as an ATCA1, was trained on this new panel and became the first female to check out as a Lighting Operator, although she later resigned in 1979 following her marriage to Iain Alexander.

PINK PIG

An advertising balloon, shaped and coloured to resemble a pink pig, was tethered between two of the four chimneys of Battersea Power Station to promote the forth-coming Pink Floyd album 'Animals' (released 23rd January 1977). One westerlies morning it broke free but the device fitted to deflate it in such circumstances failed to operate and the pig floated away eastwards gaining height. Inbound flights had to be warned that they might see a pink pig go past and there were numerous calls from members of the public reporting that pigs *can* fly. Pink Floyd's manager rang to say that he would be prepared to charter an aircraft and chase the pig with a view to shooting it down, but this was politely declined, however, and the balloon is believed to have deflated out to sea.

THE PERIPHERAL LAYOUT

The move to the central area Control Tower had been made some twenty one years earlier, and there was a feeling at Management level that the time was overdue for a radical modernisation of the VCR interior layout. Having ruled out the possibility of a revolving dais the ATCO i/c at the time, Ken Pearson, decided to move for a peripheral layout based on the design favoured by the Americans, and installed at Fort Worth, Texas. There was almost universal agreement amongst the ATC staff that the concept would not adapt to the basic structure of the VCR, and strong warnings were given to him by George Dyer of the Technical Committee and Derek Harriss, by then a Watch Supervisor, that the Air controllers' lines of sight, particularly in respect of departing traffic, would be unacceptable. Approval, however, was given for the design and construction of the relevant furniture which was duly installed, with the Ground Movement Controller isolated on a dais in the centre of the VCR while all other working positions were situated around the perimeter of the room, with a group of desks provided around the western side of the VCR for easterly operations and another group around the eastern side for westerlies. But it was immediately obvious that the fears that had been expressed were justified. Departures quickly climbed above the Air controller's field of view, making his task unacceptably more difficult to perform. The

The westerlies bank of desks of the peripheral layout with Clive George (foreground), Brandon Chapman and John Rymill visible behind. (via Clive George)

location of the desks, close to the air vents, meant that at times it became oppressively hot, and reflections from the windows and the position of the window stanchions caused annoyance. The GMC desk was too far from the other desks and created problems with data transfer, and there was chaos when a runway change occurred with almost everyone having to change their position. A return to the centrally located desk arrangement was recognised as being imperative, and in a little over a year the peripheral layout was removed, much to everyone's relief. Despite the problems associated with the peripheral layout ATCO training continued and amongst those arriving at Heathrow during this period for Tower validation were Wendy McDonald, Brandon Chapman, Tony Croft, Mike Male and Richard Harrison, all of whom were successful despite the problems that existed. When designs for the replacement dais were considered the need for extra space to accommodate trainees was taken into account and the final choice was somewhat different from that which had originally existed. Where the two Air desks had formerly been a combined central unit they were now re-arranged to be two separate desks facing out in the direction of operations from the edge of the dais, with an ample walk-in space behind them.

BRITISH AIRPORTS STAFF INFORMATION SYSTEM (BASIS)

Although they survived these re-configurations of the VCR the days of the Lamson tubes and of the ticker tape, which provided stand information, were numbered. The Lamson tubes were simply no longer needed, with strip printing taking place in the VCR, used departure strips being retained in the VCR for the cross checking of hourly totals, and used arrival strips being taken down to Approach on a convenience basis by ATCAs going on breaks. The system was switched off although the tubes remained in situ for some time without pressure before removal. The ticker tape survived for a couple of years but then also succumbed when the BAA introduced its new British Airports Staff Information

System (BASIS) in 1980, a system based on the Teletext technique which had been developed jointly by the British Broadcasting Corporation and the Independent Broadcasting Authority. A number of video receivers were installed in the VCR and Approach, each fed by a pair of BASIS transmitters. These transmitters provided identical information but to opposite ends of the main cable ring, so even if there was a single transmitter failure or a single central area main cable break information continued to be transmitted. The system had a capacity of over 400 pages covering the status of both arriving and departing flights, in event or scheduled order, for the whole Airport or just on a per Terminal or Company basis. Other pages covered ground movements, stand and jetty information and special messages. Instead of having to transfer information on inbound flights and their stands to their working sheet from a moving tape, which disappeared rapidly into a waste bin in busy periods, GMC controllers now had a video screen to view which retained this information for some time. There was also a page for the GMP controller to monitor the status of traffic he had started, and pages on which essential ATC information could be displayed - items such as runways in use, possible delays etc. With a little experience, often gained during the quiet moments of night duties, the system could be used in many ways to improve the overall service provided by ATC. The BASIS remained in service for almost twenty years, finally needing to be replaced - as did many other computers - to cope with the shift into the year 2000 known as the 'Millennium Bug', although by then its technology was also becoming old, non-standard and difficult to maintain or extend.

REMEMBRANCE DAY HELICOPTER

It had now become established practice to restrict aircraft movements at the Airport for the period of the one minute silence on Remembrance Sunday at the Cenotaph in Whitehall. Respect for the solemnity of the occasion was shown by keeping the airspace in the vicinity of the service

The BASIS display seen in April 1988. (Pete Bish)

free of aircraft noise for a bracketing period of ten minutes. If 28L, 28R or 23 were in use this was achieved by vectoring inbound traffic at least five miles clear of the area, while on easterlies no departures were permitted on routes which might disturb the silence - Daventry, Clacton, Dover and Polar SIDs. These restrictions were later extended to include all departures still on the ground at Heathrow if 10R was in use, by requiring them to be held well back from the holding point so that the Remembrance service at Stanwell could also be conducted without the background whine of jet engines. Helicopter operations were also affected, with route H4 east of Battersea being closed for a period of two hours while the service took place. A similar closure also occurred on the day of the State Opening of Parliament. However, there is a rule which says 'if it can go wrong it will go wrong', and the fickle finger of fate will always be waiting to poke you in the eye. In 1983 the closure of H4 had begun for the Remembrance Sunday service when Joe Hanbury, working the Special VFR position, received a call from a helicopter requesting a clearance on routes H4 and H2. The traffic was not visible on radar, being at 500 feet and not squawking, but Joe replied that the route was not available and instructed the pilot to remain clear of the Control Zone, to which he received the reply of 'Roger, leaving the Zone'. Joe thought nothing more of the episode until staff who had been out on tea breaks at the time came rushing back to ask what had happened. The helicopter had, in fact, already entered the Zone and passed the area of the service when it was told to remain clear so, by reversing course to comply, it went back past the assembly for a second time followed by the TV cameras. Commentators covering the service referred to the 'Police helicopter' providing security cover but the truth was much more embarrassing. In fact it was actually a German Air Force Huey - not the quietest of birds - with very visible markings and a call was received by the Approach Supervisor from the Prime Minister's office shortly afterwards asking for a full report to be submitted by the next morning. Blame was eventually laid on ATC Manston for failing to adequately brief the pilot.

CONTINUOUS DESCENT APPROACHES

Previously much of the effort to reduce aircraft noise nuisance on and around the Airport had been directed at departures, with the introduction of minimum noise routes, noise monitoring, the night curfew etc. But now attention focussed on the inbounds, many still using long established descent profiles and speeds which, studies suggested, could be altered to offer significantly lower noise levels. Observations at Heathrow showed that, under existing operational conditions, about half the westerly landing traffic made its intermediate and final approach without a period of level flight, and the hope was that a much higher proportion of the traffic could be encouraged to optimise its descent in the same way. This would involve greater input of range information from Approach and, of course, the co-operation of pilots. At the same time, by increasing intermediate approach speeds, it was hoped that greater use would be made of low-power, low-drag approaches. A six month trial of Continuous Descent Approaches (CDAs) began on 30th December 1976, initially confined to the two westerly main runways 28L and 28R, and track distances were passed with initial descent by the No.1 Director, then on first contact with the No.2 Director and again when the aircraft was turned onto its ILS intercept heading.

The most obvious way of determining track distance was by relating to preceding traffic, but the variation of speed between intermediate and final approach would often result in quite different estimates, most of them overly optimistic. For the purposes of the trial the speeds were set at 200 knots for the intermediate approach, 170 knots on the closing heading at ATC request, and 150 knots when established down to the outer marker, all with a tolerance of plus or minus 10 knots. Many of the ATCOs were concerned by the 30 knot increase in intermediate approach speed, particularly for traffic coming off the Biggin stack on a westerly heading where the 'S' bend approach might be complicated by the wider radius turns, particularly if there was a strong southerly component in the wind. But no major difficulties were experienced and three months into the trial the LP/LD speeds were re-promulgated as 210 knots intermediate, 160 to 180 knots on, or shortly before, the ILS closing heading at ATC request, and 160 knots when established to the outer marker - all speeds to be flown as accurately as possible. The trial received a generally favourable response, and at the end of the first six months was extended for a further nine months to include the easterly main runways 10L and 10R as well. By the end of this period it was obvious that there were significant benefits not only in terms of reduced noise nuisance but also in fuel saving, so on 31st March 1978 CDAs were confirmed as the standard mode of approach to Heathrow.

Sitting on Air Departures one day Brendan McCartney had just launched an Air France Airbus A300 bound for Paris and turned around to give it a final check before transferring it to London Control. Seeing that the wheels were still down he informed the pilot and received the immediate reply 'Yes, Sir. We use zem for ze take-off'.

During 1976 and 1977 the BAA focussed its attention on various projects aimed at making the manoeuvring area more user friendly for the increasing numbers of large aircraft using Heathrow, perhaps best described as 'letting out the seams'. First to receive attention were blocks 17, 30(0) and 31(0) to which concrete fillets were added early in 1977, allowing large aircraft that vacated at block 17 an easier turn back westbound towards Terminal 3. Fillets were also constructed at about the same time in blocks 98 and 99, adjacent to the turn-off at block 102. Then in May 1977 work got under way to enlarge the 28L holding area which, when completed some six months later, enabled two Boeing 747 size aircraft to be held on the eastern side of block 75 while similar sized aircraft passed on the western side. And when this was finished the 10R holding area in block 98 began to receive similar attention which lasted through the winter into 1978.

HELIROUTE CHANGES

Following a review of the helicopter route structure within the London Control Zone a number of significant changes were announced. The removal of three routes and introduction of two new routes, together with the imposition of a night time ban on the use of certain routes by single engined helicopters, were the major components of the package.

(1)   Routes H1, H8 and H11 ceased to exist.
(2)   New routes H3 and H5 were introduced.
(3)   Single engined helicopters were prohibited at night

An Air France A300 in original livery (Pete Bish)

on routes H7, H9 (from the Airport Spur to Northolt), and H10 (from Northolt to Kew Bridge).

(4)   The Iver turning point was altered and a new turning point West Drayton introduced on a revised H2 route.

DESIGNATION	ROUTE	MAX. ALTITUDES
H2	Marlow-Cookham-Iver-West Drayton-M4 Motorway-Osterley Lock-Grand Union Canal-River Thames-Westland Heliport	1,000 ft (750 ft Osterley Lock-Chiswick Bridge)
H3	Bagshot Mast-M3 Motorway-Thorpe-Shepperton Ferry-Molesey Reservoir-Bushey Park-Teddington Weir-Barn Elms Park-Westland Heliport	1,000 ft Bagshot Mast-Thorpe, 800 ft Thorpe-Barn Elms Park, 1,000 ft Barn Elms Park-Westland Heliport
H4	Zone Boundary-River Thames-Chelsea Bridge-Westland Heliport	1,500 ft Zone Boundary-Chelsea Bridge, 1,200 ft Chelsea Bridge-Westland Heliport
H5	Uxbridge Common Roundabout-Northwood	1,000 ft
H7	Banstead-Nonsuch Park-Raynes Park-Wimbledon Common-Caesar's Camp-Roehampton Park-Barn Elms Park-River Thames-Westland Heliport	1,000 ft
H9	Oxshott Station-Sunbury Lock-Bedfont-Sipson-Airport Spur-Northolt-Northwood	800 ft Oxshott-Sipson, 1,000 ft Sipson-Northwood
H10	Iver-Uxbridge Common-A40(T) Road-Hangar Lane Station-Gunnersbury Park-Kew Bridge-Barnes-Westland Heliport	1,000 ft except 1,200 ft Perivale Golf Course-North Edge of Gunnersbury Park; 750 ft North Edge of Gunnersbury Park-Chiswick Bridge

These revisions, which created a structure composed of seven routes, came into force on 19th May 1977.

1977 ATCA DISPUTE

Towards the end of the summer of 1977 industrial harmony finally evaporated bringing the first recorded withdrawal of labour by ATC staff at Heathrow. Due to a Government pay freeze the CAA refused to pay the ATCAs an agreed increase for using the IBM9020D, which resulted in a ballot of members by the CPSA - the Union representing a large majority of the assistants - over possible strike action. In the event a work to rule was voted more effective and this began in the middle of August, creating the anticipated disruption of traffic and concentrating media attention on the dispute. Threats of suspension were made to a number of assistants, followed by actual suspensions on August 25th which precipitated an all out strike. This continued for

several days until the suspensions were lifted, but feelings remained at boiling point. The assistants resumed their work to rule with Management insisting that they should return to normal working or face further suspensions. There could only be one outcome. An ATCA at LATCC was suspended and the rest walked out again in protest on 1st September and stayed out for two months. The ATCOs, who continued to work, were given strict guidelines by their Union, the Institution of Professional Civil Servants (IPCS), so that there could be no accusations of strike breaking. The assistants, meanwhile, were allowed to picket in front of the Control Tower, but not on the steps, and at the rear exit. The weather was generally fine and the Police found it necessary to restrict the initial large attendance, supplemented at times by guests from other Units, resulting in the introduction of a Watch system for the strikers covering the morning and afternoon duties - by law no picketing could take place at night. Initial support from passengers and other Airport workers began to evaporate as the dispute dragged on but there were still lighter moments. On one occasion the on-coming Watch supervisor, Len Hobbs, arrived for work in his old and rusty Renault followed by Bikash Datta driving his Rolls-Royce, who dropped off Clive George for picket duty. And during a television interview it was let slip that the strike pay the assistants were receiving was better than their normal pay. Towards the end of October, however, the Union's reserves were becoming pretty depleted and a series of meetings took place, culminating in a ballot on whether to continue the strike. Although feeling was still very strong the result was a vote to return to work, which took place on 4th November, but serious damage had been done to morale in the grade. Nationally large numbers of assistants left their Union and at Heathrow there were several resignations. Celia Hall, John Warren and Rod Watts all found alternative employment with Saudia while Mike Smith, Paul Garrett, Annette Kirby and Pete Patrickson moved to the BAA's Apron Control Unit. The wounds inflicted by this long, unsatisfactory dispute were slow to heal and when the assistants were called on a couple of years later to support similar action by other work groups within their Union the response was predictably unenthusiastic.

THE GATWICK LINK

Approval was given for the resurrection of a shuttle service linking Heathrow and Gatwick, which would operate only until construction work on the M25 motorway had progressed sufficiently to provide a satisfactory surface connection. This time a Sikorsky S-61 helicopter, jointly operated by the BAA, British Airways Helicopters and Caledonian Helicopters, would be used in preference to a fixed wing aircraft as had been the case some years earlier. Before the flights began an helicopter strip was prepared, comprising an approach aiming point and take off strip aligned east - west and located on the grass a short distance south of the threshold of runway 05. Although day markings and night lighting were provided it was not intended that it should be used as a landing area except in an emergency. The inbound 'Link' entered the Control Zone at Oxshott at 1,300 feet following a Decca track aligned with helicopter route H9, and then descended to be at 800 feet by Hersham. If visual contact had been established at this stage the pilot could stay at 800 feet up to the missed approach point at Ashford, otherwise he descended to arrive at Ashford at 500 feet and if visual contact was still not established then a missed approach had to be carried out. These procedures applied to all runway configurations, and the outbound followed the reciprocal route and altitude profile. Provided the main 28/10 runways were in use and the visibility was 3kms or more the approach from Ashford was uncomplicated. Having been cleared for its approach to the strip the 'Link' positioned visually, descending to be at air taxi height above the strip, whence it was cleared to air taxi to and touch down in block 96. It then ground taxied into block 90 and waited for clearance to cross 28L/10R into its stand H38. Again the departure route was simply the reverse of this. If the visibility was less than 3kms the Link had to be integrated with the fixed wing traffic using 28L/10R and there could be no helicopter movement between Ashford and the strip while there was landing fixed wing traffic between the outer marker and touchdown, nor until a departure from either direction had passed block 84. When runway 23 was in use the inbound used the first 1,000 feet of 28L as its landing strip while for runway 05 the procedure inbound was for the helicopter to be integrated into the landing stream, effecting a visual final down to air taxi height over block 96 before touching down in block 90. Departures in both cases lifted from the subsidiary runway in use rather than using the 'Link' strip.

The distinctive sound of the S-61, together with the frequency of the service, brought complaints from residents living beneath the route. This resulted in the introduction of a 'high profile' clearance which allowed the 'Link' to climb early to its inter-zone cruising altitude of 2,400 feet if outbound or to maintain altitude for longer when inbound. This was subject to the approval of Air Departures who needed to assess what conflicting southbound traffic he had and was, therefore, more likely to be approved on westerlies when only the Dover SID was a problem. Operations began on 9th June 1978 at a frequency of ten return flights per day (£12 single and £22 return) and ATC staff at Heathrow and Gatwick were invited to sample the service at any time free of charge if there were seats available. Among those who accepted this offer was Alan Carter, who found that he was the only passenger on his return flight from Gatwick. He was invited to sit up front by the pilot who, after they were airborne, pointed out various features on the ground which marked their route to Ashford. Alan said that he could see them all and, to his great surprise, was told to take control. Although very nervous he thoroughly enjoyed the challenge and was quite obviously excited when he surfaced from the flight deck after the landing. The stewardess took just one look at him before

Sikorsky S-61 G-LINK flew the majority of the 10 return daily flights between Heathrow and Gatwick for the 7½ years prior to the M25 being completed. (Brian Pickering - MAP)

saying accusingly 'it was you flying it, wasn't it?' The final day of 'Link' operations was the 6th February 1986.

VIP PARKING

New block number boards began to appear with black lettering on a yellow background to conform to ICAO standards, and in 1979 the runway guard lights ('wig-wags') were similarly changed to yellow. A new aircraft parking apron which had been under construction on the western side of block 90 was also completed and brought into use. Intended primarily for VIP movements it comprised two stands (330 and 331), each capable of accepting aircraft up to Super VC10 size parked nose-in to the VIP terminal or, alternatively, a single aircraft up to Boeing 747 size could be parked nose-in to the north west corner of the apron. Aircraft arriving at the stands generally presented no handling problem, but departures could cause chaos if their turn away from the stands directed a warm, smelly blast at the assembled VIPs on the apron, or worse still blew someone over. This has happened, flooring the Lord Chancellor dressed in his full ceremonial gear, and brought a furious Operations Duty Manager storming to the top of the Tower stairs demanding an explanation.

PRECISION APPROACH PATH INDICATORS (PAPIs)

Elsewhere on the Airport Precision Approach Path Indicators (PAPIs) appeared on the right hand side of runways 10L and 28L for an operational evaluation which began on 16th February 1979. VASIs, which they were intended to eventually replace, continued to serve the left hand side of these two runways, with compatible brilliancy settings. The PAPIs comprised a set of four light units, mounted as a single wing bar adjacent to the visual touchdown aiming point. Each unit of the PAPI had a sharp transition between the red and white signals, and the innermost was set a half degree higher than the required glide path, with progressive reductions of a third of a degree setting angle for each unit outboard, so that the outermost was set a half degree lower than the correct glide path. The correct approach angle was shown by two reds and two whites. In the case of 28L an additional wing bar was positioned 120 metres further upwind for use by the pilots of long bodied aircraft who would otherwise use the upper set of a three bar VASI system, but this was later removed. Following a successful period of evaluation the VASIs were withdrawn and replaced by PAPIs on all runways early in 1984, although there was a minor set-back when it was found that condensation formed on the lenses of the units for fifteen minutes or so after they were switched on, making them unusable for this period. This was rectified by June 1984 with the fitting of permanent heaters, but in the meantime the units had to be left switched on or given sufficient time to warm up if they had been off for any reason.

SOUTHBOUND CHECK

Following an incident in July 1977 when a Dart Herald took rather too close a look - legitimately - at a helicopter on route H3 a new restriction was introduced for traffic taking off from the easterly runways on SIDs to the south and west. Aircraft using these SIDs when there was a

helicopter on the route were required to climb straight ahead to 1,500 feet before making their right turn, to ensure that there was safe separation where the paths crossed. It was hoped that this would be only a short term measure until the helicopter route was re-aligned, but there were numerous environmental and flight safety considerations. For the majority of departures, on short and medium range flights, the restriction was easily met and there was minimal effect on over-all expedition, but heavily laden Oceanics and other long haul flights were a different matter, sometimes needing several miles in summer temperatures to reach 1,500 feet. Delays to succeeding departures were inevitable and unacceptable, and of course there was additional noise nuisance caused to the communities directly east of the Airport. So, in 1979, a different approach was adopted which gave priority to the Airport's traffic instead of to the helicopters. It was announced in Notam 324 / 1979 that from 1st June until 30th September 1979 (apart from Derby week) route H3 would be closed from 0900 until 1300 whenever Heathrow was on easterly operations. Despite the early optimism that a solution would be found the restriction became an annual event, being extended in 1980 to include the month of May, and again in 1981 to cover the longer hours of 0800 to 1700.

The incident between the Herald and helicopter also prompted an examination of other related procedures, as a result of which changes were found to be necessary to the missed approach procedures for 28L and 10R. From 17th April 1980 the standard missed approach was amended to require an initial climb straight ahead to 1,500 feet before the turn south towards Epsom was made. Later in the same year, on 4th September, amendments were also made to the minimum holding altitudes at the OE, OW and NE NDBs. These were now raised to 2,000 feet at the OE and NE to provide adequate terrain clearance, and to 2,500 feet at the OW to ensure separation from the White Waltham local flying area and access lane.

Although movement rates had shown encouraging annual increases in the early seventies this came to an abrupt halt. Further wide-bodied types had followed the Boeing 747 into service - TriStars and DC10s starting to appear from 1972 and the Airbus A300 in 1974 - but enormous increases in the cost of aviation fuel in 1974 due to a fuel shortage meant that total aircraft movements peaked in 1973 followed by several years where rates declined.

Total Aircraft Movements	
1970	270,286
1971	273,242
1972	279,291
1973	293,867
1974	288,179
1975	276,087
1976	278,108
1977	265,002
1978	292,055
1979	299,027

Recovery at the end of the decade moved figures up to within a whisker of the 300,000 mark but recession in the early eighties would again prevent this target being achieved for a number of years.

SST ROUTE AND SID CHANGES

The SST routes, which had been introduced a little under four years earlier, were re-named in May 1979, SMB becoming SWB2 and SNL becoming SEB3. Then, as the new decade began, they were linked to the new Organised Track Structure in the Shanwick Oceanic Control Area - SM for westbound and SN for eastbound flights. Further changes were also about to be made to the way in which SIDs were designated to remove ATC clearance ambiguities and to reflect international proposals for the standardisation of SID designation. The new designators were composed of a basic indicator followed by a validity indicator followed by a route indicator. The basic indicator was the name of the significant point where the SID route terminated e.g Brecon (BCN). The validity indicator was a number from 1 to 9, and whenever a route was amended the next higher number would be allocated. Finally the route indicator was a single letter of the alphabet, different letters being allocated to each route which terminated at the same significant point. Effectively this identified the runway used for departure so for a Brecon departure from Heathrow's runway 28R the SID now became a Brecon One Foxtrot (BCN 1F) while from 28L it would be a Brecon One Golf (BCN 1G).

28R = Foxtrot	28L = Golf	23=Hotel
l0R = Juliet	l0L = Kilo	05=Lima

A similar change was made to the SIDs at Gatwick at the same time, runway 26 receiving the route indicator Mike and 08 being allocated Papa, and the new designators came into use on 21st February 1980.

EVACUATION PLANS

After their withdrawal the Runway Caravans were given a prolonged lease of life as Mobile Contingency Units (MCUs), for use when an evacuation of the Tower was necessary. One caravan was left on the 10L caravan site but the other was moved to the disused PAR site south of block 84 in grass area 16, and a handful of staff would be despatched in the ATC vehicle 'Pixie' to attempt a limited service. Normally a recall to the Tower would come before any meaningful operation was achieved. On a routine visit to the MCUs during his spell in ATC Operations (1980/1981) Chris Harris found that the caravans were showing distinct signs of terminal decay, prompting a review of how they would be replaced. Problems of location had also begun to arise due to the imminent construction of Terminal 4 and the associated taxiway development south of 28L/10R, so a landside site was considered the best option. Initial thoughts were for a location on top of the Terminal 2 car park, but this was ruled out through problems of ensuring its security. A suitable site was eventually found, although the location is not given here for obvious reasons, and construction of the Emergency Visual Control Room (EVCR) went ahead. Choice of site, however, was not the only problem that had to be overcome. The equipment to be fitted in the EVCR had to operate independently of that in the Tower to ensure that a service could continue even if the Tower was completely disabled. The EVCR was finally completed and handed over for operational use, only to be severely damaged soon afterwards by a fire which broke out in an air conditioning unit which had

not run for some time, allowing dust to collect. During the re-equipment process continuing doubts over the security of the EVCR and now, also, over the ability of staff to safely evacuate the EVCR if there was another fire delayed completion, but finally it was declared ready for operational use on 20th January 1986. The EVCR team was now comprised of 3/4 ATCOs and 2 ATCAs, and a limited Aerodrome Control Service with single runway operation on 28L/10R would be provided, using frequencies 118.7, 121.9 and 121.0. Weather minima were laid down, which for departures was a visibility of 3,000 metres or more, provided Low Visibility Procedures were not in force, and for arrivals a visibility of 6 kms or more and lowest reported cloud 1,000 feet or above. The Approach Radar Control Service was provided from LATCC. Following the EVCR's successful return to operational service Bunny Austin, then Head of ATC Operations, gave approval for the disposal of the caravans on 30th January 1986.

THE CHIPMUNK

Very early in the morning on the 2nd November 1980, and before his move to Heathrow, Malcolm Hemming was sitting at LATCC waiting for a pending Southend departure to appear. Seeing a response to the north west of Southend Malcolm rang them to say that he could see the departure but was told that it was not yet airborne. In fact ATC Southend were unaware of the traffic but when given its position were able to see its navigation lights. Malcolm continued to watch the traffic as it tracked west and then disregarded it as it turned south into the Denham overhead, believing it to be a Denham inbound. Next morning, however, he heard that Heathrow had received an unexpected visitor during the night and realised that this was almost certainly what he had been tracking. Having left his office to take readings for an early morning weather actual the Met. observer had discovered a de Havilland Chipmunk G-BCRX parked on the grass to the north of 28R/10L. At no time had it contacted Heathrow Approach or Tower as it made its way into the Airport and there was no trace of the pilot. The Police, when asked to investigate the Chipmunk, were somewhat reluctant and suggested that the RSPCA might be better equipped to deal with it! The Press, of course, had a field day. The incident, it transpired, was the result of a late night prank. The pilot had spent the day celebrating the engagement of two of his friends and, in high spirits, had decided to fly to the Southend area to carry out some aerobatics. On his return the idea of landing at Heathrow had suddenly become irresistible, and following the successful landing he had left the aircraft, climbed the perimeter fence and been picked up by friends in a car.

As 1980 drew to its close an improvement was made to the Arrival ATIS service when the broadcasts made on the Biggin Hill and Bovingdon VORs were supplemented by a long range service introduced on 133.075 Mhz. This came into operation on 27th November.

ATCO INDUSTRIAL ACTION

Government pay policy, which continued to be dominated by the need to control high inflation, was again the cause of a number of one day strikes which took place in 1981.

Even Derek Harriss donned a headset as management provided a limited service during the ATCO industrial action of 1981 'DH' is seen here in GMP - Note the Route Map of Europe. (Roger Kunert)

Civil Service pay, which influenced CAA pay, operated with a 'Pay Review Unit' (PRU) system, which resulted in a number of years with very low increases and then a 'catch-up' year. Doug Bush, who at that time was the Chairman of the ATCO Branch of IPCS, recalls that the pay round of 1981 was particularly difficult causing the Council of Civil Service Unions to call for a day of industrial action on 9th March which was supported by the majority of staff at Heathrow. During the morning and afternoon duties of the 8th March management made strenuous efforts to dissuade staff from taking part on the grounds that it had nothing to do with ATC, but they overlooked the night Watch. When 'C' Watch came on for their night duty they worked until midnight and then went down to the outside front steps of the control tower leaving just one ATCO in the Approach room as a safety cover. They all stood on the steps for about fifteen minutes before returning upstairs to 'rest' for the remainder of their shift. The subsequent Watches then also took action and Heathrow was effectively closed to traffic until midnight 9th/10th March apart from a few flights which were handled by the one or two controllers who did not support the action. This was the first time that Heathrow ATCOs had taken any strike action but, despite the flexing of industrial muscle, negotiations failed to make acceptable progress. The two ATC Unions balloted their members to gauge support for further industrial action and this resulted in a vote by the ATCOs for limited strikes. An initial

programme covering a period of five weeks and involving all Units was agreed but the Government, who believed that the campaign would not be successful, made no improved pay offers. The plan for Heathrow was that each Watch would take strike action on one duty during the five weeks with the morning duties targeted. Action across the Country was co-ordinated for maximum effect, which resulted in Heathrow and LATCC always taking action on different days. All staff who took strike action had their lost pay made up by IPCS from a central fund, and at the end of the five weeks the CAA made an acceptable pay offer which was implemented in the September. Following this relationships between staff and management slowly returned to normal although, as Doug points out, they always remained 'lively'.

Time now for some more names, in fact a total of 175. Shown below is the main Watch roster for July 1981, all Watches having thirteen or fourteen ATCOs. Most Watches also had thirteen ATCAs, with extra cover available from the ATCA1 co-ordinator/leave relief team. Jack Hollis was about to retire (on 31st July) and be replaced as 'D' Watch Supervisor by Don Hickson. ATCOs Anne Gardner (from Cardiff) and Chris Huggett (from Manchester) were due to arrive in mid-July to start Aerodrome validation training, and Steve Moody was also expected early in August from Prestwick. Malcolm Judge (from ScATCC) was another imminent arrival while leaving the family were Bev Hull, Barry Winch and his wife Lyn who had all resigned.

ATCO MAIN ROSTER JULY 1981

	A	B	C	D	E
Watch Supvr.	F.A.Way	L.West	K.C.Williams	J.A.Hollis	D.R.Austin
Deputy Supvr.	D.Harriss	R.M.Wise	B.A.Piket	A.J.Prosser	J.C.Kiernan
1	A.McLean	J.S.Rymill	D.E.Bush	D.J.Carney	T.G.C Quantrill
2	A.Carter	R.Wadley	R.Hendry	C.R.Prentice	C.M.Ward
3	Mrs B.J.Hull	R.E.J.Dawson	R.J.Plant	J.R.Cant	J.MacDermot
4	P.J.Bish	G.B.Coates	R.Daly	N.J.Mack	C.K.Clarkson
5	A.S.Watkins	I.D.McKinna	A.C.C.Haines	P.A.Louden	R.C.Metcalfe
6	B.J.McCartney	A.J.Budd	C.A.Cosgrave	J.F.Hanbury	M.W.Lewis
7	I.H.Alexander	I.M.Callier	H.C.Hayes	A.H.Croft	R.M.Neville
8	P.Wilson	M.P.Ross	P.J.Martin-Bishop	P.S.Flynn	W.J.Ferguson
9	Mrs W.Campbell	J.P.C.Gell	B.A.G.Chapman	C.K.Herbert	I.Mason
10	M.J.Campbell	P.J.Ailsopp	M.V.Male	J.S.Siddell	R.L.Harrison
11	K.H.Miller	I.G.Sims	A.M.Denchfield		S.W.Lambert
12	I.M.Toakley	B.C.Winch	Mrs S.P.Clifford		
13		D.C.Shawe			
14		P.G.Johnson			
Consolidating	E.G.Gregory G.Hewitt		D.J.Broderick	M.L.Burlyn R.G.Boulter S.W.Forster	M.D.Taylor K.P.Meakin
U / T VCR	D.I.Lamont	D.M.Crabb	J.J.Cooke		S.C.Hobbs
U / T APC	R.A.Rowland-Rouse		R.K.Spooner Mrs J.S.Price	D.A.Rham	

Relief Watch Supervisors : D.Hickson and L.Dunn
Regional Training Unit : I.J.Culley and A.W.Jack
ATC Ops 1 : C.R.Harris   ATC Ops 2 : G.R.Bullock

ATCA MAIN ROSTER JULY 1981

1	M.Cleary	J.C.Wood	J.M.MacPherson	M.E.Davies	D.J.Moss
2	R.Kunert	E.N.Dallison	G.P.Kemp	I.J.M.Saunders	D.P.J.Treacy
3	V.A.Annett	N.K.Wales	C.H.George	Mrs S.A.Collins	J.L.Harborne
4	A.J.M.McGregor	N.A.Rolfe	B.Datta	M.McKenzie	D.P.Crizzle
5	Mrs L.P.Miller	S.P.Batham	S.P.Quinton	G.C.Riches	Mrs L.G.Keightley
6	D.K.Wilson	R.T.Kehoe	R.Darling	Mrs S.R.C.Louden	Mrs J.E.Williams
7	P.M.Richardson	F.D.Jennings	G.W.Jarvis	P.Blanchard	Miss S.M.Quest
8	Mrs J.Lambert	Mrs L.M.Winch	A.G.Bright	Mrs V.J.Pickford	Mrs E.A.Meakin
9	Mrs J.A.Ward	C.P.Beards	L.Hoey	Mrs D.M.Woodhouse	K.J.Oswick
10	K.M.Bowdler	Miss B.K.Latimer	A.Picton	Mrs M.Johnson	Miss S.J.Holland
11	G.R.Black	Miss T.A.Wilcox	P.J.Clark	M.A.Hooper	D.J.Matthews
12	D.T.London	R.M.Webb	Miss V.E.Lennon	R.A.Davies	S.J.Rawsthorne
13	D.G.Williams	P.W.Irwin	M.F.B.Williams	A.P.Thorpe	

ATC Records : B.A.Buckingham
Regional Training Unit : E.W.Percival, G.P.Foulkes, Mrs S.E.Field, J.Wornham, G.Tong and S.P.Harben
ATCA1 Coord / Leave Relief Team : D.W.Ferguson, J.H.Gleave, F.Karai, A.J.Wright, T.M.Ward, G.Bannister, K.P.Baker, M.D.Swann, P.A.Ward and M.Judge

Terry Ward was bored. Sitting at the Supervisor's desk he decided to liven up the next ATIS broadcast 'Foxtrot' by asking pilots to report that they had received information 'Fandabidozy' instead, thereby demonstating a rather worrying taste in television programmes. Anyway one of the first to check in was an Iberia flight whose initial call left the No1(S), unaware of what had been done, rather perplexed. 'Confirm you have information Foxtrot'. 'Negative, sir, we have Fandabidozy'. 'You have what?...' On another occasion Graham Jarvis was just cutting a broadcast with a warning of bird activity. Clive George, standing nearby, decided to add a touch of realism by making quacking noises in the background which were picked up by the sensitive recorder and transmitted very audibly.

FLOW CONTROL

Despite occasional setbacks air travel was becoming more generally available and affordable, not least for leisure, and this had put pressure on most aspects of the air transport system. Passenger facilities at airports in Spain, and later in Greece as holiday preferences changed, struggled to cope with demand, and the same was true of the associated ATC systems. There was considerable pressure for European ATSUs to remove bottlenecks and increase capacity, which could not be achieved overnight. The resulting periods of industrial action aimed at improving equipment and working conditions, mostly genuine attempts to protect the travelling public, drew strong criticism from the media. What was obvious was that controllers needed protection against overloads and that airlines needed a more predictable system to facilitate their flight planning and crew rostering. And so flow control was born, to adjust the flow of traffic leaving the London FIR/UIR in compliance with flight level allocation systems and traffic flow restrictions imposed by adjacent Centres. By 1981 this had developed from modest beginnings into the Air Traffic Flow Management Unit (ATFMU) at LATCC, with two Departure Flow Regulators - DFR1 and DFR2, each responsible for a specific set of routes into Europe. Airlines could contact the appropriate DFR for a departure time up to two hours before the ETD of an aircraft on a restricted route, and were normally issued with an Approved Departure Time (ADT), which allowed take off at that time and up to six minutes afterwards. This gave rise to the more popular name of 'departure slot'. Occasionally other forms of restriction such as 'take-off not before' or 'clearance expires at' might be given. The restriction was then also passed to the Tower assistant for inclusion on the aircraft's flight progress strip. Provided pilots made a realistic attempt to reach the holding point in good time the ADTs created no major difficulties but there were always optimists who arrived at the start of their slot with numerous aircraft in front of them, expecting to be accommodated somehow. And when traffic peaks required general outbound delays the re-negotiation of slots could become a real headache.

ACCOMMODATION CHANGES

On lower floors of the Tower, below the operational areas, office space had become available during the seventies due to the closure or re-location of other departments, and this enabled some of ATC's non-operational staff to occupy more spacious accommodation. The Chief Officer moved down from the sixth to the third floor and was joined here by the Head of ATC Operations, although Chris Harris (ATC Ops 1) and Geoff Bullock (ATC Ops 2) still had an office each on the sixth. ATC Training had long been established on the fourth floor and remained there. The Medical Centre also moved up to the third floor, catering for ATCO and aircrew medicals. The closure of the canteens on the ground and first floors, however, now liberated large areas for re-development although a small bar which faced Terminal 2 did linger on for a while. In fact it was here that one of the 'A' Watch controllers, Alastair McLean, used to display another of his talents playing regular gigs with a jazz band as saxophonist. The space on the first floor offerred an ideal opportunity to unite all ATC sections under the same roof and resulted in the closure of the Flight Clearance office in the Queens Building on the night of 14th/15th July 1981. They were joined in their new accommodation by Met and by a reduced AIS unit, some of their staff at this time being re-located to Pinner. The remainder stayed at Heathrow for about three years before they were also transferred out. The move across from the Queens Building went smoothly, the most obvious differences being the introduction of a security guard to control access to the Control Tower (and therefore to Flight Clearance) at its south east entrance, and noticeably fewer visits from aircrew who previously had frequently wandered in to get briefings when the office was more accessible. A new canteen - dubbed the 'Posh Nosh' - on the first floor of the Queens Building replaced the Tower facilities. Primarily patronised by Airline personnel it was nevertheless popular with ATC staff, especially a self-service salad bar in a separate room at the rear which attracted many of the mid-day D1 and D2 diners. Here, for a heavily subsidised set price, you could eat as much as you liked and many displayed amazing appetites (didn't they, Jez?). A staff canteen in Terminal 3 also had some supporters.

MORE CONCRETE

The BAA had been concentrating its attention on repairing and resurfacing large areas of taxiway, starting early in 1980 with the outer taxiway north east of the Tower and then moving in the middle of 1981 to areas near the 10R holding point. But although this involved using a lot of new concrete there was no new concrete, if you know what I mean. Notam A497, however, issued on the 21st July 1981, announced the imminent start of major work scheduled to take about fourteen months to complete, constructing new taxiways and apron areas for a fourth Terminal south of 28L/10R. A substantial amount of the work associated with this development was on or close to the threshold area of runway 05, which was withdrawn from use for the duration. The 23 ILS and the 'Link' strip were also taken out of service, but runway 23 remained available for use initially, albeit for landings only and with a reduced landing distance of 2,120 metres. Then, in April 1982, it too was closed so that extensive concrete repairs could be made to the section of the runway north of block 85. The opening of the new taxiway system south of 28L/10R eventually took place about three months behind schedule and gave GMC a nice present early in the New Year of four new blocks (93, 95, 118 and 119) and a re-located block 97 to play with. It also cleared the way for the construction of the Terminal itself and development of the three associated aprons (Sierra, Tango and Victor).

Surfacing in the VCR one morning after a hard night's rest Geoff Bullock was intrigued to find the GMC controller Dick Dawson looking through binoculars at the aircraft in the Ockham stack. Without appearing to notice Geoff's arrival Dick said to the Air controller 'Tell them they can drop the Speedbird now'. This was too much for Geoff who enquired what was happening to which Dick replied 'The radar has failed downstairs so we're doing it from up here'. Result: major consternation for Geoff who did not spot the masterly wind-up!

LOCAL COMPETENCY SCHEME

The Safety Regulation Group (SRG) were looking to standardise ATCO competency levels nationally, both at NATS and non-State units. Until this time there had been no formal checks of competency after validation at Heathrow although there might be a review of a controller's abilities with the possibility of re-training if an incident occurred. A scheme was devised whereby every ATCO would be required to attend an annual check of his/her competence with a designated 'local competence examiner', a senior Watch member with an appropriately endorsed licence. A seminar took place in London towards the end of 1981 run by ex Heathrow ATCO Roy Stayley, which was attended by Heathrow's nominated 'examiners to be' - two from each Watch and members of the training section. These were :- Alan Carter and Pete Bish from 'A' Watch, Ian Callier and Rob Wadley from 'B' Watch, Doug Bush and Ray Plant from 'C' Watch, Paul Louden and John Cant from 'D' Watch, and Terry Quantrill and Rod Metcalfe from 'E' Watch. The training office representatives were Alan Jack and Ian Culley. Following this the scheme was introduced in 1982, with technical questions being asked from a list agreed by SRG, and appeared to have settled down reasonably well when a dispute arose which was never really resolved satisfactorily. The local competency examiners (LCEs) had considered that they were extensions of SRG but then SRG tried to distance themselves, suggesting that the LCEs were more closely aligned with Management. This was not accepted by the LCEs and, following discussions, all resigned from the scheme forcing SRG to carry out competency checks for a while. Eventually a compromise solution was found which recognised that the LCEs had a degree of independence but nevertheless at the same time broke their direct link with SRG. After the scheme had been in existence for some time the annual check was extended to include a day in the training office, which included lectures on topical subjects and time on a simulator practising emergency situations and other scenarios considered worthwhile. This was known initially as Emergency Continuation Training (ECT) and was introduced as the result of AAIB recommendations following an incident at LATCC which highlighted flaws in the handling of emergencies.

LOCALISER SENSITIVE AREA

Although all four of Heathrow's main runways had been equipped for Cat 3 operations for over five years there was still no international agreement on visual aids to help pilots identify the boundary of the localiser sensitive area (LSA). Heathrow had installed white occulting lights at specified runway exit points to this end but it was generally quicker for controllers to monitor an aircraft's progress off the

runway on the ASMI (which they did anyway) than to wait for a pilot's call of 'vacated'. In an attempt to make it easier for pilots to know when they had cleared the LSA a trial of coded centre line lights (CCL), planned to last throughout the winter, began on 23rd October 1981. Only 28L was involved and all turn offs west of block 84 were modified for the trial. The standard green centre line lights were replaced between the runway edge and the boundary of the LSA by alternate green and yellow lights, and a pilot could now be sure that he had cleared the LSA when he had completely passed the last yellow light.

SID CHANGES

Changes to TMA airspace made it necessary to amend Heathrow's SIDs to the south and south west and on 18th March 1982 the Midhurst, Seaford and Ibsley departures from the westerly runways and the Seaford and Ibsley departures from the easterly runways were withdrawn and replaced by:-

(1)   the 'Drake' departure for Amber 34 - southbound.
(2)   the 'Benbo' departure for Amber 1 - southbound.
(3)   the 'Hardy' departure for Amber 1 East - southbound.
(4)   the 'Sampton' departure for White 17 and White 38 - southbound, and also for Delta Red 8 and Delta Red 37- westbound.

In addition a new 'Hazel' SID was introduced, available on request for flights unable to comply with the altitude requirements of the 'Sampton', which required aircraft to achieve vertical separation above the airspace allocated to Farnborough. These presented no problem to short haul flights but were difficult for long haul departures to destinations such as Johannesburg to achieve. An element of humour was evident in the choice of these new nautical designators since the 'Drake' would regularly be used by flights of the Spanish airline Iberia as would the 'Hardy' by Air France's many daily flights to Paris. Later in the year a further new SID was introduced as time was called on low level positioning flights from Heathrow to Gatwick and vice versa. Until now the clearance both ways had been via Epsom, originally at 2,000 feet and then later at 3,000 feet when the base of the TMA was raised, but increasing traffic levels had now made these low level transits impractical. On 28th October 1982 a new 'Detling' SID was introduced, replacing what had been a simple inter unit arrangement with a more formal and structured route working TMA (SE). The new routeing from Heathrow to Gatwick was via Detling to Gatwick's Eastwood hold at minimum stack level while in the opposite direction flights climbed up to minimum stack level at Biggin.

Around this time the Douglas DC8-73CF A4O-HM of the Omani Royal Flight appeared re-registered as A4O-HMQ and there was a strong suspicion that the 'Flow' unit had been responsible. A new Flow procedure had been introduced for occasions when a replacement flight plan was submitted with a change of route, requiring the callsign on the replacement to be amended by the addition of the suffix letter 'Q'. This also had to be used by the crew during the flight and removed any doubt as to which flight plan had been cancelled. The story has it that, taxying out one day on a re-filed plan, A4O-HM was instructed that it must in future use the call sign A4O-HMQ...

Lucy Miller with a selection of pictures of the 17 Guide Dogs purchased as a result of donations and sponsored events through the Heathrow Control Tower Guide Dog Fund. The album records the many individuals and events which contributed to this 12 year project. (via Lucy Miller)

GUIDE DOGS

The Heathrow Control Tower Guide Dog Fund, brainchild of Lucy Miller, was born on 8th August 1982 and she could never have anticipated how it would unite all sections of the Control Tower. In its early days it was simply a jar kept in Approach Control into which small change and foreign coins were dropped, the latter being sold off to Banks or staff going abroad with the aim of raising £1,000 to sponsor a guide dog and its owner. Progress was slow until 'C' Watch's Ron Daly organised a sponsored cycle ride around the edge of the London Control Zone - about 160 miles -which began and finished at the Guide Dog Kennels near Wokingham. This took place on 23rd and 24th July 1983 and apart from Ron there were nine other participants - Brandon Chapman, Jez Cooke, Joe Hanbury, Steve James, Mike Male, Ian Toakley, Tom Toy, Bob Hillier (then still at LATCC) and Keith Williams. Over £500 was raised and resulted in the sponsorship of the Tower's first guide dog, appropriately named 'Radar'. Two years later an even more ambitious project took place. This time the target was Paris and again Ron Daly was the organiser. With sponsorship from Air France and Travelscene a group of ten 'C' Watch ATCAs and ATCOs were waved off from Terminal 2 by Miss Air France on 8th October 1985. The mentally unstable participants this time were Kevin Baker, Pete Carter, Jez Cooke, Ron Daly, Malcolm Judge, Mike Male, Geoff Nash, Paul Nobbs, Tom Toy and Ian Toakley, accompanied by his wife Judy. Well over £1,500 was raised this time. Inspired by all this athleticism Terry Quantrill was next to undertake a challenge, raising over £1000 in sponsorship by cycling from Lands End to John O'Groats in April 1986. Danair, who at that time operated a service from Heathrow to Inverness, generously provided Terry with a free trip back. By December 1986 five dogs had been sponsored and there was enthusiastic support for each new fund-raising activity throughout the Tower. Regular raffles, supported by a number of Airlines (including British Airways, British Midland, Air Canada, Gulf Air and Japan Air Lines), and the collection and sale of paper for recycling by members of AIS were a steady source of income, and when Lucy handed over to Brian Piket on her posting to Hurn in 1991 the total of dogs purchased had risen to twelve.

Brian adopted a more aggresive marketing policy and in the next two years was able to raise another £5,000. By far the most successful project of this period was another event suggested by Terry Quantrill, who offered to circumnavigate the Airport on an 1876 Penny Farthing bicycle with bets being placed on how long it would take him, and prizes given for the closest guesses. In fact the distance of over nine miles was covered in just forty one minutes, most people overlooking the fact that the Penny Farthing had been designed for speed. Not long after the presentation of the seventeenth dog, and for a number of reasons, it was decided that the Guide Dog Fund should be wound up and so a memorable era came to an end. The dogs were:-

Radar, Blip, Lucy, Pixie, Terry, Laurie, Raffles, Punch, Argus, Boddly, Bunny, Holly, Prince, Kal, Roxy, Taffy and Ziggy

The representative pictures given by the Charity for each dog sponsored were hung initially in the ground floor reception area but were later moved to their present location on the first floor near the lift.

BENT CENTRE LINE FOR NORTHOLT

In August 1982, after two incidents occurred involving Airways flights inbound to Northolt, certain changes were made to existing procedures when Heathrow was on easterlies. Instead of keeping the Northolt inbound on his frequency as had formerly been the case the No.1 Director now transferred it to the No.2 Director to ensure that it was safely integrated with Heathrow traffic being sequenced onto 10L and 10R. It was then handed over to Northolt only when the separation from Heathrow traffic was constant or increasing. Later in the year a proposal was put forward by CATO1 aimed at improving the safety of the procedure even more by amending the runway 08 vectoring procedure. This involved the introduction of a new radar circuit based on an off-set final approach intersecting the extended centre line of the runway at 4nms. The new off-set centre line (bearing 100°T) would keep traffic at least 3nms north of 10L at all times and would therefore allow independent sequencing to runway 08. This new procedure was adopted on a six month trial basis which began on 7th March 1983, and although not ideal it nevertheless proved to be workable given the proximity of the two units and became permanent in February 1984.

HELLO WENDY

Having been impressed by the service given by the No.2 Director Wendy Campbell one morning the pilot of a Swissair DC9, Captain Peter Jost, asked if he and his crew could pay ATC a visit to see how things worked. They were made very welcome and obviously enjoyed themselves because soon afterwards Wendy received a beautiful cartoon of a Swissair DC9 making a request to visit the Tower. This had been drawn by Captain Jost and was displayed in the ATC

rest room for many years. In a strange coincidence similar drawings, which included one of a Saudia MD-11, were spotted by Pete Bish during a visit to Switzerland in the year 2000. Passing through the small village of Embrach near Zurich he stopped at a cafe for a beer and was surprised to see a number of the cartoons hanging on a wall. Enquiries revealed that they were indeed by the same Captain Jost, who had been a friend of the proprietors for many years. After converting to MD-11s with Swissair he had joined Saudia, also on MD-11s, and regularly sent the family postcards from around the World. Pete left him a note and received a letter back saying that he had many pleasant memories of his years flying into Heathrow.

RADAR UPGRADES

The Tels radar replacement programme of the early eighties included, amongst others, Heathrow's ACR6 and AR1. The most urgent of these was the ACR6, which was now 25 years old and occupied a site required for taxiway development. The projected replacement was an EN4008 which, like the Marconi S650 ten years earlier, was mounted for its evaluation some 145 feet above ground level on top of the British Airways multi-storey car park. The EN4008 comprised an ACR6 antenna, single channel AR1 electronics, an R/F swept gain unit and a Marconi S7100 processor. Similar but less sophisticated radars had been installed at Gatwick and Stansted and were performing well. The first series of flight trials took place during February 1983 using a CAFU HS-748 and a Cessna 172, and an interim report recommended an operational trial. Before this took place, however, changes were made to the radar to improve its performance including the fitting of a later model processor, the S7113, on loan from the manufacturers. The ATC operational trial then took place in May and June but although

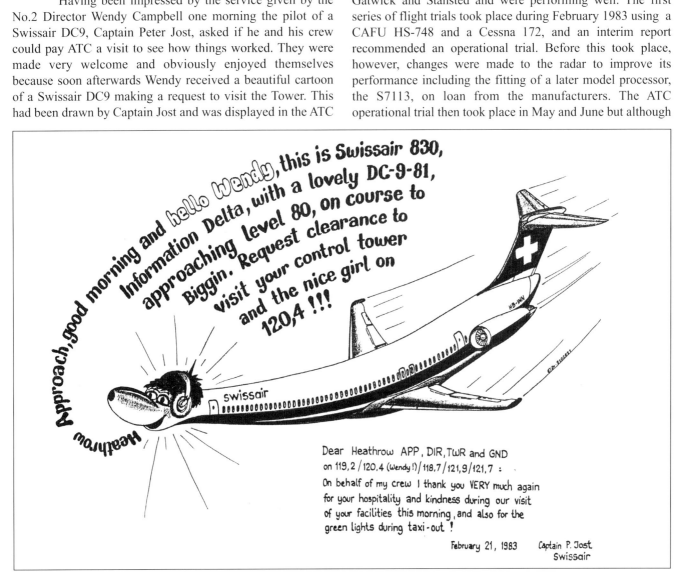

Approach, good morning and hello Wendy, this is Swissair 830, Information Delta, with a lovely DC-9-81, approaching level 80, on course to Biggin. Request clearance to visit your control tower and the nice girl on 120,4 !!!

Heathrow

swissair

Dear Heathrow APP, DIR, TWR and GND
on 119,2 / 120,4 (Wendy!) / 118,7 / 121,9 / 121,7 :
On behalf of my crew I thank you VERY much again
for your hospitality and kindness during our visit
of your facilities this morning, and also for the
green lights during taxi-out !

February 21, 1983   Captain P. Jost
                      Swissair

The long serving ACR-6 radar seen here in 1988, along with the then current 'Pixie' and a BMA DC-9 departing 27L. (Pete Bish)

satisfactory in many respects the radar's low level cover was considered unacceptable. Further modifications followed and a second ATCEU evaluation was conducted in November and December. The radar's performance was assessed as exceeding that of the AR1 with which it was directly compared and it was again recommended for operational trials, but once again it was failed by ATC for a number of reasons. Possible alternatives now had to be considered which resulted in a decision not to replace but instead to upgrade the existing ACR6 with components from the Marconi S511 radar, including a 2022 transmitter and the S7113 processor previously mentioned, while retaining the antenna. The 10cm radars at Belfast (AR1), Cardiff (AR1), Edinburgh (AR1) and Prestwick (ACR6) were given similar upgrades, all five systems being obtained at a heavily discounted price because

NATS allowed Marconi to use the sale for marketing purposes. The hybrid radar was designated the EN4000 and remained in service at Heathrow until the autumn of 1989 when it was replaced by the Watchman. The original intention had been that the extension of the ACR6's life would allow it to cover the replacement of Heathrow's non-standard AR1 with an AR15 but this did not materialise. Instead the AR1 was removed in 1986 following the entry into service of the HSA 23cm radar. The frequency of the EN4000 was 2,960 Mhz and the beam width 1.8 degrees.

MIDLAND BREAKFASTS

Jez Cooke had a friend Geoff Goodchild who flew Short 330/360s for British Midland. These used to fly several

Breakfast is served! The box like shape and ICAO type designation SHD6 gained the Shorts 360 the nickname 'Shed' and various disparaging remarks on the R/T when introduced. G-BMHY is seen arriving on the 'November' stands in late 1986. (Pete Bish)

sectors each day between Heathrow and Birmingham and East Midlands and Jez discovered that the first inbound flight of the day served, by airline standards, a magnificent hot breakfast. When it emerged that there were often a few breakfasts remaining when the aircraft landed the insatiable ATCO appetite led to Jez working the No.1 Director North position if it was known that his friend was Captain of the early morning arrival. Initially the enquiry about surplus meals would be made by Jez but later, if Jez was heard to be on the frequency, the first call from the aircraft would be something along the lines of 'Heathrow, Midland 777, Short 360, inbound to Bovingdon Flight Level 70 with information Delta and we've got five' (i.e. five breakfasts). Jez would then take a break timed so that he arrived at the aircraft's allocated stand in 'Pixie' at the same time as the aircraft, whose progress was smoothed as much as possible. Pleasantries and breakfasts would then be exchanged after which Jez would return to the Tower to distribute the first sitting. The only stipulation was that the cutlery (nothing plastic or cheap) and heated boxes should be returned to the aircraft after its next flight down.

Work began on 9th May 1983 to lay down the final section of the southern taxiway from block 106 to the full-length threshold at block 100. Its completion would remove the need for departures from the new Terminal 4 or, indeed, any of the south side parking areas to cross 10R if they needed the runway's full length for take-off. A new block 105 would be created to link the two existing blocks but its construction affected the 10R ILS glide path radiations so for the eighteen months or so needed to complete the work a full ILS approach was not possible, although landings from other types of approach were permitted. When the new taxiway was handed over for use it was unlit and therefore unavailable at night or in low visibility, but this was rectified soon afterwards during resurfacing of the Cargo Terminal taxiway.

GMC AFTER TERMINAL 4

The location of Terminal 4, south of 28L/10R, broke away from the original concept of having all passenger handling facilities inside the lattice of runways. It was, however, the only feasible site although constrained by the perimeter road and by the need to retain the crosswind runway 23/05. But the predicted activity at the Terminal made it as busy in its own right as some smaller Airports and this, combined with the unavoidable and considerable increase in runway crossings raised major questions as to whether GMC, already under pressure, would be able to cope. One possible solution was that the GMC function should be split, although the idea was generally unpopular. Most controllers felt that there could only be one logical split, north and south of 28L/10R, but that the increased co-ordination would offset the advantage of less traffic. In addition the controller working the area south of 28L/10R would have a relatively undemanding task offering little job satisfaction. Despite this strong negative feeling a number of possible splits were identified for operational trial by members of the ATC Ops and Training sections, principally Chris Prentice and Bert Hayes under the direction of Bunny Austin. The first three splits examined, which all used runways as boundaries between the two GMC areas, included the most obvious one mentioned above and also splits giving GMC2 all blocks south of 28L/10R together with those east of 23, and the same again but with the addition of runway 23. A fourth split divided the Central Area diagonally

into two by drawing a line NW - SE through the 'M' and 'F' cul -de-sacs. There were certain practical problems involved with organising the trials - arranging for the additional frequency, extra co-ordination for tugs, which would necessarily continue to work GMC1 etc - but when they were concluded Chris and Bert felt that definite benefits had been evident. Nevertheless the strong opposition to any form of split from the operational staff won the day and it was subsequently decided that there would be no immediate change.

This problem shelved, albeit temporarily, ATC Ops and the Technical Committee continued to be kept busy working up the new procedures that would be necessary to handle movements at the new Terminal and the associated increase in runway crossings. Runway transit times were obviously an important factor but after a number of practice taxying and towing movements had been carried out it was decided that no special gaps would be created for crossing traffic, which would have to accept any delays that resulted. British Airways estimated that about thirty tugs a day would need to cross the runway which was not considered too excessive although after the Terminal opened this number was often exceeded, not always for bona fide reasons, and a concerted campaign had to be waged to encourage them to use other routes when possible. Another problem was that, until now, traffic crossing a runway had been the subject of prior agreement between the appropriate Air controller and GMC and had remained with GMC for the crossing. The Air controller simply placed a 'runway obstructed' strip in his active bay in the appropriate position between other movements and received confirmation from GMC when the runway had been vacated. This might be given verbally although an accepted method of indicating 'runway clear' was to tap the metal casing of the fluorescent lights over the GMC desk with a pen or pencil to attract the Air controller's attention. But the high number of crossings now expected made this impractical, and new procedures were devised which required all crossing traffic to be transferred to the appropriate Air controller holding short of the runway at a nominated block. It would then be handed back to GMC after it had crossed although, after a little operational experience, this was found to be unnecessary when traffic was outbound towards 28R when it was transferred instead directly to the other Air controller. New methods of clearly identifying crossing traffic were also required since the 28L/10R Air controller would, as a consequence, block his runway with an active flight progress strip instead of a 'runway obstructed' strip, and a number of variations of strip holder and strip markings were tried out before an acceptable solution was found, some using magnetic tags (the product of Chris Prentice's fertile mind and a convenient hacksaw) and others specially adapted GMC strip holders. Finally consideration of the wisdom of having tugs on a frequency where poor R/T discipline might have a direct affect on the safety of the operation led to a decision to move them to a UHF frequency. This was cross coupled either to GMC (Channel 1) or to either of the Air frequencies (Channel 11) and meant that, if the frequency became blocked by a tug's open transmitter, the link could be deselected and operations continued. Unfortunately one other problem was encountered for which there was no easy solution. Traffic crossing at block 87 was found to cause a dangerous deflection of the ILS glide path radiations when it passed in front of the transmitter and so crossings at the threshold were virtually ruled out, reducing flexibility and removing what would have been a very convenient and perhaps the most expeditious crossing point.

Rod Metcalfe, working Special VFR one day, was asked by the FIR controller at LATCC if he would accept an aircraft with an unspecified problem that wished to enter the Control Zone. Thinking that the pilot probably wanted to land at one of the airfields inside the Zone Rod agreed and the aircraft was transferred. However, when asked the nature of the problem, the pilot replied that, without being a nuisance, he wished to remain in the Zone until he could speak to the Prime Minister although he would not say why. He was held to the east of Heathrow while the situation was discussed at higher level, and finally it was decided that the best option would be to land him at Heathrow. The pilot agreed and was vectored in but, after landing, was arrested by the Police who wanted to prosecute him. But there was no case to answer as he had not contravened the ANO and had complied with all ATC instructions, so they were forced to let him go. It transpired that he had supplied the Army with an item of equipment and wanted to bring attention to the fact that he had not yet been paid for it.

MIKE ROMEO

Another story, which has its origins in the mid-eighties, was obviously anticipated by the immortal bard many years earlier when he wrote 'Mike Romeo, Mike Romeo, wherefore art thou Mike Romeo?' Alan Carter No.1 Director North and Tony Watkins his No.2 Director. G-AVMR, the British Airways BAC 1-11, came into Bovingdon as a Shuttle back-up and was given a wide heading off, perhaps 260 degrees, for a landing on 10L. Having given him descent Alan handed him off to Tony, or so he thought. In fact only the strip was transferred and when Tony some time later asked Alan where Mike Romeo was the aircraft had disappeared off the left hand edge of Tony's screen and was level at 3,000 feet about to enter Wiltshire airspace. Feeling very guilty Alan turned Mike Romeo left heading 120 degrees and asked him to call established, although he did not mention his range which was around thirty five miles. The pilot did not question anything and on that day the Mike Romeo Appreciation Society was born. Never again when 'A' Watch were on duty was it held either in the air or for a stand, and rumours of the aircraft's VIP

status spread amongst the crews who would ask 'Does it help if we say we are Mike Romeo?', without knowing the reason. The story eventually surfaced in the Evening Standard on 26th February 2001 as the aircraft awaited scrapping at Hurn Airport, ten years after it was withdrawn from service by British Airways. There is an appropriate and happy postscript. Learning of the imminent scrapping of 'Mike Romeo' Pete

Al Carter with his ultimate 'Departure Strip' following his retirement in 2002. (Pete Bish)

Bish, who was on Alan Carter's Watch, saw that a piece of the aircraft might make a fitting and very unusual gift for him when he retired in 2002. However, when he approached the aircraft's owners, European Aviation, he was told that someone else had already shown an interest. But this was only a temporary setback, as enquiries revealed that the other

BAC 1-11 510 G-AVMR 'County of Tyne and Wear' as adopted by 'A' Watch, seen resting on the 'November' stands in December 1986. (Pete Bish)

request had come from Chris Huggett, another of Alan's colleagues in Heathrow Approach, who had the same purpose in mind. European Aviation were very happy to supply the 6x2 feet panel which was fashioned into an over-sized strip holder and presented to Alan at his retirement party on 16th August 2002, together with the aircraft's control column which had been obtained by Pete Evans, also at LTCC, when he read the newspaper article.

HSA 23cm RADAR

The CAA was being pressed by the International Telecommunications Union (ITU) to vacate the 50cm wavelength by the end of the decade as it sat right in the middle of the TV band. The specification for the radar to replace Heathrow's ageing Marconi 264s was, therefore, quite exacting - moderate range, suitable for SRAs, minimal weather clutter - and the 23cm wavelength was chosen because it offered a convenient compromise between the 10cm and 50cm radars currently in use. Plessey and Marconi tendered jointly although they were unable to persuade AEG Telefunken to supply the antenna they favoured due to the high rotation rate specified. A submission was also made by Hollandse Signaal Apparaten (HSA), in conjunction with Cossor, which involved the modification of a military system they were producing for ship-board use. It was water cooled and had already been bought by the Royal Dutch Navy, the Royal Navy and the United States Navy. Its purpose, however, was to detect low flying aircraft over the sea which meant that the antenna had a very low cut-off and was therefore unsuitable for civil Airport use. Nevertheless this bid

The HSA 23cm, tower-mounted in the Central Terminal area, is probably Heathrow's best ever radar from a user's viewpoint....(Dave Shawe)

was preferred for a number of technical reasons and an order was placed by the CAA who were also able to get AEG Telefunken to change their decision over the supply of an antenna and its turning gear. The radar's nominal maximum range of 250 miles was, of course, far in excess of that required for Airport use and so was reduced to 80 miles for the Heathrow system. The rotation rate was also slow but the 15 rpm required was achieved by constantly using two of the three motors fitted in the radar whereas, in more normal use, only one would have been used with the other two switching in to maintain a steady rotation as wind speeds increased. The HSA 23cm radar entered service at 0001 hours on 11th January 1986 when it also facilitated the withdrawal of the Plessey AR1.

TERMINAL 4 FOR SALE!

A meeting of the 'A' Watch 'Think Tank' was convened to decide how best they could celebrate the imminent opening of Terminal 4, and this led to it being advertised for sale. Paul Johnson somehow managed to acquire an estate agent's 'For Sale' sign and on the eve of the official opening he and three other 'A' Watch members - Martyn Swann, Berni Latimer and Alan Carter - set off south in 'Pixie' with the intention of erecting the board in some suitable spot. However things did not go as smoothly as hoped. The first problem arose at the airside security gate where Berni, who had changed her hairstyle, did not match the photo on her security pass. After some debate her identity was finally accepted and they were allowed through, wondering why the sign (which was pretty obvious inside the van) had not been questioned. Then they were faced with finding a place to plant it. The original choice of somewhere near the southern end of the 'Tango' stands had to be ruled out and finally a suitable alternative was found on the grass opposite stand T12. Sadly there were no enquiries about the price, which might have boosted the 'A' Watch barbecue fund!

The new Terminal was officially opened by Their Royal Highnesses the Prince and Princess of Wales on 1st April 1986. It had been almost nine years since planning application had been submitted by the BAA, and this had been followed by a public enquiry which lasted from May until December 1978. The architects chosen were Scott Brownrigg and Turner, Guildford and the design in technical jargon was 'linear, vertically stacked and segregated' - in simple terms aircraft would dock directly against the buildings and the arrivals and departures were on different levels. It had been designed predominantly as a long haul Terminal to relieve pressure on Terminal 3, and its first occupants were British Airways long haul together with their Paris and Amsterdam services, accompanied by KLM and Air Malta. The transfer of British Airways services to Terminal 4 allowed the BAA to begin its planned re-development and refurbishment of Terminal 3, but the move presented British Airways with a huge logistical problem. A total of almost 2,000 items of ground handling equipment needed to be moved of which around 700 had to be taken across 28L/10R. This took place on the nights of 10th and 11th April when stands J15 and K14 were closed early so that equipment could be assembled ready for transit. The runway was then closed at 2100 and movement began half an hour later. Following this massive transfer of equipment flights began to operate from the 23 new stands available on 12th April.

One of the 2 Marconi 264s alongside Block 115 which fed both Heathrow Approach and LATCC for so many years. This view in 1988. (Pete Bish)

MICROWAVE LANDING SYSTEM (MLS)

Although the emphasis during 1985 and 1986 had been on producing the new procedures for Terminal 4 a number of other changes also took place. In September 1985 environmentally friendly modifications were made to the western end of helicopter route H2 and in the following September the City Centre Helistop was finally closed. Despite its grand name this was simply a barge moored on the Thames at Trig Lane but it did see some very limited activity. On 12th April 1986 the main runway crosswind component required for the activation of either runway 23 or 05 was raised to 20 knots, considerably reducing their chances of being used. But perhaps the most interesting development was the arrival in August 1986 of a Microwave Landing System (MLS) serving runway 28R. MLS had been selected by lCAO to replace ILS and initially the choice had been narrowed down to either the British Doppler system or the Australian 'Interscan' system. While the Doppler MLS was in its infancy but had great potential the 'Interscan', known by the Americans as Time Referenced Scanning Beam (TRSB), had gone as far as it could go but worked. However it was the latter system that the Americans favoured and by applying diplomatic and economic pressure to ICAO member States they were able to force through its adoption, in much the same way as they had won the case for VOR over Decca for area navigation some years earlier. MLS offered a number of advantages over ILS and these included:-

(1)   extra channels which made siting less critical.
(2)   no beam bending due to terrain, buildings etc.
(3)   curved approaches were possible.
(4)   less subject to interference.

The TRSB system installed at Heathrow was an engineering model produced by Plessey, not for operational use but allowing experimental modifications to be made where necessary. Although it was originally intended to remain at Heathrow for just over a year it was finally removed in 1993- 94 and replaced by a production model - the P-Scan 2000 engineered to Cat 3 standards. British Airways became involved at an early stage in the evaluation of this new landing aid by installing the airborne equipment of several manufacturers in their Boeing 757 G-BIKK and carrying out occasional MLS approaches on 27R. A second aircraft, Boeing 767 G-BNWB, joined the trial some years later in 1994 to evaluate DGPS navigational data against the 27R MLS signals. By squawking 'ident' at 1,500 feet the pilot triggered a camera on the ground (at the 09L localiser site) which allowed Tels to compare the MLS approach with the known ILS profile.

While it is not strictly within the period covered by this book it is worth recording that MLS went out of favour with the Americans towards the end of the nineties when GPS systems seemed to offer the way forward, and this resulted in a declining interest in its development in Europe. However the greater incidence of Cat 3 conditions in Europe and fears that there could be major disruption if satellites were switched off for military reasons revived the fortunes of MLS resulting in an order for four Thales systems for installation at Heathrow from 2002.

One evening Dave Broderick was in charge of a quiet Air Departures (28R) when Chris Cosgrave rang from Approach to ask if a Pitts Special that he was working back to Wycombe Air Park could make a low approach and overshoot. Since there was only one aircraft taxiing out, a Trident which was early for its slot, Dave agreed and the Pitts was positioned onto final. By the time it reached the threshold the Trident was sitting at the holding point, idling away its delay, and the crew and passengers must have been as impressed as the staff in the Tower when the Pitts proceeded to perform several rolls and then switch on its smoke. What Chris had not told Dave was that the pilot was Nigel Lamb, a member of the Marlborough aerobatic team, returning from an earlier display.

Another fly-past story from the mid-eighties took place in the early hours of a beautifully clear weekday morning, around the time when the USAF went on their unannounced visit to Libya. Approach was asked by London Mil if an F-111 could be accepted for a look at London and since the Tower had no traffic to affect it the request was approved. The F-111 was given vectors from north of Bovingdon to Tower Bridge whence it ran in towards Heathrow at 4,000 feet. ATCO Chris Huggett and his lighting operator Dick Griffiths in the VCR wanted to extend a greeting to the unusual visitor so, when the aircraft was about two to three miles out, Dick flashed the runway lights up and down through the brilliancy settings to which the aircraft responded by igniting fuel in its after-burner, a party piece known as 'torching'. There was a massive bang, audible for some distance, and a flash which bathed the VCR desks - and probably much of London too - in an orange glow, following which the F-111 vanished northbound at a high rate of knots. Chris and the Watch Manager Bunny Austin, who had to be summoned, were busy for some time afterwards answering phone calls from people who were convinced that they had seen an aircraft explode in mid-air!

THE HEATHROW TEN

Heathrow has always struggled to reach and maintain its agreed ATCO staffing levels. High failure rates among staff fresh off Cadet courses and inability to attract experienced staff from other units have been contributory factors. In 1986 the situation was no different from normal and it was decided that drastic action should be taken. A number of ATCOs at West Drayton were chosen for compulsory transfer to Heathrow and these included Pete Hamer, Bob Hillyer, Rod Jackman, Phil Layton, Rick Morton, Steve Sharpe, Dick Tilley and Brian Wildey. They, together with Colin Cordery and Graeme Wilson who were also named but avoided the move across, came to be known as 'the Heathrow Ten' and, with the exception of Steve Sharpe who quickly returned to ATC Ops at LATCC, did much to alleviate Heathrow's shortfall. Malcolm Hemming arrived at the same time via Farnborough, whilst Brian Jones followed the next year. At the end of 1986, with the first of the arrivals from LATCC now undergoing training the Watch list looked like this :-

ATCO MAIN ROSTER DECEMBER 1986

	A	B	C	D	E
Watch Manager	L.Dunn	D.Harriss	J.M.Toy	N.D.Bunn	D.E.Bush
Asst Watch Mngr	Mrs W.Campbell	T.G.C.Quantrill	R.Daly	A.J.Prosser	W.J.Ferguson
1	A.McLean	J.C.Kiernan	B.A.Piket	J.R.Cant	C.M.Ward
2	A.Carter	R.G.Boulter	R.Hendry	P.A.Louden	J.MacDermot
3	N.W.Wright	J.S.Rymill	J.F.Hanbury	M.J.Gunston	G.K.Clarkson
4	P.J.Bish	G.B.Coates	P.N.Q.Carter	A.H.Croft	R.C.Metcalfe
5	G.Hewitt	I.D.McKinna	C.A.Cosgrave	P.S.Flynn	M.W.Lewis
6	R.A.Robinson	J.E.E.J.Przygrodski	D.J.Broderick	D.G.Nicholas	R.M.Neville
7	A.S.Watkins	I.M.Callier	A.E.Barnes	D.A.Rham	R.L.Harrison
8	B.J.McCartney	M.P.Ross	S.V.James	S.C.Hobbs	R.K.Taylor
9	I.H.Alexander	N.E.Wood	J.J.Cooke	Mrs S.P.Clifford	S.W.Lambert
10	P.Wilson	M.G.Edwards	B.A.G.Chapman	M.J.B.Inglis	N.P.Le Gros
11	C.K.Herbert	M.J.Mothershaw	R.K.Spooner	J.C.Siddell	K.P.Meakin
12	P.G.Johnson	D.C.Shawe	M.V.Male	S.W.Forster	A.J.Fleming
13	K.H.Miller	K.McMahon	R.A.Cowell	Ms J.S.Price	C.C.Huggett
14	J.D.Oram		I.M.Toakley	S.J.Dominic	
U/T VCR	J.P.Bate R.J.Morton	B.T.Wildey	M.P.Hemming	M.R.Halverson	G.D.Howlett
U/T Radar	R.H.Tilley	M.S.Walker	C.J.Wilson	P.D.Layton	Miss S.P.J.Simmonds P.B.Hamer

Relief Watch Managers : R.Wadley and E.Wood
Heathrow Training Unit : C.R.Prentice and H.C.Hayes
Regional Training Centre : L.H.T.Wellard
ATC Ops : I.M.Mason   ATC Ops 2 : G.Morehouse

ATCA MAIN ROSTER DECEMBER 1986

	A	B	C	D	E
1	M.Cleary	J.C.Wood	G.P.Kemp	M.E.Davies	D.P.J.Treacy
2	R.Kunert	J.H.Gleave	A.J.Wright	G.Bannister	R.D.M.Griffiths
3	A.Marsh	F.Karai	M.Judge	A.J.M.McGregor	M.P.Dyer
4	M.D.Swann		K.P.Baker		
5	Mrs L.P.Miller	N.K.Wales	C.II.George	Ms S.A.Appleby	D.P.Crizzle
6	K.M.Bowdler	S.P.Batham	B.Datta	M.McKenzie	P.W.Hayes
7	Mrs J.E.Darling	F.D.Jennings	R.Darling	R.T.Kehoe	Mrs E.M.Shoesmith
8	Mrs S.R.C.Louden	C.P.Beards	G.W.Jarvis	Mrs M.Johnston	Miss S.M.Quest
9	D.T.London	Miss T.E.Wilcox	Mrs P.Neale	M.A.Hooper	S.M.Neale
10	Miss B.K.Latimer	P.R.Irwin	A.G.Bright	Miss T.L.Girdler	Miss S.J.Holland
11	Mrs E.S.Findlay	R.M.Webb	Miss V.E.Lennon	M.F.B.Williams	C.L.Fishpool
12	S.L.Barnes	C.D.Ibell	M.S.Settle	T.M.Fallows	Miss L.S.Freedman
13	M.A.Granata	C.A.Peake	F.W.Hayes	R.A.Gatfield	M.Tayte
14		Mrs P.Harkins			

ATC Ops 3 : C.J.Warner and P.G.Stephens
Heathrow Training Unit : E.W.Percival
Regional Training Unit : D.G.Williams, S.P.Harben and Miss J.M.E.Watkins

STATION GRADING

Negotiations had, however, been taking place between IPCS and NATS aimed at encouraging greater mobility in the ATCO grade through the introduction of station grading. Until now there had been no salary differential between the quietest and the busiest units and there was therefore no incentive to request a move to a busy station such as Heathrow. A draft agreement on restructuring of the ATCO grade, which was circulated in June 1987, recognised Heathrow and LATCC as the busiest units, Scottish Oceanic, Manchester and Gatwick as the next busiest, and then finally came all other units. Implementation of the agreement was conditional on the breaking of the civil service pay link and the negotiation of revised working practices and, if this was achieved, watchkeeping ATCOs 2 and 4 at the smaller units would be re-graded as ATCO 3s while those at the five busier units would become ATCO 2s. Assimilation onto the IPCS pay spine and the award of extra spine points to the busier stations in 1989 (all five units) and 1990 (LATCC and Heathrow only) would create a pay differential between Heathrow and the quietest units of just over five thousand pounds per annum at the top of the scale from 1st April 1990. The proposed scales for Heathrow were:-

ATCO 1		ATCO 2	
Scale point from		Scale max from	
1.4.90	25,943	1.4.90	23,986
1.4.89	24,945	1.4.89	23,064
1.4.88	23,986	1.4.88	22,176
1.4.87	22,176	1.4.87	20,503

N.B Shift Liability and Unsocial Hours payments not included in these rates.

The conditions for re-grading and the proposed new pay scales were accepted and discussions ensued on the subject of revised working practices, which resulted in an agreement implemented in August 1988. Each of the five Watches now comprised an ATCO 1 as Watch Manager and (theoretically) 16 ATCO 2s - one of these the Deputy Watch Manager. The shift times became:-

Morning	0700-1445
Afternoon	1430-2215
Night	2200-0715
D1	0800-1700 (three supplied)
D2	1000-1900
D3	1130-2030
D4	1200-2100
D5	1600-2330

The number of ATCO 2s available, however, was well short of the eighty required and it was agreed that the change over from afternoon to night duty would initially be at the earlier time of 2130 until there were seventy five fully validated ATCO 2s on the unit, which was not expected imminently.

NEW RUNWAY EXITS AND DESIGNATIONS

Out on the field, meanwhile, various changes had been taking place. Despite its high landing rates Heathrow suffered from a lack of decent high speed runway exits and on the preferred, and more regularly used, westerly runways there was also a frustratingly long distance between the turn offs at block 11 and block 9 (28R) and between block 83 and block 79 (28L) if vacating to the south. Indeed in the latter case it was at times necessary for traffic bound for the south side to vacate north at block 81 to prevent a go-around. The opening of Terminal 4 had not improved the situation, greatly increasing the number of aircraft needing to vacate to the south and many of these were now heavier types such as the Boeing 747, which normally missed the turn at block 83 but could manage something sooner than block 79. What was needed on both runways was a new, preferably high speed, exit to resolve these problems and the first to be completed was a turn off to the south from 28L linking block 81 to block 109, which was opened early in 1987. A turn off from 28R mid-way between blocks 11 and 9 leading onto the outer taxiway at block 37(0) did not follow until ten years later (in June1997). A little later in the year, on 1st April, the helicopter landing pad north of block 15 and the aiming point in block 94 were withdrawn from use, the latter being replaced by an aiming point in block 96 to supplement the other existing location in block 111. Being unlit they could only be used by day and night time landings and take-offs had to use 28L/10R. But it was a change that came three months later, for only the second time in Heathrow's history, which was to prove the most challenging. Back in 1952 runway 16/34 had succumbed to the inevitability of magnetic change and been re-designated 15/33 and now, on 2nd July 1987, the designators for 28L/10R and 28R/10L were changed to 27L/09R and 27R/09L respectively. It was some time, however, before controllers and pilots (particularly those with extensive experience of Heathrow) were able to stop themselves inadvertently referring to the runways by their previous designators.

THE AVERAGE BLOCK

During one of their rare night duties together, under-employed ATCOs Bob Robinson and Malcolm Ross put their highly intellectual, enquiring minds to the exacting task of determining the sum of all the block numbers on the Airport. Later, with this accomplished, Malcolm propounded the theory that if this total was now divided by the number of blocks that existed then you could identify the 'average block'. This turned out to be block 63 and because of its regular, geometrically rectangular shape block 63(0) was awarded the honour over 63(I). Their efforts did not receive official recognition, but block 63(0) - which later became 63(I) when the 'Delta' stands were extended - is now used as a transfer point between GMC1 and GMC2, and it is interesting to consider what some carriers would make of being told to hold in the average block!

The 'Heathrow Mushrooms' with Angela Rippon at their appearance on BBC 1's quiz 'Masterteam'. L to R, Graham Jarvis, Angela Rippon, Mike Settle and Roger Darling. (via Graham Jarvis)

TV STARS

Over the years it has not been unusual for Heathrow's ATC staff to feature in radio and television broadcasts. TV presenter James Burke spent a week in the Tower gathering material for an edition of his science based programme 'Burke's Law' - a spin-off from 'Tomorrow's World' - and Mike Smith and Sarah Greene were present for a time recording a series of shows which followed a week in the life of the British Airways Boeing 757 G-BIKF 'Raglan Castle'. An edition of 'Horizon' and a documentary 'Red One to London' also saw recordings made in the Ops rooms while Robert Spooner has taken part in three interviews for the BBC. One of these was for transmission on the BBC's World Service in Uzbekistan - suitably translated although Bob can speak some Russian - while the other two were for Airport programmes on their Internet website. In the reverse direction staff were invited to visit the studios of Capital Radio to meet Chris Tarrant as a thank you for their services to the 'Flying Eye' in its patrols over London, but a new dimension was added to these exchanges by three 'C' Watch assistants who were accepted to appear on a BBC1 quiz programme 'Angela Rippon's Masterteam'. They had been selected from 1,400 entries and would be competing with teams who were taking part in two or three competitions each week. For the programme Roger Darling, Graham Jarvis and team captain Mike Settle adopted the team name of 'the Heathrow Mushrooms', which they explained to their hostess was derived from being kept in the dark in Heathrow Approach and fed a load of s**t. Although amused she felt that this would be an inappropriate response on the actual show. Their first appearance was on October 11th 1987 against a team who had already won three games, but talent could not be held down and the 'Mushrooms' progressed to further appearances on 12th and 13th when they were finally defeated by the eventual winners of the competition, an Irish team from Carrick. For their achievements the Heathrow team received bronze medals, having commendably come tenth out of the sixty-five eventual participants.

THAMES RADAR

The 14th October 1987 saw a significant extension to the service provided from Heathrow when, two weeks later than originally planned, Thames Radar began operations from the Approach room on frequency 132.7 Mhz to coincide with the opening of the new London City Airport. There were a number of postings in to provide the staffing required - the Heathrow ATCOs had refused to undertake the extra duties without a pay increase - and these included Christine Deamer from Edinburgh, Dave Deamer from Birmingham, and both Mike Martin and Ray Redford from Farnborough. Mike had first heard of Thames Radar at an IPMS meeting earlier in the year and, dissatisfied with the limited demands of his current work at Farnborough and aware that station grading would soon penalise him financially, had been quick to apply for a transfer. Ray followed suit for the same reasons and both were accepted, albeit initially only on detachment until the end of the year. They were, however, given progressive extensions as a result of their OJTI endorsements until they became permanent fixtures. The newcomers were joined by Heathrow ATCOs Chris Prentice and Bert Hayes, who were responsible for the initial training programme, plus Ian Mason and John Rymill. This gave an interesting mix of experience, some being used to working within the protected environment of controlled airspace while others were more accustomed to operating in the open FIR. The establishment of a Special Rules Zone was intended to give a measure of protection to the traffic using London City but transfer of aircraft to and from LATCC was not formalised and led to public transport aircraft being worked by Thames outside controlled airspace. The situation was exacerbated by numerous infringements of the SRZ by pilots unaware of the new Airport and its associated airspace and a number of airmisses resulted. This brought about the suspension of the Thames Radar service for a short while in December 1987, while intensive work was done by Pete Allsopp and Colin Atkins (TMA Ops) to achieve a workable solution. In recognition of the success of this work the London City holding facility was named 'Alkin'.

When Thames Radar arrived in the 6th Floor Approach room they occupied the console originally set aside for SVFR plus a similar one alongside. Two positions, Thames Radar and City Director were available. These were therefore back to back with the main Heathrow bank, including SVFR. This view was in September 1988 with Kevin Mallam nearest the camera. (Pete Bish)

FIRST GENERAL MANAGER

In 1980/81, while attending a management course at Henley, Keith Williams was in a team which put forward in their thesis the suggestion that there should be an overall manager at each unit to unify the separate sections (ATC, Tels etc). At the time this did not appear to evoke much interest and Keith was therefore surprised to see the same idea presented a couple of years later in glossy brochure form by a group of PA consultants and welcomed for implementation. Keith was among those selected to fill one of these new posts and, having impressed with his determination that it should be Heathrow, was posted in as the first General Manager in 1988. The new structure was in its infancy but most staff were in favour although there was some dissent from senior engineering managers who saw this as a further erosion of their empire by ATC. Unfortunately for Keith one of the early decisions he faced was whether to make the Control Tower non-smoking. A pipe smoker himself he was faced with the dilemma of whether he personally would be able to comply if he imposed a ban. As he was about to go on a ski-ing holiday he decided to defer his decision to see if he could resist smoking while he was away, and having just about survived agreed to the ban at the next meeting of the LJNCC. He remembers being approached by some staff who were adamant that they could not control safely without smoking but there was a large majority who supported the decision. Because smoking had previously been permitted in the building certain rooms had to be designated as smoking areas and one of these was the ATC rest room on the seventh floor.

From that time on it required strong nerve for a non smoker to enter the room and a machete to cut through the stale smell of smoke within.

This year also saw the start of a major re-work of the space available on the ground floor of the Tower. Tels remained in firm control of the east wing but part of the area which had originally been the staff cafeteria and bar was prepared as a new office for Flight Clearance and Met, who moved down from their rather more spacious accommodation on the first floor. This in turn enabled the return of AIS from their office building in Pinner, which had been sold for re-development, on 17th September 1988. There was still a requirement for STPOs in Flight Clearance which led to a rather unsuccessful attempt to cross train them for ATCA duties and vice versa. Jackie Green was the only STPO to validate and she was later absorbed into the ATCA grade. After a while the STPOs moved back upstairs again necessitating the installation of a new Lamson tube link from Clearance to convey any data inputs that were required. This had pressure from the ground floor to the first but relied on gravity for the returns. Plans had also been drawn up for the west wing where, it was hoped, Approach Control would be re-housed together with a new rest room and kitchen in 1989.

The next major piece of equipment to arrive at Heathrow was a Plessey Watchman 10cm primary radar fitted with an on-mounted Marconi SSR antenna, which was delivered in March1989. It was the third such installation in the NATS airfield radar replacement programme and was designed from the outset to provide plot extracted primary and secondary radar data. Following a successful series of flight trials in March 1990 it entered service on 25th April 1991, permitting the withdrawal of the EN4000. Beam width was 1.5 degrees and scan rate 15 rpm. The siting of the new radar, however, would cause its premature withdrawal from service some ten years or so later (together with the D/F equipment and R/T receivers) when the area in which it was located needed to be cleared for the construction of Terminal 5. Rather than re-site the Watchman a replacement Raytheon ASR lOSS radar was purchased - paid for by Heathrow Airport Limited - and the Watchman was re-located to Edinburgh.

The AFS called one morning for an emergency crossing of 27R which resulted in a Singapore Airlines Boeing 747 being sent round just as its wheels were about to touch. The ambulance sprinted across and the VCR Supervisor rang the AFS to find out more about the emergency 'We have been called to meet a sick passenger on the Singapore Airlines flight ….' was the embarrassing reply.

The time had come again for the surface of the main runways to receive attention. Re-surfacing of 27L/09R began on 10th April 1989 and involved night time closures from Monday to Friday from 2100 to 0500. Following its completion at the end of the year there was a short break and then similar work was undertaken on 27R/09L starting on 5th March 1990. Towards the end of 1989 the Airport's approach and taxiway lighting were also in the news. USI 15/89 gave notice that the SHINGALS (Supplementary High Intensity Narrow Gauge Approach Lights) had been conveniently re-named SALS - just lose the HING and off you go. But much more worrying was the discovery that omni-directional

green taxiway light fittings would soon become unavailable as both manufacturers (GEC and Thorn EMI) had been forced to switch production to a bi-directional fitting to meet the light intensity requirements for Cat 3 operations. Until now it had been easy to confirm the correct selection and serviceability of all green routes that comprised Heathrow's unique system, but this would become progressively more difficult as the new fittings were installed. Co-ordination between the GMC controller and his lighting operator would necessarily be increased and areas of the Airport would appear, in effect, unlit and require greater monitoring of all movements to ensure that the expected progress was made. Despite strong protests to HAL, which included concern over the possible effect on movement rates, ATC were forced to accept that there was no alternative to this retrograde step with its associated safety implications.

NEW APPROACH ROOM

Work on the preparation of a new Approach Control room on the ground floor progressed well and 19th May 1989 was set as the last full day of operations from the sixth floor. The new room with its lower ceiling - you will remember that the sixth floor accommodation was two floors high - seemed smaller and had no windows but this gave it a somewhat cosier atmosphere. The opportunity was taken to remove the Special VFR controller from the line of Heathrow suites and to locate him more logically beside the two Thames Radar consoles with which he constantly liaised. This gave a

Proof of concept - The Ground Floor Approach room in mock-up form. (via Bill Billing)

Heathrow line up (facing north) of an ATSA at the western end of the room, APC(N), Dir 1(N), Dir 2, Dir 1(S), APC(S). Behind them, facing south, were the low level suites, and at the eastern end of the room was a desk for the Supervisor and Supervisor's assistant. An impressive 20 inch diameter Ericsson DS86 radar display was provided for each of the operational controllers including APC (N and S) who no longer needed to lean across to confirm radar derived data in their acceptance of releases and could also monitor operational safety more effectively. Data displayed on the screens was selected using the new Heathrow Airport Radar Processing System (HARPS), and allowed a wide variety of choice. An office was provided for the Watch Manager and another small room for individual Watches to store their admin. records such as rosters and training reports. Finally a large rest room and kitchen were provided next door, but not exclusively for ATC use. The move downstairs took place during a 'C' Watch night duty and thirty four years of operation from the sixth floor passed quietly into history with a brief entry by Hank Prosser in the Approach Watch log at 0142 on 20th May which read 'Operations transferred to new Approach Control Room'. Although the service to aircraft was essentially unaffected the change did have a number of practical and social disadvantages for the operational ATC staff. A certain dimension had been added to the Approach operation by being able to look out of the windows at times

and this was obviously no longer possible, while exchange visits of a social nature between the two ops rooms - until then a common break-time activity - were also made less convenient, particularly from Approach to the VCR.

NEW VCR DESK DISPLAYS

While this construction work was going on downstairs an unexpected problem arose in the VCR involving a new piece of equipment which had arrived for installation in both Ops rooms. The Airport Display Information System (ADIS) was one of three items ordered for the VCR and all were confidently expected to fit into the panels available on the existing desks. The ADIS, however, was found to need more space than had been allowed, forcing a major decision to replace all the operational desks in the VCR, with some inevitable inconvenience to staff. The new furniture had a lower profile and, when installed, gave the VCR a sleeker more modern appearance.

The ADIS responsible for this make-over had been acquired from Praxis as the result of a suggestion by Paul Johnson that certain items of data on the control desks could be combined. It consisted of a colour monitor and keypad, and displayed both dynamic and paged data on a horizontally divided screen. The dynamic data at the top of the screen included the time, pressure settings, IRVR readings, the

...and in final form. Subdued lighting was still used (which many of us believe makes for a quieter ops room!). The Approach Supervisor position in the foreground has ADIS (left) and BASIS (right) displays. The operating positions each have a single 20' Ericsson radar display and back lit maps and data above. In this picture all seats are occupied by staff from Ops and Training, hence Eric Percival acting as Supervisor! (via Bill Billing)

anemometers and runway/approach lighting selected. Below the line the paged data consisted of 1,000 pages, almost half of which were allocated to ATC for the display of any information considered pertinent such as emergency call phraseology and speed groupings. The manual supplied by Praxis was difficult for the non-computer literate to understand and Chris Prentice found it necessary to translate relevant parts into layman's language so that the ATSAs could input weather information. Having said that some ATC staff became quite adept at using the equipment and very acceptable pictures of a Constellation, a Hercules and various Porsches appeared. A new DFTI also arrived. This had a 12 inch diagonal raster scan display and a display control panel. Radar inputs were avaiable from Heathrow, Debden and Pease Pottage and the control panel enabled controllers to select their individual preferences of range, height filter, label size and brilliances etc. At this stage the secondary data was not code-callsign converted, but this would follow a year or so later. Finally the ASMI was replaced. A definitive requirement had been originated in 1987 when the ASMI Mk.5 currently in use was recognised as having become too difficult and expensive to maintain due to the shortage of components and obsolete technology used. In fact it dated back partly to 1967 when the Decca Mk.3 ASMI had replaced the original installation. This had been re-furbished in 1975 and re-designated the Mk.5 but now was the last of its type in the World. The Thomson CSF 'Astre' Ground Movement Radar - as ASMI was now known - was chosen as its replacement and this was installed during the summer of 1989, entering service in the October. This had a scan-converted colour picture with a wide array of user options, perhaps the most useful of which were mapped overlays of block boundaries and LSAs. These three pieces of equipment and the HARPS in Approach were impressive advances in technology offering considerable selectability but with the disadvantage that changes of the display, sometimes requiring a number of computer inputs to reach the correct menu, could be difficult to make if it was busy. Quite a contrast with earlier times when an on / off switch and a brightness control were considered adequate.

As a 'thank you' for their tolerance during this period of transformation all ATC staff were given a black Parker ball pen on which the CAA logo and the words 'EGLL - a new approach in '89' were printed in gold. Unfortunately it came in a presentation box designed for two items and one or two were returned in protest, although most were accepted with the less than gracious thought 'What must I do to get the other pen?' A buffet meal and drinks were also provided at a Langley hotel. The vacation of the sixth floor enabled this area to be re-developed into conference and presentation facilities, segregated from the rest of the Tower and only accessible by the lifts. The future of the new Approach room, however, was already in some doubt as planning for a Central Control Function - which would see the Heathrow, Gatwick and Stansted Approach Controls relocated to the TMA room at LATCC - continued to progress. At this stage the 'O' date for Heathrow's move to West Drayton (stage 2) was December 1991, only two and a half years away.

TOWER SHAKES

Normally it is Heathrow's ATC staff who have to demonstrate their ability to be flexible but the Control Tower building has also been known to display the same quality from time to time. On one occasion Malcolm Hemming was supervising in the VCR when everyone felt a thump, as though something had hit the base of the Tower. Having made a number of enquiries inside the building with no success he ended up ringing the National Physical Laboratory who told him that at the time mentioned there had been a minor earth tremor with its epi-centre in Shropshire and that this was almost certainly the cause. Another incident, which happened during a 'D' Watch night duty in the early seventies, involved Sue Clifford, Eric Dallison and Alan Carter. About half way through their first half they became aware of a bubbling noise which became louder and louder until eventually it was quite frightening and made R/T transmissions difficult to hear even though they were wearing headsets. The Police, the BAA and the Fire Service were all informed and meanwhile the Watch Supervisor Jack Hollis appeared and found that the walls were shaking. By now the noise was so loud that Alan had to tell an aircraft that evacuation was being considered but the day was saved by the Fire Service who arrived and traced the sound to a calorifier located at the foot of the stairs which was obviously in the last stages of a nervous breakdown. But the final story in this collection, and possibly the most dramatic, took place in the summer of 1989 when the support structure for the new Thomson GMR was being installed. Staff working in the VCR felt the Tower begin to shake alarmingly for no immediately obvious reason and assistance was sought to locate the cause which was eventually found to be two workmen who were checking the security of the safety hand rail on the new GMR gantry. By pushing and pulling on the rail, which was imbedded in the Tower brickwork, they were inducing an oscillation which had been discerned as far down as the third floor.

REMOTE HOLDING

At times a stand which was urgently required for an incoming flight was still occupied by a departure which had received an ATC route delay. This resulted in an agreement, initially involving Heathrow Airport Limited and British Airways only, that if an aircraft was fully ready to depart some time ahead of its slot it would be allowed to absorb the delay at a 'ground holding point' if it was operationally feasible. This offered a number of advantages to the Airline - releasing the stand and the associated despatch staff while improving the 'on-time' departure statistics - and also put the aircraft in a good position to take an earlier slot if it became available, but of course gave GMC an extra movement to handle. The most logical position for remote holding was the holding point of the landing runway in use e.g blocks 74 and 75 when 27R was in use for departure, although any convenient block which did not interfere with the general traffic flow or, indeed, an alternative stand such as the 150s might be selected. The scheme was introduced on 24th July 1989 and was later extended to include progressively more airlines.

One day a British Airways Captain arrived in the Tower foyer to renew his medical and was sent up unescorted to the third floor where the Medical Centre was located at that time together with the offices of ATC Management. Having successfully negotiated the first part of the route he looked around for the entrance to the Centre and spotted a name plate inscribed 'D R Austin' on one of the doors so went in, mistakenly thinking that this was Dr. Austin's office when in actual fact it was the office of Bunny Austin, the Head of ATC Ops, whose initials just happened to be D R. Unknown to the Captain Watch Manager Derek Harriss had arrived in the office moments earlier to see Bunny and had decided to wait hidden behind the desk and surprise him on his return, so as the door opened Derek sprang out to the consternation of both parties....

1000 MOVEMENTS IN A DAY

Following the period of depression at the beginning of the eighties increasing confidence in the industry led to a sustained period of growth with total movements passing the magic 300,000 mark for the first time in 1985. The first day with over 1,000 movements also occurred in that year on 7th June. Only 4 years later the average was over 1,000 per day.

Total Aircraft Movements

1980	294,619
1981	267,117
1982	273,068
1983	283,060
1984	297,431
1985	309,344
1986	315,753
1987	329,977
1988	351,567
1989	368,430

HOST COMPUTER SYSTEM

One of the major NATS projects at this time was the upgrading of the IBM 9020D computer which had been in operation at LATCC since 1975. This was known as 'Rehost' and involved the replacement of the earlier computers with four standard commercial IBM 4381 computers - one pair to run the operational software, processing radar and flight plan data, and the other pair to provide a software test and development system. Technical transfer took place during December 1989 and then, following operational trials, the Host Computer System (HCS) went into service on 7th April 1990. The official launch was carried out by HRH The Princess Royal later in the year on 18th June.

LONDON CONTROL ZONE CONTRACTS

The ever improving climb performance of Heathrow outbounds was, by now, making it difficult to justify a Control Zone which extended fourteen miles to the west. Increasing general aviation traffic wishing to route around to the west of the Zone was being forced into confliction with the Booker circuit or over the built up areas around Camberley and so, on 3rd May 1990, the Zone boundary was drawn in by two miles to reflect these changed requirements. The free lane associated with White Waltham, now on the Zone boundary, became redundant and to celebrate the newly bestowed freedom two hot air balloons - piloted by Pete Bish, Roger Kunert and friends - made the most of a bright start to the day by lifting from the airfield and drifting west on the light easterly wind.

MAYFIELD SID

Otherwise during 1990 and 1991 things were fairly quiet in Approach Control, the only procedural change worthy of note being the classification of the existing arrival routes into the four stacks as Standard Arrival Routes (STARs) on 7th February 1991. In contrast to this a number of changes occurred in Aerodrome Control, amongst these the withdrawal of the Departure ATIS on 121.85 Mhz when it was combined with the Arrival ATIS from 5th April 1990 as

The Air Arrivals desk following installation of all three 1990 advances in electronic displays. Now mounted in the desk are, left to right, ADIS, the DFTI (now re-dubbed ATM - Aerodrome Traffic Monitor) with labels and the Thomson GMR. The updated Runway Override panel appears on the desk below the GMR. (CAA Archives)

'Heathrow Information'. A trial procedure where aircraft landing and take-off times were no longer broadcast was also brought in as a result of the BAA no longer needing this information. While this was found acceptable in relation to landing traffic a safety audit at LATCC subsequently made a strong recommendation that the broadcasting of departure times should be resumed to reduce the workload of TMA controllers when an aircraft made its first call and so this was done. Later in the year, on 23rd August, the 'Detling' SID used for aircraft positioning out to Gatwick was replaced by a new 'Mayfield' SID which provided a more direct routeing via Epsom (Midhurst DME 20 on easterlies) to Mayfield at 5,000 feet and removed the need for the aircraft to be worked by LATCC. The simple inter-unit co-ordination, however, was often overridden by the TMA controllers to whom a courtesy call had to be made before the aircraft was given take-off clearance. If they saw that Gatwick was busy, which it nearly always was, they would often refuse to allow the aircraft to get airborne, even if it had received an EAT and been released by Gatwick's Director. On one occasion the aircraft was allowed to get airborne but was then climbed to enter the Gatwick stack at flight level 120, reducing the procedure to a farce. Inevitably there were numerous irate phone calls to the LATCC Supervisor to explain the working of the procedure but it was still some time before it was understood by all. Finally, turning to equipment, a new membrane style of runway override panel was installed in the Air desks, replacing the old raised button version but initially giving some problems until controllers became accustomed to the degree of pressure required to effect a change of selection. Then, as 1991 began, the DFTI - although still the same piece of equipment - was re-named the Aerodrome Traffic Monitor (ATM).

On a hazy day in the summer of 1990 the pilot of a Robinson R22 helicopter, making only his second solo cross country flight, found himself 'temporarily unsure of his position' and quite correctly decided to call ATC for assistance, choosing Luton who squawked him but were unable to see his response on radar. Next they asked him if there were any features on the ground which might help them to determine his position to which he replied 'Affirmative. I can see two runways, one marked 27R and the other 23. Oh, and I can also see a Concorde parked outside a hangar.' Problem solved, thought Luton. He must be at Duxford where the Concorde G-AXDN is preserved. 'Call Duxford on ..'. Almost immediately, of course, he was back with Luton and now the penny dropped. He was transferred to Heathrow's Special VFR frequency allowing the chaos he was causing to be resolved.

A little later in the year on Battle of Britain Day an impressive total of 168 aircraft were involved in the flypast over London, their exit routes being determined by whether they were slow (Hercules, Nimrods, 146s etc) or fast (fighters). The route for the 'slows' was direct to Northolt but the Red Arrows, who were included in this group, delayed their turn north west and ended up flying directly over Heathrow. As they passed over Terminal 4 the leader showed commendable panache by requiring the team to 'smoke on'.

ASSESSMENTS FOR WATCH MANAGER POSTS

The nature of work in ATC meant that the Watch Manager was more closely involved with his team than was the case in other industries, becoming almost a paternal figure looking after the needs of his family, but this was about to change. Promotion from ATCO2 to ATCO1 had traditionally followed the Civil Service procedure with a general review board interviewing large numbers of candidates who were all expected to be career minded, and who were invited for interview if they had received three consecutive 'well fitted' markings in the promotability section of their annual staff report (ASR). Those who sufficiently impressed the board were then held in readiness for anticipated vacancies although this sometimes meant a relatively long wait. There were obvious shortcomings in this system and when in 1991 it became necessary to find replacements for a number of Heathrow Watch Managers who were leaving it was done using the newly introduced system of 'assessment'. Now when a post was about to become vacant it was advertised by a vacancy notice and only those interested in that particular post needed to apply. From these a short list of candidates was chosen and assessed using a series of modules designed to identify the applicants most closely fitting the character profile established for the post. Different modules might be necessary for different posts but for the Heathrow Watch Manager these consisted of six elements - a maths test, an English comprehension test, a lengthy self-assessment, a group discussion, a presentation on a chosen subject and a technical interview to finish. The two day assessment was enough to deter some who would otherwise have applied and been strong contenders, and others who took the tests were not impressed by having to demonstrate their ability to count and understand their native tongue. Overall it felt very synthetic but the net result was that it produced Managers with similar personality traits who were also clearly management orientated. They were generally much younger than had previously been the case and this, together with their stronger attitude to dealing with staff, inevitably led to them being remoter figures, which many felt did not reflect the needs in the Air Traffic environment although it might suit other industries.

DISPLACED THRESHOLDS - OR NOT.....!

Chris Huggett enjoyed being out on the field in 'Pixie' and was often asked to take new arrivals with him for night time familiarisation. One of his favourite stunts was to get permission to enter 27L or 27R and then to say to his passenger 'let's see how fast this van will go'. Having floored the van in each gear until it reached maximum speed he would then say 'I'll leave it as late as I can before braking at the other end', but as the red end bar sprang towards them he would stamp his foot on the floor a couple of times and shriek 'Oh no, the brakes have failed'. Usually the passenger was so new they did not realise the 09L and 09R thresholds were displaced and Chris would take a sadistic pleasure from seeing them firstly brace in horror in expectation of hitting the grass at 100 mph and then relax with a look of confusion as they shot past the bar uneventfully. This, he would explain, was a really effective way of demonstrating to them that the thresholds were displaced. One of his victims was Matthew Bethel who enjoyed the joke as much as Chris, in fact so much so that a few years later he decided to play the same trick on newly arrived 'Spike'. Unfortunately, being an ATSA, he did not really need to know that the runways were only displaced at the western end and called for clearance to enter 09R. Everything went to plan except that when they passed the red end bar at the 27L threshold they ran onto the grass at around 90 mph. If anything Matthew was more surprised than Spike as he really had not expected this to happen but after a very uncomfortable few seconds the bucking van slid to a halt without injury to its occupants. Spike, with amazing restraint, turned slowly to Matt and said calmly 'What the f*** did you do that for?!'

FLOW UNIT ARRIVES AT HEATHROW

By now the ATFMU at LATCC, which had been re-named the London Flow Management Unit (LFMU) in 1987, had seen its task grow in complexity to the extent that a major re-think of methodology and manning had become necessary. The regulation task was normally being performed by either one or, at most, two ATCO2s from the duty Watch under the direction of an ATCO1, but the radar validations held by the ATCO2s concerned were becoming a valuable resource and the wisdom of using them in flow control was being questioned. Following a major review a decision was taken to recruit and train fifty new ATSAs to take on the high volume task of flow regulation under the supervision of one ATCO2 Supervisor and the overall management of one ATCO1 Flow Manager. This massive increase in the size of the Unit presented an immediate problem of accommodation but space became available on the first floor of the east wing of the Control Tower and so, after the necessary preparatory work had been completed, the LFMU - like AIS in 1988 - moved across and became part of the Tower's ATC complement in April 1991. The Head of Flow Management at the time was John Douglas with Ian Finlay, an ex Heathrow ATCO, as Head of Operations. The presence of the Unit on the Airport yielded certain benefits derived from its greater accessibility to Heathrow operators and, of course, Heathrow's ATC staff, which allowed for discussion and appreciation of each others problems face to face. Equipment when they arrived was fairly basic although there was a system known as the Airline Request Communication System (ARCS) which facilitated the allocation of slots to a number of major airlines. This was later replaced by an upgrade called National Air Traffic Flow Management System (NATFMS), and other equipment - including radar displays - also appeared so that delays could be more easily monitored. The LFMU, however, was destined to operate from its office in the Control Tower for less than three years as European States had already begun to take steps to form an organisationally more efficient Central Flow Management Unit to replace the existing system, which was administered by five separate Units. Control was transferred to the new central location in Brussels on the night of the 13th/14th January 1996 when the LFMU was re-named the London Flow Management Position (LFMP) with a resultant major reduction of staff. Although it had been hoped that the newly created LFMP would be able to move directly into the new ACC at Swanwick slippages in the programme saw it transitionally return to West Drayton in January 1997.

MULTIPLE AIRCRAFT RAMP SYSTEM (MARS)

The BAA meanwhile were facing something of a problem - how to improve their use of the aircraft parking space available, which at times was less than efficient. Having provided facilities for the ever-increasing numbers of wide-bodied aircraft operating into Heathrow there were occasions when the only option they had was to park smaller types on stands which were larger than required. The situation was resolved by the introduction of a scheme known as 'Multiple Aircraft Ramp System' where a stand could be used either for one large aircraft or two smaller types. Stands on the 'D', 'N' and 'R' aprons began to be re-configured and when two smaller aircraft used the stand the bays were referred to as 'Left' and 'Right' i.e. D48 for a large aircraft became D48 Left and D48 Right for two smaller types. The scheme was also applied to stands 327, 328 and 329 which were re-aligned and re-named Xray 1 and Xray 2, both with MARS markings allowing each to accept either a Boeing 747-400 parked tail inward or two smaller types. Capacity at Terminal 4 was also becoming a problem and this lead to the introduction of a remote parking area designated Whisky 1 adjacent to and west of the 96/123 stop bar. This could only be used with ATC approval and was restricted to daytime only with a visibility of 1,500 metres or more provided that runways 23 and 05 were not in use. Initially it took only a maximum of thirty minutes to clear the stand if ATC required it but as more Whisky stands were introduced the warning time required increased to two hours and made activation of the subsidiary runways a much more complicated procedure, requiring the Supervisor to be able to predict exactly when the wind would increase to the extent that they needed to be used.

AUTO DM

In Aerodrome Control the additional capacity offered by the Host computer signalled a further reduction of the ATSA complement. In an extension of its functions the HCS was now programmed to track aircraft as they became airborne and to trigger the printing of flight progress strips for the squawk that appeared. Auto DM, as it was known, made the ATSA input position redundant and left just two in the VCR to fulfil the support function - plus, of course, the lighting operator. The rather simplistic removal of one of the ATSAs because his position had ceased to exist served to highlight the fact that in the past he had been able to offer assistance to the others in busy periods in addition to carrying out his own tasks and now left them stretched under pressure. The new procedure also affected the Air Departures controller since it became vital to ensure that a departure had the correct squawk selected - too often not the case - otherwise strips would be produced for some other unrelated aircraft, causing confusion with possible safety implications.

CRATCOH

Back in 1972 a Committee under the chairmanship of Group Captain Douglas Bader CBE DSO DFC had been set up by the Authority to investigate the adequacy of existing measures to prevent fatigue in the flight crews of public transport aircraft, which might adversely affect their aircraft's safety. Its recommendations, which included specific limitations of hours and minimum rest periods, were accepted and made legally enforceable under the ANO. There had, however, been no corresponding exercise as yet to determine whether controller fatigue could similarly affect ATC safety, although the Radley Committee had made a number of general recommendations on working hours in its report in 1964. During 1986 and 1987 a computer failure, increasing flow control delays and an apparent rise in reported airmisses attracted media attention which aroused greater public interest in ATC safety, and in 1988 ATS Standards expressed concern following their annual inspections at a number of smaller aerodromes which revealed developing or unresolved rostering problems due to staff shortages and increased traffic. It was therefore no surprise when, in January 1989, the CAA announced that a Committee had been formed to consider whether measures should be taken to regulate the duty hours of civil ATCOs to ensure that fatigue did not endanger aircraft. The Committee on the Regulation of Air Traffic Controller's Hours (CRATCOH) included two members with Heathrow experience - Keith Williams and Roy Staley - and its wide ranging investigation included consideration of written submissions (from GATCO, IPMS, NALGO, NATS, IAL and the AOA amongst others) and of a study of stress in ATC commissioned from the RAF Institute of Aviation Medicine. A number of oral hearings also took place and visits were made to nineteen ATC Units during the peak summer period of July and August 1989. Their report, which was published on 15th February 1990, made a number of recommendations:-

(1)   No period of duty shall exceed 10 hours. Within 720 consecutive hours the aggregate of periods of duty shall not exceed 200 hours.

(2)   There shall be an interval of not less than 12 hours between the conclusion of one period of duty and the commencement of the next period of duty. Within 720 consecutive hours there shall be not fewer than three intervals of a minimum of 60 hours each between the conclusion of one period of duty and the commencement of the next period of duty.

(3)   Upon the conclusion of six consecutive periods of duty within 144 hours, or upon consecutive periods of duty within 144 hours reaching a total of 50 hours, whichever is the earlier, there shall be an interval of a minimum of 60 hours before the commencement of the next period of duty.

(4)   Not more than two night duties may be worked in immediate succession.

(5)   Upon the conclusion of two night duties in immediate succession there shall be an interval of a minimum of 54 hours before the commencement of the next period of duty.

(6)   No operational duty shall exceed a period of two hours without there being taken during or at the end of that period a break or breaks totalling not less than 30 minutes.

(7)   During any consecutive period of 365 days not fewer than ten days of total holiday entitlement shall be taken in periods of not less than five consecutive days.

The recommendations were accepted by the CAA and the new regulations were introduced at Heathrow on 1st October 1991. While significant changes were necessary to the rosters worked at some non-State airfields only one amendment needed to be made to the existing Heathrow roster for it to comply with all of these requirements. To satisfy the conditions of para (2) a day off had to be introduced between the second afternoon duty and the first D1 duty where currently there was only a ten hour interval, but this was easily achieved. However, because the regulations were now legally enforceable, much stricter monitoring of an individual's work pattern became necessary. This was particularly important where the taking of breaks during a duty was involved and resulted in Supervisors having to maintain a record of the time breaks were taken so that the two hour limit was not exceeded.

APPROACH LEVELS CHANGE

Down in Approach a change of procedures was deemed necessary following an airmiss north east of Heathrow between an aircraft that had left Bovingdon and another at the same level tracking west off Lambourne prior to turning back downwind for a westerly landing. The minimum stack level at both Biggin and Ockham had long been allocated for Approach use, allowing the No.1 Director (S) to run Biggin traffic underneath the Ockham stack on easterlies and permitting vertical separation to be provided between traffic leaving the two stacks on westerlies until lateral separation could be guaranteed. This, however, was not the case north of the field where the two stacks were much further apart and the airspace less confined but, as a result of the incident, the minimum stack level at Bovingdon was assigned to Heathrow from 1st April 1992 for use on both easterlies and westerlies, allowing the No.1 Director (N) similar flexibility. At the same time the lowest level at Biggin when Heathrow was on easterlies was re-allocated to CCF Biggin, since descent to minimum stack level had normally to be given in any case prior to, or very soon after, the VOR as an aircraft began its intermediate approach.

SPECIAL CUSTOMERS

Over the years a number of customers, including Eric Raffles who was mentioned earlier, have earned themselves special affection and recognition for a variety of reasons. Take, for example, Captain Charlie Adams of TWA. Flying Boeing 707s and, at a later stage, 747s he would use aerodynamic braking when he landed, keeping the nose of the aircraft so high in the air that it seemed impossible for the aircraft not to settle back onto its tail. Many an Air Arrivals controller reached out towards the 'Crash' button before seeing the nosewheel lowered gently onto the runway as the aircraft reached taxying speed. Michael Coady, the Irish pilot of Smurfits Learjet G-JJSG, was another who always had an audience. He would acknowledge take-off clearance for an easterly departure to Woodley and then ask 'Are you watching?' This was a signal for everyone in the VCR to look as the aircraft got airborne and came down the runway very low and gathering speed. Then, as he passed the Tower, he would make full use of the Lear's fighter like performance and pull it up into a very steep, climbing right turn. Highly watchable. He later flew for the parent company in the United States and has now retired and is living in St. Louis. The Fokker F.27-600 OO-SCA, which flew the Antwerp -

Sabena's F-27 'Charlie Alpha' airborne on its regular run to Antwerp on 9.9.71. (Brian M Service)

Heathrow service for Sabena from 1970 until 1972, became a firm favourite through the willingness of the crews to fit in with any ATC requirements. This earned them certain benefits, in particular the use of 28L/ 10R as landing runway whenever it was possible, to reduce their taxying distance to the 'Foxtrot' cul-de-sac where they parked. When the service was terminated ATC received as a 'thank you' a Rolls-Royce Dart turbine blade mounted on a wooden base inscribed 'To

The turbine blade trophy presented to ATC by the Sabena 'Charlie Alpha' crews (Celia Kunert)

London ATC with sympathy. The Sabena F.27 pilots OO-SCA March 70 - October 72'. This was handed over at a small ceremony arranged by Ian McConnell and performed at the stand on the last day of operations and the crew in return were presented with a framed picture of the aircraft.

SPLIT GMC

Richard Taylor, the Manager ATC, was under considerable pressure from the airlines to split the GMC

position. The frequency was often extremely congested and there was concern that an aircraft with an emergency might not be able to get access to the R/T. Accepting that the split was now inevitable Derek Harriss (Head of ATC Operations and Training) was tasked to put together a group to formulate the implementation of Split GMC operations. The GMC Implementation Group had its first meeting on 19th February 1993 and consisted of the Manager ATC (Richard Taylor), a Watch Manager (Alan Haines), a controller from each Watch, a lighting operator and Derek Harriss as Chairman. Following the previous study of possible splits carried out some ten years earlier it was agreed that there were three main options to be explored:-

(1)   North and south of 27L/09R.
(2)   North and south of 27L/09R plus east of 23.
(3)   A diagonal split changing with the runways in use.

Before this could be done, however, certain software modifications needed to be made to the lighting panel to allow dual input, and the GMP frequency had to be changed from 121.7 to 121.97 (on 27th May 1993) to release 121.7 for the second GMC frequency. The first series of trials, assessing option (1), took place over three days in June and involved ATCOs Chris Wilson, Ian Callier, Keith Miller, Steve Hobbs, Alan Haines, Brendan Kelly, Mike Holdstock and Bob Robinson. The results were very disappointing. A number of problems were identified but the most critical was that the workload split achieved was GMC1 = 80%, GMC2 = 20%. A slight increase in the total amount of work was also noticed, which meant that overall the GMC1 workload was only reduced by about 10%. Option (2) was then tested, again over a three day period, although GMC2's area of responsibility was expanded by the addition of all blocks on runway 23. This, too, showed little promise and finally attention turned to option (3) with a trial scheduled for the last week of August. With minor modifications to a split proposed by Chris Wilson the areas allocated were:-

GMC2   All blocks south of 27L/09R.
             The inner taxiway from 68(I) clockwise to 20(I).
             The outer taxiway from 67(0) clockwise to 20(0).
             Block 57(0) to block 98.
             Block 36 and west to block 115.
GMC1   All other central area blocks and the maintenance
             areas north of 27L/09R.

At this point Steph Simmonds and Julia 'Jules' Hunt joined the evaluation team and the results of the first trial were felt to be very encouraging. The perceived workload split was estimated as GMC1 = 67%, GMC2 = 33%, and the concept was generally well received although changes of the interface blocks were considered necessary. Further trials took place incorporating and developing these suggestions, and by the end of the year the areas of responsibility had become:-

GMC2   All blocks south of 27L/09R.
       The inner taxiway from 63(I) clockwise to 37(I).
       The outer taxiway from 77(0) clockwise to 37(0), 78,73, 74.
       Block 65 and west to block 98.
       Block 36 and west to 115.
GMC1   All other central area blocks and the maintenance areas north of 27L/09R.

When tried out in February 1994 this arrangement achieved a 50% - 50% split and was considered very promising, although noise levels in the VCR were a cause for concern, particularly when Martyn Swann was around. Following one last series of trials through March there was fairly unanimous agreement within the working group that the correct split had been achieved and the plan entered the development stage on 13th June 1994 with, essentially, the same allocation of responsibility as above except that the north western limits of the GMC2 area were pulled back around the corner to blocks 28(I) and 28(0). Throughout the period of the trials the views of the lighting operators, represented by Martyn Swann, Roger Kunert, Geoff Bannister, Andy McGregor and Andy Marsh, had been carefully considered and, where necessary, incorporated into the procedures used but there were still many ATCOs who were sceptical of the need to split GMC and even more so of the split chosen. This negative feeling was aggravated by management insistence that GMC2 should

be open whenever possible during its scheduled hours, even if there was little traffic, and lead to situations where both GMC controllers were at times working aircraft in the other's ground space, ostensibly saving the aircraft a frequency change but really just demonstrating how undemanding they felt the task had become. Management of ATCO operational times also became a nightmare as there were now three ninety minute positions - negotiated reductions of the normal two hour maximum due to the demands of the position - to consider. Keeping a break to thirty minutes was difficult since the rest room was on the ground floor but any excess time taken was cumulative during the duty until eventually it became necessary to either find extra help or to close GMC2. Henceforth the joy of controlling a busy GMC session bandboxed could only be savoured on those days when staff shortages occurred in ATC or amongst the BAA staff who monitored the frequencies, requiring GMC2 to remain closed.

MORE SPECIAL CUSTOMERS

Other customers who have attracted special recognition when on the frequency include Dave Ward, who flew a Beechcraft King Air into and out of Denham for United Biscuits. Although he was not a Heathrow Airport user this former Vickers Valiant pilot was a pleasure to work on Special VFR due to his extreme courtesy and obvious professionalism. Two other regulars on this frequency also deserving mention stand out because of their strong links with ATC. The first is Peter Cadbury who, during his time with Westward Television, used to commute between his home at Hawthorn Hill (near White Waltham) and Plymouth in a Britten-Norman Islander. An invitation was extended to all ATC staff to join him for flight experience - and a day out in the West Country - which led to some becoming more deeply involved as safety pilots, notably Doug Bush who made twenty one return trips. Gama Aviation, based at Fairoaks but

Atmospheric shot of Pete Kemp having just 'lit up' for the night. Note the duplicate BASIS and GMR displays to accommodate GMC(2)'s own Lighting Operator. (CAA Archives)

also regularly seen at Heathrow, was another operator enjoying frequent ATC presence on the flight deck in the form of Chris Cosgrave, John Cant or Roy Hendry. The nature of many of their flights - delivering live organs - conferred on them a priority status in any case but it is fair to say that they were afforded an unusually high degree of expedition because they were Heathrow controllers and therefore could be trusted not to cause embarrassment. Finally a quick mention of Ian Ramsey who flew for British Midland and Virgin Express. Recognisable by an up-turn in his voice at the end of each transmission he was always chirpy and co-operative, and became an honorary member of 'D' Watch whom he visited regularly in the VCR until he moved to France.

On the 4th March 1993 the Daventry SIDs were permanently withdrawn and replaced by Wobun SIDs (for westerly ops) and Buzad SIDs (for easterly ops), while downstairs the helicopter routes were once again under review. Following increases of the permitted maximum altitudes on H5, H7, H9 and H10 which were introduced in February 1992 further revisions took effect on 1st April 1993 aimed at alleviating the problem of helicopters infringing Rule 5 of the low flying regulations whilst at the same time complying with standard operating altitudes as they joined a route at the Zone boundary. These raised the Zone entry altitudes to a maximum of 2,000 feet and applied to all routes. Attention was also being given to the section of H2 between Kew Bridge and the Heathrow Airport Spur. Although deemed separated from ILS approaches to 27R and 27L its proximity to the approach was a constant cause for concern and this was fuelled by an increasing number of requests from pilots of fixed wing aircraft for traffic information in response to TCAS alerts. There was obvious resistance from the Helicopter Operators to the removal of any section of the route structure but a decision was made late in the year to permanently close this section of H2 and this took effect on 6th January 1994. It was out on the field, however, that the most significant changes were taking place. Work began on 19th April, initially involving the closure of a large part of the outer taxiway south east of the Tower, which would see this area re-designed to accommodate the construction of the new 'Europier'. This outward expansion of the 'D' apron, which would involve the disappearance of the existing inner taxiway from block 77(I) to 38(I), was completed in the November when the outer taxiway in this area became the 'new inner', leaving runway 23/05 to serve as the outer when required - a further nail in its coffin.

REVISED VORTEX SEPARATIONS

A Wake Vortex Study Group had been established by CATO in January 1992 to review the existing wake vortex procedures, which had last been revised in 1982, and to consider whether any changes were necessary. This was intended to be a short term solution as a major wake vortex modelling programme had commenced at the Chief Scientist's Division of NATS which, it was hoped, would enable future decisions on separation criteria to be made on a sounder scientific basis. In general the separations used in the UK were based on ICAO recommendations although some had been increased, but analysis of reports on the wake vortex incident data base suggested that some of these were too generous and therefore created delay. Conversely there was also substantial evidence that the Boeing 757 needed to be re-classified into a

heavier group than its current 'medium' as it was frequently the lead aircraft when wake vortex reports were filed by lighter 'medium' types such as the Douglas DC-9 and Boeing 737. The Group put forward a number of proposals and these were introduced at Heathrow on 20th September 1993, initially for a trial period of six months but later made permanent. The most significant of these was the creation of a fifth weight group by the sub-division of the 'medium' group into 'upper medium' and 'lower medium' groups. The 'upper medium' group included the Boeing 757, Boeing 707, Douglas DC-8, Vickers VC10 and Ilyushin IL-62 together with the Airbus A310, demoted (but only temporarily) from 'heavy' as its weight was between that of the 757 and the 707 / DC-8. The 'lower medium' group was formed of the rest of the existing 'medium' group plus the BAe 146, which had previously been anomalously classified 'small'. In addition a number of reductions of vortex separation were introduced while a suggestion was also made by the Group - but not at this time trialled - that minimum radar separation between aircraft on final approach could, where there was no requirement to provide wake vortex separation, be reduced to 2.5nms.

Lead aircraft	Following aircraft	Spacing reqd
Heavy	Heavy	4nm
Heavy	Upper medium / Lower medium	5nm
Heavy	Small	6nm
Heavy	Light	7nm
Upper medium	Heavy	*
Upper medium	Upper medium	3nm
Upper medium	Lower medium / Small	4nm
Upper medium	Light	6nm
Lower medium	Heavy / Upper medium / Lower medium	*
Lower medium	Small	3nm
Lower medium	Light	5nm
Small	Heavy	*
Small	Upper medium / Lower medium	*
Small	Small	3nm
Small	Light	3nm
Light	All groups	*

* Where spacing is shown by an asterisk wake vortex separation was not required.

Although there was a significant increase in the separation between 'upper medium' types and 'lower medium' followers (now 4nms instead of 3nms) Heathrow's arrival capacity was calculated by ORA 1 to be virtually unchanged. On the benefit side a noticeable drop in wake vortex incidents involving Boeing 757s was expected.

One really wet day a swan landed on the threshold of the landing runway 27L, presumably thinking that it had found a quiet stretch of river. Landings continued while the services of Checker were awaited and the swan was seen to stand with its wings outstretched and neck fully extended, hissing abuse at the very large (metal) birds that flew overhead. This continued until it saw a Boeing 747 on final when, obviously accepting that there comes a time when you have to put discretion before valour, it crouched down to become just a small white bump on the runway surface.

APPROACH MOVES OUT

Development of the project known as the Central Control Function (CCF), to which a brief reference was made earlier, had continued steadily but the 'O' date for stage 2 - the

TO STAY (AT HEATHROW)

A	B	C	D	E
W.Campbell	G.Coates	R.Daly	B.Piket	R.Metcalfe
B.Jones	J.Przygrodski	B.Wildey	R.Dawson	I.Callier
C.Herbert	R.Robinson	J.Cooke	S.Hobbs	A.Fleming
R.Cowell	I.Mason	R.Spooner	S.Clifford	M.Doyle
K Barsh	B.Kelly	S.Simmonds	J.Siddell	K.Day
C.Wilson	M.Walker	M.Holdstock	J.Price	R.Lodge
D.Brindley	R.Goddard	M.Hockin	A.Weir	M.Bridge
N.Cooper	R.Glynn	R.Clarke	N.Reed (u/t)	R.Lane
I.Wheatley (u/t)		J.Hunt (u/t)	Q.Fox (u/t)	M.Darling (u/t)
		A.Mercer (u/t)		

TO GO (TO C C F)

A	B	C	D	E
A.Carter	J.MacDermot	P.Carter	D.Nicholas	R.Neville
P.Bish	R.Hendry	D.Broderick	D.Rham	R.Harrison
B.McCartney	J.Hanbury	A.Barnes	M.Inglis	G.Clarkson
I.Alexander	C.McClelland	G.Hewitt	A.Croft	M.Lewis
P.Johnson	M.Mothershaw	R.Hillyer	C.Huggett	A.Budd
R.Tilley	K.McMahon	I.Toakley	M.Hawkins	M.Hemming
S.Dominic	G.Coffey	J.Bate	M.Turner	S.Lambert
N.Bainbridge	J.Ellis	G.Foulkes	K.Fowler	P.Hamer
N.Crawford (u/t)	W.Lapworth (u/t)	J.Kennedy (u/t)		R.Rodway (u/t)

Following transfer to CCF West Drayton, the Heathrow element was soon moved to the Southwest corner of the banks of suites. Operating positions seen here are: (l to r) Dick Tilley INT S (Director South as was), Andy Garrett FIN (No 2 Director), Al Carter INT N (Director North) and Mihiri Wajayaratna (u/t) LL Support (Approach North). A fifth position, looking after EATs, sequence numbers and general phone calls etc. used to be in the line, but now occupies a dedicated position back to back with INT N. Light levels are near to daylight. Following the move of the area function at LATCC to Swanwick, CCF/Terminal Control became LTCC (London Terminal Control Centre).(Pete Bish)

transfer of Heathrow Approach to the CCF Ops room at West Drayton - was put back due to the need to modernise other LATCC systems and to allow for the early introduction of the London Upper Sector, which would significantly increase system capacity in the upper airspace. The date for the most dramatic change that Heathrow ATC had ever undergone, however, was eventually finalised as 23rd/24th October 1993. The need to create a new operating concept within the London TMA had become evident when the decision was made to develop Stansted as London's third airport. Simulations at the ATCEU showed that the TMA (NE) sector became overloaded when a figure of just twenty movements an hour was generated by Stansted and, of course, developments at London City, Northolt and Farnborough amongst others would only contribute greater congestion and complexity. A detailed study of Common IFR Operations in the New York area, where IFR traffic rates were almost twice those in the London TMA, saw a number of their ideas tried out in simulations at the ATCEU. The result was a decision to re-organise operations within the TMA and to operate the service from a new control facility called the Central Control Function. An integral part of this new system called for the collocation of the TMA and Approach Control functions and, although other sites including Heathrow were considered, LATCC was chosen as the most suitable location. Original plans envisaged Special VFR, Thames Radar and City Approach moving across into the CCF Ops room at the same time as Heathrow's Approach team but this decision was later reversed, allowing an element of radar to remain in the Control Tower. The thought that Approach would disappear from the Control Tower was difficult to come to terms with, and very strong arguments

were made for its retention. Perhaps the greatest concern was that the enforced specialisation in Aerodrome or Approach Controls would waste a wealth of cross experience and create a situation where, after a time, neither discipline would fully understand the other's problems. Reduced job satisfaction and, for those going to LATCC, loss of identity through no longer being physically at Heathrow were also considered important factors against the move. Notwithstanding this each controller at Heathrow was asked early in 1992 to indicate his/her work preference for the split - whether they wished to stay as an Aerodrome controller at the Tower or to go across to West Drayton as an Approach/Radar controller and the result, shown above, meant that almost everyone would get their wishes. Although changes of option were allowed the list was virtually unchanged when 'O' date arrived some eighteen months later.

It fell to 'B' Watch to complete the actual transfer of Approach Control to West Drayton. Their night duty ATCOs rostered for Approach went straight to West Drayton while Brendan Kelly (Head of ATC Ops) and Keith Miller (ATC Training) took over from the off-going 'C' Watch in the Control Tower. They then saw out the last hours of operations in the 'old' Approach room, Keith dealing with the penultimate movement while Brendan pulled rank and handled the last. The log entry for 0001 on 24th October reads 'Heathrow Approach has now been transferred to CCF. Still awaiting final stand down. Heathrow Approach is dead, long live Heathrow Director'. This is followed, at 0235, by a further entry 'Final stand down declared. Heathrow Directors fully operational'. Staff arriving for their morning duty on the 24th found a scene reminiscent of the 'Marie Celeste' with

Following the 'split' only SVFR (Ian Wheatley right) and Thames Radar (Dick Gallop left) plus the City Radar position (unoccupied at far end) were left on the ground floor at Heathrow. (CAA Archives)

only the Thames and City positions manned. At this time of day a Supervisor with four, possibly five, controllers and an assistant would normally have been very busy dealing with Heathrow's inbound traffic but now there were just empty seats although the radar consoles, which were still switched on, showed business mysteriously as normal.

GNOMES

Three of the Approach staff leaving the Tower for West Drayton were looking for a special way to mark their departure and this led to Steve Dominic, Pete Bish and Alan Carter setting off in Pixie during their last duty in the Tower to carry out their plan. Alan had brought into work with him a garden gnome which was deposited at the foot of the wind sock south of block 74 with an appropriate commemorative message while Pete planted a packet of daffodil bulbs nearby. Despite the rigours of life at a busy international airport, Alan's gnome was still watching aircraft taxying out to 27L some ten years later - having been moved along with the windsock for taxiway development - and had been joined by a number of companions from other airside workers, including

By May 1998 the collection of gnomes at the 27L Windsock had grown after Al Carter left the first one. (Ian Callier)

the Police. However, HAL had other ideas and the front page headline of the airport newspaper 'Skyport' of 10th December 2004 reported the destruction of all the gnomes as they were not in keeping with the airside environment. Even the Sunday Times of Boxing Day 2004 covered the story! The more stealthy daffodils continue to make an annual show in their original location......

RUNWAY 05 OPS

The use of a subsidiary runway always adds interest to routine and this was particularly true of runway 05. On that handful of days in a year when howling northerly winds allowed no other choice its operation was a complex and demanding task and therefore was thoroughly enjoyed by all. Fifty weeks a year on the sausage machine for a few days of gourmet delights! The combination of runway 05 for landing with 09R for departure - the normal configuration - was effectively a single runway operation requiring the Air position to be band-boxed although there would always be a second controller plugged in to carry out any coordination required. The problem they faced, of course, was that the intersection of the two runways was almost two miles from the threshold of runway 09R and that take-off clearance could only be given when landing traffic on 05 had crossed block 85. The favoured R/T patter here was to ask a departure if he could see the traffic on final for 05 and, if he could, he would be told 'as soon as that traffic clears your runway cleared for take-off' which would normally see the departure start to roll as the landing aircraft came over the threshold of 05. In this way spacing on final could be reduced although it did rely on the cooperation of all pilots concerned. One day, however, a British Airways flight had begun its take-off roll when a voice - believed to have been from another aircraft waiting for departure - transmitted 'Speedbird xxx there is traffic on final for 05' which caused the Speedbird to abandon its take-off, giving the Air controller a few anxious moments. There were also problems for GMC who found most of the landing traffic vacating in the area of the northern and southern dual taxiways where he had a constant stream of traffic towing to and from the maintenance areas. In Approach the traffic pattern was similar to that used for runway 23 in that traffic from all four stacks was integrated into one stream running downwind. Inbounds from Biggin and Ockham crossed the approach before turning left to join the stream from Bovingdon and Lambourne coming down from the direction of Burnham. The intermediate approach from Lambourne for runway 05, incidentally, must have been one of the longest on record - west from the stack for about thirty miles and then downwind for another twenty or so before turning back onto final - but even from Ockham could become quite extended. In fact this was a major contributory factor in an incident which happened one busy December afternoon when 'E' Watch were on duty. A British Airways BAC 1-11 had taken off from Heathrow for Jersey but was unable to land there due to the high cross winds and so had elected to divert back to Heathrow where it was virtually 05 single runway operation. The pilot was obviously concerned about his fuel state but declined offers to be given a priority and was therefore held at Ockham for a while before beginning his approach. He had, however, seriously underestimated the distance that he would have to travel from stack to touchdown and was almost out of fuel when he landed.

Apart from the demands presented by vectoring traffic for a visual final to a rarely used runway in strong winds there were other interesting technical questions posed by the combination of this subsidiary runway with 09L and 09R, including how to handle 09R departures to Woodley. The standard clearance of 'right heading 240 degrees' might find a heavily laden Oceanic flight struggling to get above the inbound stream and many preferred to ask for 'straight ahead to 1,500 feet' before the turn to at least ensure a good start. There was also the question of whether there should be a stagger in the ranges to touchdown when there was landing traffic on both 05 and 09L. Differences in the ground speeds of the aircraft involved, in the lengths of the two runways, and just the sheer improbability of a double go-around led most to agree that no stagger was required but it was nevertheless an interesting discussion point which became rather academic when the runway was permanently withdrawn from use in the latter part of 1993 to accommodate the continued sprawl of Terminal 4. By now the Whisky stands had increased in number to five, which also caused the shortening of the reciprocal runway 23 to 1,966 metres.

To illustrate the sort of knock-on tangle 05 could produce, this story from some years earlier seems appropriate here…..This is the picture. Runway 05 in use for landing. 10R for departures with 10L available for use. Alan Haines in the Air position had given take-off clearance to a Paris bound Trident 3 on 10R and also to a KLM flight to Amsterdam on 10L using a rather tight gap in the landing stream. On final for 05 was a JAT Boeing 727 battling with the wind and, watching its progress, Alan was concerned when he noticed an application of power - characteristic plumes of black smoke from its Pratt and Whitneys. Thinking it was beginning a go-around Alan aborted the Trident's take-off but could not be sure if it would be able to stop short of block 85. The 727 meanwhile was still continuing its approach and so Alan was now forced to send it around. Over on 10L the KLM was airborne and to keep the JAT clear of it Alan had no option but to give the 727 an immediate right turn onto a heading of 120, which was completed over the threshold of runway 05 and looked very exciting. Turning his attention back to the Trident Alan asked if he wished to taxy back for another try to which the pilot replied 'I think I shall have to go to the hangar first to get some new brakes'.

MORE AIRFIELD DEVELOPMENTS

The first of two major taxiway development projects began in January 1994 and involved the re-configuration of the taxiway system west of Pier 7 and the construction of three new stands. The building which had housed the ACR6 radar had by now been demolished, enabling the BAA to extend both the inner and outer taxiways west from block 60 to give dual access to the 09R holding point. The outer taxiway south of block 52 was also re-aligned onto a north-south axis which allowed the three extra stands - 147,148 and 149 - to be fitted in to the south of the existing stand 150. This resulted in the creation of several new blocks (46, 55, 59(I), 125 and 126) while east of the Tower a new link taxiway (block 53) was also taking shape between blocks 50 and 54. At the same time block 75 was divided with the northern half being designated as block 131. This was the initial phase of the much needed second development which began early in 1995 - the construction of a taxiway connecting block 131 to block 118 south of 27L via block 86. When completed this additional route allowed taxying and towing movements to cross the runway much closer to the threshold of 27L than before without affecting the glide path transmissions and also offered the Air controller a useful intermediate line-up position from both north and south at block 86 when 27L was in use for departure. This was of particular benefit when a Boeing 747 was lining up from the south at block 87 - a lengthy process

which regularly found the aircraft still not ready to roll when take-off clearance was given. An appropriate intersection departure could now be used to fill what previously had been wasted time and help to maintain high departure rates.

IRA ATTACKS

A few weeks after the start of the first of these works projects the Irish Republican Army (IRA) made its presence felt at Heathrow by carrying out three terrorist attacks over a period of five days, aimed at causing as much disruption and anxiety as possible for Airport users and staff. The campaign began in the second week of March and validated recently published ICAO statistics which showed a dramatic increase in terrorist acts involving civil aviation. On the 9th March the Police had a particularly difficult day, receiving numerous coded messages from the IRA warning of 'a large number of bombs' at Heathrow. Searches, however, failed to reveal anything suspicious in the Terminals or out on the manoeuvring area and operations were allowed to continue. Iain Alexander, the ATC Watch Manager, recalls that his afternoon by contrast had been pretty quiet with only a routine Local Standby to deal with and he was enjoying the view outside when the closure of 27R/09L was ordered so that the runway and area around it could be searched for possible mortar shells. The Police had been called out to a burning car at the Excelsior Hotel and had found home made mortars inside, with indications that others might already have been fired. Following the closure of the runway at 1840 GMT the inner and outer taxiways north of the Tower and stands from the 'B's to the 'R's were also closed and a thorough search was made, resulting in the discovery of three complete mortars although it was thought that four had been fired. Taxiways and stands were progressively returned to service but the continued search for the missing mortar kept 27R/09L closed until almost ten o'clock the next morning (10th). Further bomb threats were received late that night and just after midnight three more mortars were fired into the 'V' apron, narrowly missing a Boeing 757 parked on stand V18. Of these two were recovered intact while one was found in fragments. Once again a large area around the impact site was closed off and a fourth mortar was found close to the 'V' cul-de-sac. This time normal operations, except in the 'V' apron and block 118, were resumed soon after the arrival of the morning Watch. By now, of course, everyone on the Airport was working to a high state of vigilance but the IRA were still able to carry out a third and final assault soon after 0800 GMT on the 13th March, once again targeting Terminal 4. Malcolm Hemming, working GMC, was watching the British Airways Boeing 737 G-DOCR repositioning around the Terminal when it stopped abruptly and then began to reverse at high speed with the driver explaining 'there's a flare on the taxiway'. On this occasion the Airport was closed for about fifteen minutes before a restricted service was resumed (27R SRO) with everything back to normal by early afternoon. There was one final flourish later that day before the IRA brought hostilities to a close. Coded bomb threats were again received just before 1900 GMT and considered genuine enough for both Heathrow and Gatwick to be closed to all traffic for extended periods - Heathrow for almost two hours. The five days had seen runway and taxiway closures together with disruption to schedules but, fortunately, there had been no hurnan or aircraft casualties.

LANDING RATES

Flow control had, by now, become a mature, if sometimes inexact, science with occasions when delays inbound to Heathrow became and then remained obstinately excessive. This brought about the introduction of new procedures in March 1994 designed to ensure that the highest possible landing rates were achieved at Heathrow and that airborne holding was kept to an acceptable level to contain the workload of the sectors at LATCC. The installation of a new telephone conference line, linking the Supervisors in the VCR, LFMU, Area Control and Terminal Control, enabled the declared landing rates for the morning and evening peak periods to be reviewed (at 0530 and 1500 local respectively) and amended if considered necessary. The VCR Supervisor was also tasked with phoning the achieved hourly landing rates across to Terminal Control's Tactical Traffic Co-ordinator (TTC) for general display and if these varied from the declared rates by two or more movements in periods of holding then a further conference was required, to investigate and if necessary remedy the problem. In normal circumstances, of course, scheduled demand into Heathrow required the full capacity of the landing runway for significant periods of the day and any excessive demand would lead to extensive holding which was difficult to reduce. In July 1994, however, a further new procedure was introduced involving the tactical use of the departure runway for landing traffic to improve capacity, known as Tactically Enhanced Arrival Mode (TEAM). Although this was already possible on easterlies an easing of the landing runway alternation procedure was required before it could be used on westerlies, and this was achieved by recognising that severe inbound congestion was a valid reason for non adherence. Terminal Control could now request landings on the departure runway (not more than six an hour on westerlies) when there was more than 20 minutes delay on easterlies and 30 minutes delay on westerlies and, by careful selection of the aircraft involved, achieve reductions in the wake vortex spacing that would otherwise have been required to increase the landing rate.

COPPERCHASE

Down in the Flight Briefing Unit (FBU) a new piece of equipment known as 'Copperchase' became operational on 12th April 1994, signalling the end of the line for the STPOs. Three terminals - one 'Master' and two 'slaves' - enabled up to three assistants to process flight plans simultaneously, and flight plans and associated ATS messages could now be received, checked, actioned and despatched on screen. Until now this had been a paper intensive task involving the services of two STPOs, one employed to send out the flight's details on the AFTN and the other to input the data into the Host computer, and this had involved the assistants in hand addressing the flight plan they received and preparing a slip with the details required by the Host computer. The STPO responsible for inputs to the AFTN was withdrawn immediately while the other remained for a short period awaiting the arrival of a Host add-on.

GMC2 FACES SOUTH - BRIEFLY

Part of the work of the GMC Implementation Group had been to plan a desk layout suitable for the Split GMC operation, with the intention of GMC1 facing north and GMC2 facing south, both if required with a trainee. Construction of the agreed design was authorised and

GMC(2) faced south for just 10 months, August 1994 to June 1995, before turning back through 180 degrees. Seen here are Ivor Simms (GMC 1), Kevin Crowley (GMC 2) and Mike Doyle (Tower Supervisor). (CAA Archives)

installation of the new furniture took place during the week of 22nd August 1994, taking three nights. It quickly became obvious, however, that this new layout was unpopular and on 17th March 1995 Derek Harriss reported that the working group were unanimous in recommending that both GMC desks should revert to north facing due to:-

(1)   The cramped location of GMC2.
(2)   The need for the GMC2 controller to face his lighting operator.
(3)   The need to improve lines of sight.

Although a questionnaire was issued to all operational staff to assess opinion there was a pretty apathetic response with an inconclusive result but the decision to revert to north facing was upheld, and the repositioning of the furniture was carried out on the night of 24th/25th June 1995. An option was retained for six weeks, however, to revert to a south facing GMC2 if there was sufficient demand but this did not arise.

FLYPASTS AND MICROLIGHTS

Ad-hoc flypasts by aircraft of, shall we say, an 'exotic' nature were finally banned at Heathrow in 1994. During the morning of 11th July Mike Crutch in ATC Ops received a phone call from the Tri-National Tornado Training Establishment at RAF Cottesmore asking if two aircraft could make an approach and overshoot at Heathrow that day as part of a navigational sortie being planned. Mike was able to obtain approval from both HAL's Operations Duty Manager - provided the aircraft did not touch down - and from ATC's Watch Manager and the two Tornados duly appeared just after one o'clock, making a gentle 200 knot flypast at 300 feet watched by a myriad Airside Ops vehicles that had somehow congregated line abreast on the grass beside the active runway 09L. Since the run had taken place in the 'firebreak' period of the day scheduled traffic was not affected. However, later in the afternoon there was an exchange of phone calls between HAL and NATS Management which resulted in the imposition of a ban on any further flypasts by military and historic aircraft which, it was felt, could adversely influence the case for a proposed fifth Terminal. There is, incidentally, no truth in the rumour, which circulated at the time that Mike's subsequent posting out to ATO Hillingdon House was an admonishment for his part in this episode - he had been promoted and given the job a month earlier! Nevertheless, despite the ban …..

Single engined light aircraft, predominantly Pipers and Cessnas, had once been fairly common visitors to Heathrow. Occasionally much rarer types (including a Mustang, a Sea Fury, a Beaver, a Jungmann and a Viima) might be seen arriving for maintenance or spraying at British Airways, but now in the 1990s the BAA's pricing policy left no room for such 'light entertainment'. It was, therefore, something of a surprise when microlight enthusiast Brian Milton managed to get agreement for no less than twenty three microlights to take off from Heathrow on 25th August 1994 in commemoration of the 75th anniversary of the start of international air services. Although the original flight, in a DH.4a piloted by Lt. Bill Lawford, had been from nearby Hounslow Heath to Le Bourget a mass departure from a point only a couple of miles east of Heathrow was not considered practicable due to the disruption it would cause and so, following discussions between the Manager ATC Richard Taylor and the BAA's Head of Heathrow Operations Mike Seller, Heathrow itself was offered and accepted as a substitute. Richard's enthusiasm for the re-enactment of this historic event saw him nominated to 'flag off' the participants and to this end a special starter's flag was constructed from half a broomstick and some green baize. The day, of course, dawned damp, grey and windy causing a delay of two hours to the original planned departure time of 0830 by which time conditions had worsened to 2kms visibility, 600 feet cloud base and heavier rain. Since there was no possibility of delaying the start any longer a decision was made to set off despite the weather, and the microlights - which had been brought in by road - were released at ten second intervals from block 105 with minimal effect on Heathrow's normal operations (27L was in use for landings). The pilot of the lead aircraft, the Arrivals controller and Richard Taylor were in

3 of the 23 microlight crews lined up on a wet and windy 25th August 1994 observe Concorde getting airborne before it was their turn…..(Mike Crutch)

constant radio contact as 22 of the 23 microlights took off, many of them carrying representatives of the media although there was no major sponsorship. Specially franked commemorative covers were also carried, to be sold later in aid of the MacMillan Nurses Appeal. But this was not the end of the story. Having spent almost four hours out on the Airport a bedraggled Richard returned to his office only to find that the French had withdrawn their permission for the microlights to land at Le Bourget - due to the weather! A number of urgent phone calls were necessary before he was able to get this decision reversed and arrangements made for a high ranking French General to greet the successful participants on their arrival. Of the 22 aircraft that departed from Heathrow one landed safely a few minutes later next to the Staines reservoirs while others made intermediate landings near Reigate (unplanned) and Headcorn and Abbeville (planned) but a creditable total of 16 finally made it to Le Bourget - although mostly on the next day.

2.5 MILE SPACING

Following studies made in the 1980s the FAA had reduced spacing on final approach from 3nm to 2.5nm between aircraft pairs where wake vortex spacing was not required, and its use was now widespread although not popular with aircrew who still had reservations about possible wake vortices. The most critical factor involved, not surprisingly, was runway occupancy time (ROT) - the time taken by an aircraft from crossing the runway threshold to clear of the runway - and this depended on the type involved and the availability of suitable turn offs, particularly rapid exit turn offs (RETs). The US traffic mix, however, of predominantly medium types on domestic flights allowed an increase of up to five movements an hour when 2.5nm spacing was being used. Heathrow's mix, of course, was completely different and the lack of RETs indicated that there would be less benefit derived, perhaps as little as half a movement an hour. Nevertheless plans went ahead for a trial of reduced final approach spacing as part of the Runway Capacity Enhancement Study (RCES) for Heathrow but this had to be put back due to the move of Approach Control to CCF where controllers needed time to become accustomed to their new Sony displays. Finally, towards the end of 1994, the trial got under way with Air Arrivals the arbiter of whether conditions were suitable for 2.5nm spacing but a number of problems were soon apparent:-

(1)   The 'land after' procedure could not normally be used due to uncertainty over whether the preceding traffic would vacate in time and landing clearances were being given at an uncomfortably late stage (for controllers and pilots).

(2)   The term 'expedite' was being used more frequently with the probability that its effectiveness would be reduced.

(3)   Final approach spacing could be erratic and when the gap was particularly tight the Final Director would normally hold on to the traffic until the four mile mark while he watched for his corrections to take effect. This left the Air Arrivals controller with little option but to sit it out.

(4)   When spacing on final reduced to two miles it triggered an alarm on the Separation Monitoring Function (SMF) at CCF, requiring the Final Director to provide an explanation of the circumstances. In addition the location of the SMF in the TC Ops room allowed the discussion and rumour which followed an alarm to distract the Final Director and discourage him from applying minimum separation on final.

A general reluctance to initiate 2.5nm spacing was soon evident and there was no dissent from operational controllers when the trial was suspended on 10th July 1995 by ATS Standards, who questioned the legality of the Air Arrivals controller's use of the ATM under the existing conditions. This took several months to resolve but approval was eventually received in October allowing the trial to be re-started on the 2nd January 1996 for an initial period of one year. The concerns felt by operational staff, however, still existed and on 13th May a number of changes were made including a restriction to daytime use only, increased weather criteria and the introduction of a headwind component of 'approximately ten knots'.

APPROACH MONITORING AID

While the short-lived south facing GMC2 desk layout was under evaluation a new ATM display was installed in the Air desks, the result of a number of incidents around the World which demonstrated a need for automated monitoring of aircraft on final approach. Although the ATM performed very well it was still possible for an aircraft to deviate dangerously from the correct final approach path without it being noticed due to the display scale, and this had indeed happened at Heathrow when a British Airways Boeing 747 went well right of centreline on short final for 27R and almost hit an hotel. The ATM had, therefore, been combined with an Approach Monitoring Aid (AMA) which tracked aircraft in a predefined, wedge shaped tracking zone overlaid on the extended centre line of the relevant landing runway. Any aircraft moving off the centre line and outside this zone would now trigger an alert comprising both an audible alarm and an enlarged graphical display of the event in a pop-up window in the bottom third of the ATM display showing the aircraft's identity, the runway involved and a short history of the aircraft's track before it left the zone. If the alert was received when an aircraft was still over a mile from touchdown then the approach could be allowed to continue provided that the pilot was visual or able to correct onto the ILS but from one mile in there was no option - the pilot had to be given immediate instructions to carry out a missed approach. The new ATM with its AMA display was installed on the night of 27/28th February 1995 but, because of the accuracy required for the display, the AMA element could only be used when the Watchman radar was in use.

At Terminal 4 a further stand in the 'Whisky' series (W6) came into use and stands 330 and 331 were re-named Royal Suite 1 and 2 (RS1 and RS2) while, continuing their efforts to improve runway access from the holding points, the BAA now turned their attention to 27R and work began on 26th April 1995 to lay down additional taxiways and provide a new intermediate take-off point at block 18. This involved the creation of five new blocks - 132, 133,134,136 and 137- and when completed early in 1996 afforded the Air controller a great deal of flexibility when deciding the departure sequence since he could now make use of blocks 18, 17 and 16 for intermediate departures with even an occasional departure at times from block 15. There was, however, an early set-back on 23rd November 1995 when the port wing of a Gulf Air Airbus A340 taxying through the new block 137 struck a British Airways Boeing 757 waiting for departure from block 18, damaging its rudder and fin. This caused an additional item to be added to the ATIS broadcast reminding pilots that they remained responsible for wing tip clearances in good visibility when the greens were not in use.

NDBs AND OUTER MARKERS WITHDRAWN

During the five year period from 1991 to 1995 many of the navaids that had long been available to Heathrow ATC and its inbound aircraft were taken out of service and not replaced. First to go was the NDB 'NE' (serving runway 23) which was withdrawn permanently at the beginning of 1991, followed on 19th September 1992 by the withdrawal of the ILS serving runway 23, reducing it to the status of a visual runway with only a DME to its name. Next, in October 1993, it was the turn of the ILS fan markers on the main runways, their purpose and future having become questionable with the introduction of DME on the landing systems. This, of course, deprived the Air Arrivals controller of his 'report outer marker' response to an aircraft checking in established on the ILS but after an initial period when its use was only recommended the most logical alternative 'report DME 4' became mandatory. Speed control imposed by Approach was also now applied down to DME 4, slightly further from touchdown than the outer markers had been, allowing spacings to close up rather more than had previously been the case as the lead aircraft reduced speed. Finally came the withdrawal of the 'OE' and 'OW' NDBs (serving the 27s and 09s respectively) on 14th September 1995, which left Heathrow with no emergency holding facilities on final approach although this was not a major set-back as they had only rarely been used for this purpose over the past thirty years.

DINING - 1990s STYLE

Time now, as this book enters its final stages, to take a last look at the way in which the dining predilections of ATC staff continued to evolve until they were now a far cry from those pioneering days almost fifty years earlier when the Airwork canteen reigned supreme. Staff canteens were still kept busy by other Airport workers but the arrival of universally popular fast food restaurants in the Terminals - to cater for time pressed air travellers - immediately attracted many ATC staff, for whom the walk to and from the Queens Building facilities together with the frequent lengthy queuing on arrival there left little time to enjoy the food purchased, even in longer meal breaks. Harry Ramsden's, Burger King and a small snack shop just across the road in the coach station were all able to claim some ATC patronage while other staff preferred to bring in their own food. The opening of the new rest room and kitchen on the ground floor had made dining in more attractive, offering the facility to re-heat ready prepared meals in a microwave oven, but perhaps even more significant were the legal implications of CRATCOH which, when introduced in 1991, required much stricter observance of break periods. Time wasted outside the Control Tower

obtaining a meal was now bad news and invited indigestion. On a more social level 'A' Watch enjoyed a number of barbecues on the balcony below the VCR - with a 'hot work' permit obtained by Manager Bunny Austin after their first attempt at 'alfresco' set off the Tower fire alarms. 'D' Watch, on the other hand, developed a fondness for the spicy offerings of the Anarkali Restaurant in West Drayton, enjoying take aways during night duties and paying occasional visits to the establishment itself when there was sufficient reason. On one such excursion Kevin Day put away an unusually large meal and was promptly given the nickname of 'Bunter' by John Siddell, but the staff of the Anarkali obviously heard and thought that this was his real name. When they came over to the Tower as invited guests some time later they were heard to ask 'Mister Bunter' various questions as he explained the intricacies of ATC to them.

FLOW CONTROL IMPROVEMENTS

As the date for centralised flow control moved nearer a number of transitional changes took place, intended to give the maximum amount of flexibility to Aerodromes and to reduce co-ordination to a minimum. On 1st August 1995 ADTs were renamed Co-ordinated Take Off Times (CTOTs) with an extended tolerance of minus five to plus ten minutes, and in addition up to 45 aircraft a day could be given a CTOT tolerance of minus five to plus fifteen minutes at the Supervisor's discretion. A further relaxation of the rules required an aircraft's slot time to be re-negotiated now only if the initial call for start up was made too late. If it had been given start up in good time for its slot but was delayed for any reason - perhaps congestion at the holding point or a runway closure - then it could be allowed to depart without co-ordination. But these new CTOT parameters and rules addressed only part of the problem that the move to Brussels was about to present and Ian Finlay, the Manager of ATFM Development, was concerned that the amount of slot related paperwork generated by centralisation would be overwhelming for the assistants. Working with two software engineers who were already contracted in to the Flow Unit he was able to design a system that presented all the relevant information on screen, together with the facility to transmit messages back to the CFMU, under the name of Departure Slot Monitor (DSM). Trials in the Flow Unit, and at Jersey where the change over took place some months earlier, were very encouraging but there was initially little enthusiasm from the Airport General Managers who considered that the equipment would not be needed. Rather late in the day, however, they were forced to concede that a problem did exist and the software was passed on to Copperchase for development which took a couple of months, following which it was sold back to NATS and throughout Europe. While these units were awaited existing units from Flow were installed in the VCR and the Thames/SVFR rooms and went operational on the afternoon of 5th February 1996, since when the system has been widely adopted throughout the U.K.

CROSS TRAINING

Having been posted in effectively to invalidate a pay claim being made by Heathrow's ATCOs the Thames/City staff were given a less than enthusiastic reception when they first arrived, although the bad feeling slowly disappeared.

They were, however, operating as a separate unit - not the most ideal arrangement - and in 1992 it was decided that cross training should begin before Heathrow Approach moved to West Drayton so that a high degree of interchangeability could be achieved with a view, eventually, to complete integration of the Thames staff onto the Heathrow Watches. This resulted in Phil Hardwick becoming the first Thames controller to validate in the VCR, and Bob Robinson the first from Heathrow to validate on Thames Radar (on 23rd March 1993). A high level of training continued after the departure of Approach Control creating something of a problem for validated controllers looking for quality solo time but by May 1996 sufficient progress had been made for integration to take place, as a result of which two new day duties, a D6 (0630 - 1430) and a D7 (1530-2245), were introduced to cover the different operational demands made on Thames Radar by the opening hours of London City Airport.

Movement rates generally continued to rise, with a minor setback in 1991, so that by 1995 - the last full year covered by this book - the annual total was just over 11 per cent higher than that recorded in 1990. The busiest month in 1995 was July with 38,051 movements and the highest day's total was 1298, perhaps surprisingly late in the year on Friday October 13th - obviously no room for superstition at Heathrow! Hourly rates were frequently in the eighties and occasionally exceeded ninety in the evening peak period when traffic mix was at its most favourable.

Total Aircraft Movements

1990	390,393
1991	381,724
1992	406,483
1993	411,173
1994	424,557
1995	434,525
1996	440,343

50TH ANNIVERSARY FLYPAST

The BAA's chosen way of celebrating Heathrow's fiftieth birthday was to arrange a flypast on the 2nd June 1996 of a representative collection of aircraft that had graced its aprons over the years. Planning, as might be imagined, took several months and employed the consultancy services of the International Air Tattoo organisation who appointed Wing Commander David Roome as flypast co-ordinator. An impressive assortment of aircraft was assembled although, sadly, it was not possible to find a Stratocruiser or Constellation to take part. The display was to be led by the RAF Battle of Britain Memorial Flight's Lancaster - representing the Lancastrian G-AGWG, which had been the first commercial aircraft to take off from the Airport - and the running order was established as:-

(1)	Avro Lancaster PA474
(2)	De Havilland Rapides G-AGSH and G-AIDL
(3)	Bristol Freighter C-FDFC, De Havilland Dove G-OPLC, De Havilland Heron G-AORG
(4)	Douglas DC-3 G-AMPZ, Douglas C47A G-DAKK
(5)	Douglas DC-4 ZS-BMH
(6)	Douglas DC-6 G-SIXC
(7)	Vickers Viscount G-BFZL
(8)	Handley Page Herald G-CEAS, HS748 G-AVXJ
(9)	De Havilland Comet 4C XS235
(10)	Douglas DC-8-71 N805DH
(11)	BAC1-11 G-AVMT
(12)	Boeing 727 EC-GCK
(13)	Boeing 737-500 G-OBMY
(14)	Boeing 747-400 9V-SMS
(15)	Boeing 767 C-FMWP
(16)	MD-11 N1768D
(17)	Airbus A340 G-VBUS
(18)	Concorde G-BOAA with 9 Red Arrows Hawks
(19)	Boeing 777 G-ZZZD

Penultimate item of the 50th Anniversary flypast on 2nd June 1996 was Concorde 'AA accompanied by the Red Arrows - this angle secured from the 8th floor balcony of the Tower. (Pete Bish)

Extensive media coverage of the event included a visit to ATC by the BBC's 'Blue Peter' programme during May as a result of which a supply of 'Blue Peter' badges were sent to 'B' Watch via Bob Robinson for their co-operation during filming. There was nevertheless an accompanying stern warning from Caroline Bacon, the assistant producer, that the Badges were for adults only and not to be given to children, who have to earn their badges in other ways.

Many of the aircraft gathered at Stansted before the event, setting course to make good their required times at the threshold of runway 27R which began with the Lancaster at 1523 local. Stansted's Essex Radar and Heathrow Approach's 'W' Watch provided surveillance and any fine tuning required during the approach while Rod Metcalfe on Special VFR acted as 'catcher' as aircraft completed their flypast, seeing them safely en route out of the Zone. During their approach the crew of the Iberia Boeing 727 caused some confusion by descending to give their passengers a look at central London from very low altitude and making it difficult for the following aircraft to pick them out. By the time that the Boeing 777 made its pass at 1539, there were few amongst the assembled watchers who had not been affected by the emotion of the occasion which had been not only a worthy tribute to the Airport but also a significant illustration of how far aviation had advanced in the fifty years since it opened.

And so we reach the end of our journey through the first fifty years of civil ATC at Heathrow although, of course, the story continues. I hope that everyone has learnt at least a little more about the background to decisions that have shaped the system that exists today - I certainly have during several years of research - and that the lighter side of ATC depicted by the stories chosen here shall continue to play its part. The book has been written principally as a family album and I shall be disappointed if anyone who has worked in ATC at Heathrow fails to find something that triggers nostalgic memories. Fortunately it is that same feeling of 'belonging' that has enabled the book to be written and my thanks go to all those many colleagues who have contributed stories, sometimes embarrassing to themselves, which have shown the human side of ATC. Inevitably there are a number of larger than life characters who have not been mentioned, the best known of whom must be John Kiernan whose methods of controlling traffic, often unconventional, were nevertheless always guaranteed to delight aircrew. But like a true family everyone has played his or her part and it is my pleasure and good fortune to have been involved for thirty seven years.

Our final watch list, from early 1997, shows how the watches had settled down after 'the split'. It must be remembered that Thames Radar had by then been absorbed by the watches - hence 'Thames only' names are here who do not appear in the Staff list later.

ATCO MAIN ROSTER APRIL 1997

	A	B	C	D	E
Watch Manager	E.Przygrodski	N.E.Wood	I. .Alexander	D.C.Shawe	A.C.C.Haines
Asst Watch Mngr	B.T.Jones	G.B.Coates	R.Hillyer	R.J.Lodge	R.Metcalfe
1	R.Gallop	R.A.Robinson	B.Wildey	(B.Piket)	M.P.Hemming
2	Mrs S.Clifford	R.Redford	S.C.Hobbs	P.Kerby	M.Martin
3	C.K.Herbert	K.Miller	Miss M.E.Hockin	R.E.Dawson	I.Callier
4	C.J.Wilson	G.Howlett	K.Malam	J.Siddell	M.Baggaley
5	T.Picton	P.Smy	M.P.Holdstock	S.Forster	J.J.Cooke
6	Miss K.Nuttall	R.H.J.Glynn	Mrs M.Reed	M.Willis	M.Doyle
7	M.Stratford	J.Stafford	R.Goddard	Miss A.E.Weir	A.J.Fleming
8	N.Bainbridge	S.McKee	A.J.Mercer	K.Fowler	K.Day
9	D.G.C.Brindley	Miss K.N.Simpson	K.Crowley	R.Clarke	Mrs M.Bridge
10	I.A.Wheatley	P.Tipping	P.Hardwick	A.MacCormick	I.Montgomerie
11	J.Ogilvie	P.Hooper	I.Sims	Miss S.Woodhouse	C.Greenfield
12				K.Waud	
U/T VCR	S.James	A.Stewart-Taylor	S.Hayes		G.Kemp

*Brian Piket receiving training to regain his validation following the fitting of a 'Pacemaker', which resulted in a period of medical suspension.

*Ian Wheatley, Shane McKee, Kevin Crowley, Angus MacCormick and Marilyn Bridge training on Thames Radar.

ATSA MAIN ROSTER APRIL 1997

	A	B	C	D	E
Watch Mngrs Asst	M.D.Swann	J.H.Gleave	K.P.Baker	A.J.M.McGregor	R.D.M.Griffiths
2	A.Marsh	R.Kunert	G.P.Kemp	M.E.Davies	M.P.Dyer
3	Ms E.S.Blake	Miss T.Wilcox	M.Judge	G.Bannister	K.Gilchrist
4	P.Baber (U/T)			C.Lofting (U/T)	
5	G.Wilson	S.P.Batham	C.H.George	R.A.Gatfield	R.Kehoe
6	Mrs L.Miller	Ms P.Harkins	G.W.Jarvis	J.King	S.M.Neale
7	M.Lander	Ms J.Mitchell	Mrs P.Neale	A.Fielder	R.P.Hutchings
8	J.Freeman	L.Adby	Ms V.E.Lennon	Ms R.E.Crosswell	A.Hutchings
9	I.Forster	Ms S.Houston	J.Carson	D.Langley	A.Flower
10	D.Hadfield	J.Stemp	Miss W.Bruce	N.Partridge	Ms H.Middlemass
11		Miss S.Wayman-Hales			Ms H.Daniel

MISCELLANEOUS FACTS NOT COVERED ELSEWHERE

- The location indicator for London Airport was originally GALA.

- FIDO (Fog Intense Dispersal Of) gulleys were dug on 28R/10L but the equipment was never installed.

- The ATC vehicle assumed the name 'Pixie' from the registration letters PXE109 on an early vehicle.

- The pedestal-mounted binoculars in the VCR are believed to have come from a German 'U' boat, which is borne out by German writing on the casing. Date of arrival not known but definitely by 1958. They were refurbished in the late 1980s.

- Runway 15L/33R was permanently withdrawn from use in 1959.

- The radio ranges at Epsom and Watford were permanently withdrawn from service on 30.9.60 and replaced by NDBs.

- The term 'graunch' came into use as a way of requesting the selection of the runway over-ride. It is used as both verb and noun. The word's use even became the subject of letters to The Times newspaper.

- There was a lowerable ILS glide path aerial on 10R - lowered when runway 05L was in use.

- A rolling ball was situated on the radar desks on the sixth floor for transfer of traffic from No.1 to No.2 Director as part of the CAAS trials. This found little use and was often misused as an ashtray.

- Leave reliefs were provided for St Mary's Airport in the Scilly Isles from Heathrow until approx 1970. Des Crouch and Mike Perry are known to have holidayed in this way.

- Operational DMEs were introduced on both main runways in July 1979.

- Security firms who have safeguarded the Tower and its ATC staff over the years include Reliance, Burns, Sigma and Group 4.

- AIS Briefing Officer, Les Smith, constructed his man-powered bicycle plane in the late 1960s. Whether it flew is somewhat dubious!

Les Smith's man-powered bicycle plane seen here in PanAm's southside hangar on 24.11.67. (Frank Tyler)

The 10R glide path aerial being lowered (CAA Archives)

POSTSCRIPT

Because this book has taken rather longer to complete than originally anticipated the following brief details of events that have occurred in the meantime are included to bring the story up to date.

- Between June 1996 and June 2003 new blocks 138,139, 140, 141,160,161,162 and 163 and new stands V29, V30, V31, V32, W40, W41, X6, X7, X8 and X9 were introduced.

- Over a short period Heathrow ATCO Keith Waud and Thames ATCOs Ray Redford, Mike Baggaley and Mary Reed died prior to retirement age - in 1999, 2000, 2001 and 2002 respectively. Following the deaths at Thames Radar, GM Steve James and Manager Equipment Malcolm Aldridge commissioned an external independent company to investigate radiation levels in the Thames/SVFR room - such was the concern amongst staff. Levels were well within recognised safe standards, leading to the conclusion that the deaths were a tragic co-incidence.

- On 26th July 2001 a deal was completed whereby the Airline Group became a part owner (49%) of NATS through a Public Private Partnership (PPP). The proposal for a PPP was originally announced in July 1999 and the legislation enacted in the Transport Act of year 2000. The other final stage contender was Nimbus.

- The BASIS was replaced by a new Staff Information System (SIS)

- On 26th September 2002 a new Raytheon ASR10SS 10cm primary radar and co-mounted Condor Mk.2D Monopulse SSR entered operational service, commissioned and paid for by HAL. This benevolent gesture resulted from their need to use the space occupied by the Watchman radar, which it replaced, for construction work associated with Terminal 5. The new radar was adjacent to Stand 145 in the former 'C' cul-de-sac.

- On 7th November 2002 the Surface Movement Radar was enhanced by the addition of aircraft labelling. This was achieved using data from a Mode S multilateration sensor system using fifteen receivers around the Airport.

- A new numeric stand numbering system indicating the associated Terminal replaced the existing alphanumeric system in 2003. First to change were the 'X' and 'Z' stands which were re-numbered on the night of 24th/25th March, followed on the night of 4th/5th April by the remaining stands. Flow control was imposed to ease early problems.

- On 1st April 2003 the new Heathrow only post of Air Traffic Operations Manager (ATOM) was introduced to fill a perceived void in the management structure. The conditions of service, however, were not popular with existing Watch managers and resulted in some reverting to ATCO2. Following assessment Jem Dunn and Paul Johnson arrived to take up ATOM posts, with Alex Bristol also selected but unable to be released to come to Heathrow. The scheme, therefore, could not be

implemented immediately as four ATOMs were required for its operation.

- New Thales MLS systems were installed during 2003.

- In July 2003 the letters identifying cul-de-sacs were replaced by block numbers. 'B' became block 1, 'C' = 2, 'E' = 3, 'F' = 4, 'J' = 5, 'L' = 6, 'M' = 7, 'S' = 124, 'V' = 128, 'Z' = 127. This system lasted until 26th November 2003 when a partial move towards full taxiway lettering was implemented.

- On 10th July 2003 Thames Radar were forced to move prematurely to West Drayton as the result of a burst water pipe on the first floor of the Control Tower. Water drained down into the radar room during the early hours making the equipment and room unusable. The planned date for the move had been 27th November 2003.

- Taxiway designations changed from the block number system to letters, completed on 14th March 2004. At the same time runway holding points were given names - examples being Pluto, Rokit, Satun and Titan.

- In anticipation that AIS would move out of their first floor accommodation - probably in 2004 - to join AIDU (military publications) at Northolt, work began in 2003 to refurbish the entrance area and part of the first and second floors of the south east corner of the Control Tower for commercial letting. As this book went to press the move seems unlikely to happen.

- Stand 366 (L26) was taken out of service so that the foundations for a new Control Tower could be laid. Preliminary enabling work took place during the winter of 2002/2003. The 32 metre high cab weighing 868 tons was constructed on the southside of the airport and moved intact across 27L/09R on the night of 30th/31st October 2004. Pre-constructed sections of the Tower structure, brought in from Sheffield were inserted on site enabling the assembly to rapidly reach its full height of 87 metres. The 'topping out' ceremony was performed by General Manager Martyn Jeffery and BAA's Managing Director T5 Tony Douglas on 1st April 2005. On the same day the second Control Tower celebrated 50 years of operation and a party attended by over 100 former staff was held on the 6th floor. A nostalgia show was presented by Al Carter and Pete Bish. The new Tower is expected to be operational in October 2006.

- Terminal Five is due to open in 2008

The new Control Tower cab arrives in the Central Terminal area, passing behind an American Airlines Boeing 777 on the night of 30th/31st October 2004 (BAA Heathrow)

Reproduced with kind permission from Peter Shea and 'Skyport'

APPENDIX A

AIRCRAFT ACCIDENTS AT HEATHROW AIRPORT

This book has confined itself exclusively to the ATC operation at Heathrow and for that reason this appendix records only those accidents which have occurred within the Airport's boundaries although other tragic accidents have happened when aircraft were en-route, having taken off for or from Heathrow, and these were felt no less personally. There must be many who will read this book who, like me, were directly involved with one or more of the accidents remembered here, and the excellent safety record of recent years is a tribute to all concerned, including ATC. Permission from the AAIB to publish the accident information is gratefully acknowledged.

19.11.46 : Avro Anson : No details available

05.06.47 : Halifax C8 G-AIHW : Following a flight from Valencia with a cargo of apricots the aircraft made a heavy landing due to the pilot failing to level off correctly. The aircraft was written off and the wireless operator slightly injured.

25.07.47 (2115) : Avro York C1 G-AIUP : The aircraft was on a flight from Moscow via Berlin with a crew of seven and seventeen passengers. The flight was uneventful and a normal approach and landing were made on runway 23. After landing it over-ran the runway on to hard turf, jumped a ditch, passed over a concrete road and finally stopped across the Duke of Northurnberland River. The aircraft was severely damaged but there was no fire. Most of the occupants sustained superficial cuts and bruises, but four were more seriously injured. The cause of the accident was found to be failure of a brake cable due to the excessive wear over the steel fairlead or rubbing block.

23.10.47 : Lancastrian G-AGUL : During the landing run the aircraft ground-looped due to an error by the pilot in using incorrect technique for controlling the aircraft after touch-down. There were no injuries.

02.03.48 (2115) : Douglas DC-3C OO-AWH : After a routine flight from Brussels a GCA was made to runway 10L, with visibility 200 yards. A satisfactory approach was made, but it seems that the pilot was confused on passing the last of the sodium light fittings installed on the runway, failed to regain satisfactory visual contact, and stalled from a height of fifty feet. First impact was taken by the nose, port wing, port landing wheel and port propeller. Fire broke out immediately killing nineteen of the twenty two occupants, with the other three seriously injured. One of these later died from injuries sustained.

12.09.48 (2004) : Languedoc F-BATX : The aircraft over-ran the runway on landing causing damage to the port inner engine and undercarriage. There were no injuries.

28.10.49 (0100) : Grumman Mallard NC2956 : After taking off the aircraft reached a height of between 30 and 50 feet and then swerved to port approximately 40 degrees to the line of take off. Height was lost and the undercarriage wheels struck the grass 150 yards from the edge of the runway. The aircraft continued across the aerodrome a few feet above the surface for a further 450 yards and then crashed and burst into flames. The Captain, Radio Officer and four passengers were killed and the Engineer Officer injured.

31.10.50 (1954) : Vickers Viking G-AHPN : The aircraft took off from Paris for Northolt but a decision to divert to London was made due to poor visibility at Northolt (50 yards). London had a similar visibility but the pilot indicated that he would make one GCA before diverting to Blackbushe or Manston. A normal and well conducted approach was made to runway 28R, during which the visibility was passed to the pilot as 30 yards. At the completion of the approach the pilot reported 'I am overshooting' and the GCA radar appeared to confirm this. However, a few seconds later, the aircraft struck the runway with its undercarriage retracted, skidded 140 feet damaging both propellers, became airborne again and impacted again some 3,000 feet further on. The starboard wing was torn off and the aircraft skidded across the runway and across the disused runway, coming to rest alongside a pile of drain pipes where it burst into flames. The fog was so dense that the fire engines, although ready, took five to ten minutes to reach the scene. Of the four crew and twenty six passengers all but two were killed.

03.01.51 (0850) : Boeing B.377 Stratocruiser N1036V : The co-pilot was making the landing and as there was some slush on the runway the Captain intended to up the flaps to prevent them from being damaged. However, he inadvertently activated the landing gear switch to the 'up' position and the right gear retracted.

30.05.52 : Boeing B.377 Stratocruiser N1029V : Damaged after electrical failure on the approach, ending in gear retraction on landing.

01.08.52 (1849) : De Havilland DH.89A Rapide G-ALBB : This accident took place at the end of a five minute pleasure flight as the aircraft was approaching to land on runway 23L. It was following a Stratocruiser and had reached a point between the beginning of the approach lights and the Bath Road when it encountered turbulence at a height of 300 feet. The pilot lost control and the aircraft crashed just inside the Airport, 475 yards from the runway threshold. On impact the nose of the aircraft disintegrated and the pilot was thrown out and severely injured. Five of the eight passengers also received injuries, but of a lesser degree.

29.11.54 :Airspeed Ambassador G-ALZR : Both nose wheels fell off during take-off. After holding at Epsom to burn off fuel an approach was made to runway 10R. The passengers and baggage were moved to the back of the aircraft to move the centre of gravity back. The engines were cut as the aircraft touched down and the nosewheel leg eventually contacted the runway at about 60 knots. The aircraft stopped in about 100 yards. The aircraft was removed from the runway by getting further people to enter the aircraft and walk slowly to the back. The aircraft slowly tipped onto its emergency tail wheel and the engineers were able to refit the nosewheels.

16.01.55 (1150) : Vickers Viscount 701 G-AMOK : The flight taxied out as BE130 to Rome, having waited for the RVR to improve to the Company minimum of 150 yards. Runway 15R was requested to expedite the delayed departure although the Captain had only used this runway once before for take-off, and his first officer had never used the runway previously for take-off. Having taxied down 28R the aircraft was mistakenly lined up on the disused runway 15 (closed since 1949) and the take-off roll begun. The aircraft crashed into a barrier erected in connection with construction work in the Central Area, and suffered considerable damage. But fortunately there were no casualties amongst either passengers or crew.

22.06.55 (2152) : De Havilland Dove Srs.2 G-ALTM : The aircraft was engaged in making a colour film of the approach lighting at London Airport. Three runs had been made, and the aircraft was positioning for a fourth - to runway 10R - when the pilot noticed a decrease in airspeed. During a check to ascertain the reason a low oil pressure reading and rough running caused the pilot to shut down the port engine. Shortly afterwards power was also lost on the starboard engine and the aircraft crash landed just short of the first bar of the approach lights. There was no fire and no one was injured. The report blames the pilot for mis-identifying the problem engine.

18.08.56 (1953) : Vickers Viscount 748D VP-YNE : This accident occurred at dusk during a landing on runway 23L after a scheduled flight from Salisbury, Southern Rhodesia. The aircraft had taken off that afternoon from Rome and the flight appeared normal until the aircraft was losing speed during the landing run. The touchdown was smooth but very soon afterwards severe vibration was felt and the Captain presumed that both starboard tyres had burst. The aircraft came to rest on the runway with the starboard undercarriage leg retracted. There was no fire and all 46 on board disembarked safely. The accident was caused by a failure in the up-lock release mechanism which prevented the extension of the starboard undercarriage leg.

01.10.56 (1006) : Avro Vulcan B.1 XA897 Callsign MPQK 11 : A GCA was made to runway 10L. More than normal attention was needed to get the aircraft on to the centre line, and oscillations above and below the glide path were also noted. The weather conditions were wind calm, visibility 1,100 yards in heavy rain, scattered low cloud down to 300 feet with seven oktas at 700 feet. The aircraft struck the ground 2,000 feet short of the threshold, sustaining damage, and then crashed on the runway. Of the 6 persons on board, 4 were killed, whilst the Captain and Air Marshall Sir Harry Broadhurst ejected safely.

11.08.57 (2009) : Lockheed L-749A G-ANNT : At the end of a flight from Frankfurt the undercarriage could not be lowered due to a hydraulic fault. The starboard main undercarriage and nose wheel were unlocked by manual release but the nose wheel did not extend fully. The aircraft held for over an hour and then an approach was made to runway 23L. After landing the aircraft's port wing came into contact with the runway. There were 23 people on board.

02.05.58 : Vickers Viscount 735 YI-ACM : The aircraft sustained structural damage during a heavy landing. There were no injuries to the 38 passengers and 6 crew.

07.01.60 (1922) : Vickers Viscount 802 G-AOHU : After an uneventful flight from Dublin the aircraft was vectored for runway 28L with visibility deteriorating rapidly. The aircraft was monitored from five miles final by London Precision and then, at the pilot's request, given instructions from two miles when it was 400 feet left of the centre line. The Captain was able to see the first bar of the approach lights when about three quarters of a mile from it, and a normal flare out was made but touchdown was rather heavy. Immediately afterwards the Captain had the impression of running into a wall of fog and applied full braking. The nose wheel collapsed and by the time the fire service arrived some nine minutes later a fierce fire had taken hold. All five crew and fifty four passengers escaped injury. This accident was attributed to the failure of ATC to pass a critical deterioration of RVR to the pilot, which encouraged him to land in conditions which gave him insufficient visual reference.

02.03.60 (1957) : Vickers Viking 1 G-AGRV : Following a normal touchdown the aircraft swung to the left and came to rest with the lower forward part of the fuselage in contact with the ground and the port main gear tyre deflated. The aircraft sustained substantial damage.

08.03.60 (1127) : Handley Page Hermes G-ALDH : During the landing roll after a normal touchdown the starboard main gear collapsed. Subsequent examination revealed that the failure resulted from a fracture of the radius rod attachment lugs on the main undercarriage leg casing. No one was injured, but the aircraft sustained substantial damage.

24.12.60 (1138) :Boeing 707-436 G-APFN : The aircraft made a PAR approach to runway 23L at the conclusion of a scheduled service from Chicago. Surface wind 260/5 knots. The final stage of the approach was too fast and the point of touchdown was nearly halfway along the runway (3,500 feet from the threshold). When the Captain realised that the aircraft would not stop on the remaining length of the runway he attempted to steer the aircraft through 100 degrees on to runway 33L, but after an initial change in direction the aircraft started to skid left. Having left the runway the aircraft skidded only a short distance on the grass before the main landing gear units collapsed and the aircraft came to a standstill on a heading of 350 degrees. The aircraft was substantially damaged but there were no injuries to the 95 passengers or 11 crew.

14.08.62 :Boeing 720B D-ABOM : The aircraft was on a scheduled flight from Frankfurt, with a crew of 9 and 42 passengers. On final approach the crew discovered that the nose landing gear could not be lowered. After going around the crew tried again by all means possible to lower the nose landing gear, but were unsuccessful. The landing was made on runway 10L. The cause was a blockage at the retracted position of the hydraulic system of the jack for retracting and lowering the nose landing gear, caused by small pieces of rubber.

Boeing 720-030B D-ABOM on 10L 14.8.62. (B N Stainer - Aviation Photo News)

11.10.62 (2110) : De Havilland Comet 4 G-APDA : When power was applied for take-off an explosion occurred in No.3 engine. The take-off was abandoned and No.3 engine shut down. Half a minute later there was a fire warning from No.3 engine and the fire drill was carried out, but the warning persisted. Fire appliances arrived quickly and the fire was extinguished, but the engine was extensively damaged and damage also occurred in the secondary structure in the No.3 engine bay. It was subsequently established that the fire was the result of a fatigue failure of an '0' stage compressor blade.

TCA DC-8 54 CF-TJM's trail of destruction into 'the cabbage patch' 6.11.63 (Brian M Service)

06.11.63 (2115) : Douglas DC-8F-54 CF-TJM : Operating as flight TCA861 the aircraft experienced a start-up delay of approximately thirty minutes due to fog and then taxied out to runway 28L needing the extra length of this runway due to weight, although 28R was also available. Take-off roll was commenced with the RVR 150 yards (below his minima) but abandoned after 400 to 500 yards as the Captain could not see sufficient runway lights. The performance figures were rechecked and showed that 28R (RVR 500 yards) was acceptable, so the aircraft taxied over for departure from that runway. Take-off roll was begun, but as the speed increased the Captain became concerned with the hammering of the nose wheel on the cent re line lights. Attempts to relieve this by moving the control column back were ineffective, and the Captain concluded that he had no elevator control. He therefore decided to abort at a speed well above V1. Spoilers were not used, and the aircraft over-ran the end of the runway by 800 yards before coming to a rest in a cabbage field. The aircraft was extensively damaged but there were only five minor injuries sustained among the 90 passengers and 7 crew. Due to the location and visibility the first emergency vehicles took 23 minutes to arrive.

27.10.65 (0123) : Vickers Vanguard 951 G-APEE : The aircraft was on a scheduled flight from Turnhouse to Heathrow where the RVR was 400 metres. An unsuccessful ILS approach monitored by PAR was made to 28R followed by a full talk down to 28L from which another go-around resulted. After a period of holding at Garston a third approach was requested, this time to 28R again. The ILS approach was again monitored by PAR, and again the pilot reported 'overshooting'. The aircraft was seen on the PAR to start to climb and then dive steeply on to the runway (some 2,600 feet from the threshold). All 30 passengers and 6 crew on board were killed. A number of reasons were felt to have contributed to this disaster, none of which on its own would have caused the accident. These included :-

(1)   the RVR lights which were giving an inaccurate reading. Calibration later indicated that for the 350 metre light on 28R the reading was in the region of 50 metres too high. Had the correct value been passed (300 metres) then the approach could not have commenced.

(2)   the pilot who was not at his freshest. The overshoot was initiated with a coarse up-movement of the elevator.

(3)   Company drill, which could cause unnecessary distraction at a critical moment, even when carried out correctly. But on this occasion an incorrect flap setting was selected, affecting the pitch attitude of the aircraft.

(4)   the lag in the aircraft's instruments which gave a misleading picture of what was happening.

(5)   lack of experience of overshoots in real fog conditions.

31.12.65 (1424)   : Beechcraft Travel Air G-ASZC : After a flight from Manchester the aircraft, carrying two passengers in addition to the pilot, landed on runway 28R. While taxying to the south side of the Airport it was routed to cross 28L at block 87, and the pilot was instructed by GMC to cross behind a Britannia which was lined up ready to take off. He asked for confirmation of this instruction, which was repeated. As G-ZC taxied behind the Britannia the engines of the latter were opened up for take-off and the slipstream blew G-ZC sideways, causing the port undercarriage leg to collapse. There was substantial damage but no one was injured. As a result of this accident the standard phraseology was changed from 'behind the departing' to 'after the departing'.

31.03.67 (1328)   : Boeing 707-436 G-APFP : The aircraft was returning to Heathrow after a crew training detail at Stansted. When the undercarriage was selected down the main wheels locked down normally but the nose gear failed to extend although the nose gear door opened and the gear unlocked. Numerous attempts to lock the nose gear down were unsuccessful and a landing was made with the nose gear retracted. A small fire caused by burning magnesium in the nose leg fairing was quickly extinguished by the Airport Fire Service. Investigation showed that the nose gear had retracted with the wheels offset a few degrees to starboard; when the gear was subsequently selected down the port nose wheel tyre lodged on the edge of the wheel bay and stalled the activating jack and the emergency lowering systems.

22.06.67 (1807)   : Piper PA-30 G-ASOO : The pilot decided to land without flaps as there was an 18 to 20 knot headwind and he made the approach at 105 mph. Before landing on runway 23 he checked that the undercarriage green light was on but, after flaring out for the landing, the propellers struck the runway and the aircraft slid to rest on its belly. The aircraft was substantially damaged.

08.04.68 (1530)   : Boeing 707-465 G-ARWE : The aircraft was operating flight BA712 from Heathrow to Zurich. Approximately twenty seconds after take-off from runway 28L the No.2 engine failed and a short while afterwards caught fire. The aircraft was offered a landing back on 28L, but a 'Mayday' call was broadcast and ATC then offered runway 05R to expedite the return - surface wind was almost calm. This was accepted although the aircraft was high (3,000 feet) and fast (225 knots), making the approach difficult. Although the engine fire drill was carried out the fire continued to burn, and during the approach the No.2 engine and part of its pylon fell away from the wing into a gravel pit at Laleham, unknown to the crew. The aircraft made a good landing on 05R and when it came to a stop the fire, which had continued to burn near the No.2 engine position, increased in intensity and the fuel tanks in the port wing exploded. Emergency evacuation began as soon as the aircraft stopped, but four of the 116 passengers and one stewardess from the crew of eleven were overcome by heat and smoke and did not escape. The fire was caused by the fatigue failure of the engine's fifth stage low pressure compressor wheel, and continued to burn because of an omission to close the fuel shut off valve by pulling the fire shut off handle when the engine fire drill was carried out. The overall efficiency of the AFS was also criticised. Following this accident ATCO John Davis received an MBE and a new Fire Service alert category of 'Aircraft Accident Imminent' was introduced. The Fire Service also developed a new vehicle, smaller and faster than standard vehicles, which could reach an accident scene before the others and contain a fire until the rest arrived.

The dramatic arrival of 'WE on Runway 05 with number 2 engine missing as viewed from the Queens Building 8.4.68. (Frank Tyler)

03.07.68 (1628) : AS57 Ambassador Srs 2 G-AMAD : The aircraft was on a flight from Deauville to Heathrow carrying eight horses and five grooms. The approach to runway 28R was normal until the aircraft reached the runway threshold when it started to bank steeply to the left. The bank increased and the aircraft turned through about thirty degrees, finally crashing into aircraft parked in the Bravo cul-de-sac (where there was construction work) and ending up inverted. Investigation showed that the accident was caused by the fatigue failure of a flap operating rod which allowed the port flaps to retract while the starboard flaps increased their extension from 40 to 50 degrees. This resulted in a rolling movement to port which could not be controlled. The three crew and three of the passengers were killed. The two other passengers and twenty nine people on the ground sustained injuries, four of them serious. Aircraft involved were :-

(1)   Trident G-ARPT - destroyed. It was severed forward of the rear toilets, the entire aft part including the engines becoming detached and thrown thirty feet away.

(2)   Trident G-ARPI - severely damaged. The fin and tailplane were severed at the line of junction with the fuselage.

(3)   Viscount G-APKF - damaged. The Ambassador struck a catering vehicle, driving it against the fuselage of the Viscount damaging the skin and underlying members.

The aftermath of Airspeed Ambassador G-AMAD crashing into the 'Bravo' cul-de-sac 3.7.68. The Trident pictured furthest away, G-ARPI was repaired after this accident - only to crash itself near Staines less than 4 years later. (Brian M Service)

05.12.69 (2130) : Beechcraft Travel Air G-AWCW : The aircraft landed on 28L after a flight from Brussels and vacated at block 85. Soon afterwards it left the paved surface and struck a junction box, causing damage to its port wheel and oleo leg.

22.01.70   : Vickers Viscount 814 G-AWXI : Shortly after take-off from 28R, when the aircraft was at approximately 1,000 feet, there was a loud explosion accompanied by a fire warning on No.4 engine. Although the fire drill was carried out the engine fire could not be extinguished since the propeller continued to windmill, feeding the flames with engine oil. An immediate return was made to runway 28R, and an emergency evacuation carried out. The fire was extinguished by the AFS. Five passengers were injured in the evacuation, one of them severely.

13.11.73 : Boeing 707-436 G-APFB : While the aircraft was taxying prior to take-off, with 10 crew and 102 passengers, the main undercarriage starboard bogie was fractured just forward of the central pivot and the front wheels and axle became detached. The aircraft sustained substantial damage.

25.03.78 (1628) : Boeing 720-047B TF-VLB : The aircraft was being landed by the co-pilot when it bounced. The Captain took control to complete the landing, but during the recovery the nose gear struck the runway hard and partially collapsed. The aircraft stopped on the runway. At the time the surface wind was along the runway at 19 knots gusting to 29 knots. No evidence was found of any pre-existing defect in the nose gear assembly. The aircraft was on an Aer Lingus flight prior to joining Air Malta.

27.12.79 (1839) : Boeing 747-121 N771PA : The aircraft was operating a scheduled cargo flight from New York to Heathrow with only three flight crew on board. After a heavy touch-down the No.4 pylon forward bulkhead, which supports the front of the engine, began to break free of the pylon causing the engine to tilt down. This ruptured the engine fuel feed pipe and several other connections with the engine including the engine monitoring and fire warning circuitry. A severe fire developed which was observed by ATC and the crew as the aircraft turned off the runway towards block 77(0). The crew carried out the engine fire drill and the residual fire was rapidly brought under control by the AFS who had been alerted by ATC. There was substantial damage to the No.4 engine support structure, and also fire damage to the outer starboard wing, engine and pylon fairings. There were no injuries.

12.02.80 (1459) : Cessna 421 HB-LFQ : The aircraft was inbound from Vienna and had been cleared to land on runway 23 with a wind velocity of 200/13 knots. Just after touchdown the pilot noticed that the starboard landing gear was bouncing erratically and suspected a blown tyre. The aircraft veered away from the runway centre line to the right and after rolling about 200 metres the starboard landing gear leg broke off, causing the aircraft to turn sharply to the right and come to a stop at the side of the runway. Eyewitnesses watching the aircraft land saw the starboard wheel begin to swivel about the axis of the oleo leg just after touchdown, and then saw the leg bend backwards and collapse. Examination showed that the torque link coupling bolt, which was found near the point of touchdown, had fallen out allowing the wheel to pivot freely without restraint.

16.09.80 (1031) : Douglas DC-10-30 N83NA : The aircraft was outbound on flight PA99 to Miami with 237 on board. During the take-off run on 28R the BAA 'Checker' vehicle saw debris from a tyre burst appear behind the right hand side of the aircraft and immediately informed the Tower on the departure runway frequency in use. This transmission was heard by the aircraft's commander who abandoned the take-off. Full reverse thrust and hard braking were used and the aircraft stopped about 110 metres from the end of the runway. Two localised fires developed which were extinguished by the AFS. One passenger broke a leg during an otherwise successful evacuation.

12.05.81 : HS-125 G-BHSU : On approach to land at Brussels the left main landing gear failed to move when selected down, and the emergency drill was also unsuccessful. The aircraft diverted to Heathrow for a two wheel touch and go on runway 10L in an unsuccessful attempt to shake the gear free. A two wheel landing was made on runway 05. Subsequent investigation revealed that the left main landing gear pressure line was blocked by rubber material. The aircraft was substantially damaged.

05.05.82 (1540) : Boeing 707-347C OD-AGV : At the end of a flight from Beirut a normal approach and landing on 28L was made by the First Officer and upon selection of reverse thrust control was handed to the Commander to terminate the landing run. As the nose wheels contacted the runway vibration and bumping was felt by the crew. The Commander, sensing that something abnormal was occurring, selected full reverse thrust and held the nose wheels off the runway as long as possible. When the nose wheels touched the runway for the second time a loud bang was heard and the nose of the aircraft dropped approximately 18 inches. The aircraft came to rest on the centre line of the runway at which point the engines were shut down. The Airport fire and rescue services were quickly on the scene but as there was no fire the Commander elected to disembark the passengers using steps provided by the rescue services. There were no injuries. Initial examination indicated that the nose gear was in the down locked position at touchdown and that the oleo outer casing had fractured vertically at a very early stage in the nose wheel's landing run.

08.12.96 (1254) : Fokker 50 PH-KVK : At the end of a scheduled service as KLM483 from Rotterdam the left main gear showed an unsafe indication when the landing gear was selected down. The gear was raised and a go-around from 27L was made, following which the aircraft held at Epsom. Various attempts were made to lower and lock the gear but to no avail, and ATC were advised that there was a high risk of the gear collapsing after the aircraft touched down. While the aircraft was still in the holding pattern a change of runway was made due to the surface wind (140/4-7knots) and the crew were advised that 09R would now be the landing runway. The aircraft touched down normally at 92 knots but after five seconds the left main landing gear collapsed and the aircraft's left wing tip, left propeller and the rear left portion of the fuselage contacted the runway. The aircraft veered to the left, coming to rest on the hard surface clear of the runway at block 81. A full evacuation was carried out, and there were just three minor injuries sustained. One of the two bolts used to secure the platform which forms one half of the over-centring stop in the lock-link was found to be missing and the other was loose, allowing it to become slightly displaced. This had prevented the lock-link from achieving the over-centred condition.

05.11.97 (1620) : Airbus A340-311 G-VSKY : At the end of a scheduled flight from Los Angeles the aircraft had a landing gear problem on its first approach to Heathrow. A skillful emergency landing was carried out on runway 27L with the left main landing gear only partially extended. An evacuation was completed with minor injuries to five passengers and two crew members. Examination of the left main landing gear found that it had been jammed by the No.6 wheel brake torque rod which had disconnected from its brake pack assembly and become trapped in the keel beam structure. The associated torque rod pin was subsequently found beyond the end of the departure runway 24L at Los Angeles International Airport.

Finally a look at collisions on the ground, which illustrate just how difficult it is for the crews of large aircraft to judge wingtip clearances in confined areas. All occurred close to, or at, holding points.

08.03.72 (1123) : Pan American N738PA and Pan American N797PA : Whilst moving along the taxiway towards the main holding point for take off on runway 10R the port wing of the B747 struct the elevators and starboard stabiliser of the B707 which was waiting at a runway access point for 10R.

07.05.73 (0958) : Pan American N751PA and Aer Lingus EI-ASG : While attempting to pass behind the B737, which was stationary behind two other aircraft in block 75, the leading edge of the B747's starboard wing tip struck the underside of the B737's port tail plane.

16.05.75 (1240) : British Airways G-AWNP and Aer Lingus EI-ASK : Whilst taxying along the extension taxiway for 10L the B747's right wing tip struck and seriously damaged the port elevator of the B737 which was stationary at a runway access point (block 36).

21.06.75 (0943) : Air India VT-EBD and Alitalia l-DIBJ : Whilst taxying down the extension taxiway for 10R the port wing of the B747 struck the rudder of the DC9, which was waiting for an intersection departure at block 99/102.

20.09.80 (1104) : British Airways G-AWNN and Scandinavian Airlines SE-DAR : Whilst taxying down the extension taxiway for 10R the left wing tip of the B747 struck the rudder of the DC9 which was stationary at block 102.

23.11.95 (1031) : Gulf Air A4O-LB and British Airways G-BIKG : As the Airbus A340 moved along the taxiway centre line in block 137 to the rear of the Boeing 757, which was waiting for a block 18 departure, the port wing tip struck the 757's rudder and fin.

Another incident which caused serious damage but was not a reportable accident occurred on 26.2.68. Comet 4B G-ARGM was engine running at the BEA Maintenance Area when it 'jumped the chocks' and collided with the hangar. The Comet went on to fly again. The hangar upright prevented damage to the brand new Trident 2 inside. The moral apparently is not to use Viscount chocks when running up a Comet! (Brian M Service)

APPENDIX B

SOME DATES OF INTEREST

INTRODUCTION

No story of ATC at Heathrow would be complete without mention of some of the planes and landmark events at the airport. This appendix compiled by Pete Bish, with assistance from Rog Kunert, Ian Callier and Tony Merton Jones tries to relate the developments in ATC in the earlier pages of this book with the introduction (and withdrawal) of key aircraft types. Also, some of the events and antics that once were common place, but now seem inconceivable in relation to the continuously busy nature of Heathrow. The important aviation dates are spiced with the odd useless fact - probably suitable for repetition only at a trivia quiz!

01.01 46   The airport was handed over from the Air Ministry to the Ministry of Civil Aviation.
            First passenger carrying London Airport departure was British South American Airways (BSAA) Avro
            Lancastrian G-AGWG 'Star Light' on a proving flight to Buenos Aires, Argentina.

British South American Airways Avro Lancastrian, G-AGWG 'Star Light'. It was this aircraft which departed 1st January 1946 on a proving flight to Buenos Aires, via Lisbon, Bathhurst, Natal, Rio de Janeiro and Montevideo.(Stephen Piercey collection)

25.03.46   The Airport was officially named London Airport by the Minister of Aviation, Lord Winster. A selection of air
            craft expected to use the Airport were on display.

16.04.46   Panair do Brasil's L-049 Constellation PP-PCF, which arrived from Rio, was the first Constellation and also the
            first foreign registered aircraft to land at London Airport.

31.05.46   London Airport was officially opened by Lord Winster.

21.01.47   First offical visit to London Airport by a member of the Royal Family. Her Royal Highness Princess Elizabeth
            named Avro Tudor 1 G-AGRF 'Elizabeth of England' for BOAC. The type was later rejected by the airline and
            taken over by BSAA.

04.04.49   Boeing Stratocruiser N1028V 'Clipper Flying Cloud' arrived on a Pan Am proving flight as the first of the type
            at London Airport. The double deck Boeing was the height of luxury travel and remained in service till the late
            1950s.

24.10.49   The first DH.106 Comet, G-ALVG, arrived at London Airport and made a return flight to Castel Benito, Libya
            the next day.

15.06.50   First visit of the Bristol Brabazon G-AGPW. Two demonstration flights were made witnessed by a number of
            MPs.

31.01.51   Charles Blair, flying a P51 Mustang N1202, arrived non-stop from New York's Idlewild Airport in a record time
            of 7hrs 48mins - average speed 442 mph.

N1028V was London Airport's first Boeing Stratocruiser (Stephen Piercey collection)

08.10.51   HRH Princess Elizabeth and the Duke of Edinburgh departed on BOAC Boeing Stratocruiser G-AKGK 'Canopus' on the first Royal tour to be made by air from the UK. The aircraft departed soon after midnight for Gander and Montreal.

07.02.52   HM Queen Elizabeth II arrived back in the UK from Nairobi on her accession to the throne. She flew in on the BOAC Argonaut G-ALHK 'Atalanta' having cut short a tour of East Africa.

02.05.52   BOAC DH.106 Comet G-ALYP departed on the world's first jet passenger service to Johannesburg via Rome, Beirut, Khartoum, Entebbe and Livingstone.

18.04.53   BEA's G-AMNY departed on the world's first scheduled Vickers Viscount service to Rome, Athens and Nicosia.

08.10.53   Eight aircraft departed on a handicapped air race from London to Christchurch, New Zealand. The unlikely mix of entrants comprised five Canberras (three RAF and two RAAF), a Handley Page Hastings (RNZAF), a KLM DC-6A and the prototype Vickers Viscount 700 G-AMAV. With four refuelling stops the winning Canberra arrived at Christchurch in a total elapsed time of 23hrs 51 mins.

13.06.54   The 1954 annual RAeS Garden Party was held on the Airport on this Sunday afternoon. The programme (on page 118/119) lists the arrivals and departures that guests could expect to see.

15.06.54   A memorial statue was unveiled adjacent to the northside spectators enclosure on the 35th anniversary of Alcock and Brown's epic trans Atlantic flight.

17.04.55   The Europa Building (re-named Terminal 2 in 1968) opened for domestic/European services.

16.05.55   Lufthansa resumed services to London after World War 2 using Convair 340s from/ to Munich and Hamburg.

24.07.55   BEA began helicopter services to the South Bank Heliport, Waterloo with Westland Whirlwind G-ANUK. The fare was 35 shillings (£1.75) and 3,822 passengers were carried in the ten month operation which ended on 31.5.56.

One of the first group jet pictures at London Airport - 3 Tupolev TU-104s together on proving flights 25.4.56. (Brian M Service)

22.03.56	First visit of the Soviet-built Tupolev Tu-104 jet airliner (CCCP-L5400).

25.04.56   Three Tu-104s (CCCP-L5400, 5412 and 5413) arrived from Moscow on proving flights. They parked in formation in the area which later became the 'H' cul-de-sac.

01.10.57   TWA L-1649 Starliner N7307C departed to set the record for the longest ever non-stop scheduled commercial flight - to San Francisco - 23hrs 21 mins.

The eternally elegant shape of the ultimate piston-engined airliner - the Lockheed L-1649 Starliner. A sister ship in the TWA fleet set the endurance record from London on 1.10.57 (Brian M Service)

08.09.58   The first visit by a Boeing 707 - Pan American's N709PA 'Clipper America'.

04.10.58   BOAC DH.106 Comet 4 G-APDC departed for New York's Idlewild Airport under the command of Captain Roy Millichap as the first trans-Atlantic jet passenger service. Another Comet 4 G-APDB left New York at the same time bound for London Airport under the command of Captain Tom Stoney.

31.03.59   BOAC inaugurated a round the world service - Bristol Britannia via Atlantic/Pacific and DH 106 Comet 4 Tokyo to London.

18.10.59   Pan American Boeing 707 N719PA 'Clipper Windward' inaugurated the first all jet round the world service.

06.05.60   Five Avro Vulcans departed from London Airport to various Commonwealth destinations carrying copies of the film of HRH Princess Margaret's wedding.

XA901, one of the 5 Avro Vulcans to visit Heathrow in May 1960 to fly film copies of Princess Margaret's wedding to Commonwealth Countries. It was a similar aircraft that crashed at the Airport on 1.10.56. A somewhat slower Avro (Skyways York) appears in the foreground. (Brian M Service)

The very idea of the Royal Aeronautical Society holding a garden party between the runways at Heathrow would be pure fantasy for most of us - This is the list of arrivals and departures from noon onwards which guests could expect to see at such an event in 1954! Wonderful…………

SCHEDULED SERVICES FOR

ARRIVALS

Time: p.m.	Operator	Aircraft	From
12.05	B.O.A.C.	Constellation	New York/Prestwick
12.10	B.O.A.C.	Argonaut	Bahrein/Düsseldorf
12.25	T.W.A.	Constellation	New York
12.45	B.E.A.	Viscount	Copenhagen
12.45	Air France	Viscount	Paris
1.00	S.A.S.	DC-6	Oslo/Stavanger
1.15	S.A.S.	DC-6	Stockholm/Copenhagen
1.30	B.O.A.C.	Argonaut	Nairobi/Rome
1.50	B.E.A.	Elizabethan	Paris
1.55	B.E.A.	Viscount	Stockholm/Oslo
1.55	B.O.A.C.	Argonaut	Nairobi/Rome
2.15	B.O.A.C.	Constellation	New York/Prestwick
2.25	Air France	DC-4	Paris
2.50	B.E.A.	Elizabethan	Paris
3.00	B.O.A.C.	York (freighter)	Singapore/Castel Benito
3.50	S.A.A.	Constellation	Johannesburg/Rome
3.50	B.E.A.	Elizabethan	Paris
4.20	Alitalia	Convair	Milan
4.20	Sabena	Convair	Brussels
4.20	B.O.A.C.	Argonaut	Colombo/Rome
4.25	Swissair	Convair	Geneva
4.35	Air France	DC-4	Paris
4.35	B.E.A.	Viscount	Geneva
4.35	B.E.A.	Elizabethan	Hamburg
4.50	B.E.A.	Elizabethan	Paris
4.55	K.L.M.	Convair	Amsterdam
5.00	Swissair	DC-6B	Zürich
5.15	B.E.A.	Elizabethan	Amsterdam
5.30	B.E.A.	Viscount	Zürich
5.50	B.E.A.	Elizabethan	Paris
6.00	B.E.A.	Viscount	Frankfurt
6.05	Swissair	Convair	Zürich/Basle
6.10	Swissair	DC-3	Berne
6.15	B.E.A.	Viscount	Istanbul
6.15	B.E.A.	Elizabethan	Nice
6.25	P.A.A.	DC-6	Frankfurt
6.30	B.E.A.	Viscount	Madrid
6.30	B.E.A.	Elizabethan	Cologne/Brussels
6.45	B.E.A.	Viscount	Barcelona
6.55	B.E.A.	Elizabethan	Amsterdam
7.05	Air France	DC-4	Paris
7.05	Qantas	Constellation	Sydney/Frankfurt
7.50	Qantas	Constellation	Sydney/Frankfurt
7.50	B.E.A.	Elizabethan	Paris
8.00	K.L.M.	Convair	Amsterdam
8.05	T.W.A.	Constellation	Frankfurt
8.10	Air France	DC-3	Nice/Marseilles
8.20	B.E.A.	Viscount	Athens/Rome
8.25	B.E.A.	Elizabethan	Rome/Nice
8.25	B.E.A.	Viscount	Vienna/Zürich
8.25	Air France	DC-4	Paris
8.50	B.E.A.	Elizabethan	Paris
8.55	Air India	Constellation	Calcutta/Paris

Page Thirty-Two

DEPARTURES

Time: p.m.	Operator	Aircraft	To
12 noon	B.E.A.	Elizabethan	Paris
12 noon	P.A.A.	Stratocruiser	Frankfurt
12.20	Air France	DC-3	Dinard
12.25	B.E.A.	Viscount	Frankfurt
12.30	Air France	DC-4	Paris
12.40	Sabena	Convair	Brussels
12.50	B.E.A.	Elizabethan	Amsterdam
1.00	B.E.A.	Elizabethan	Paris
1.00	K.L.M.	Convair	Amsterdam
1.10	T.W.A.	Constellation	Frankfurt
1.30	Air France	Viscount	Paris
1.35	B.E.A.	Viscount	Palma
2.00	B.E.A.	Elizabethan	Paris
2.05	B.E.A.	Viscount	Oslo / Stockholm
2.45	B.O.A.C.	Argonaut	Rome / Accra
2.55	B.E.A.	Elizabethan	Amsterdam
3.15	Air France	DC-4	Paris
3.25	B.E.A.	Viscount	Copenhagen
3.35	S.A.S.	DC-6	Gothenburg / Stockholm
4.00	B.E.A.	Elizabethan	Paris
4.20	S.A.S.	DC-6	Copenhagen / Stockholm
5.00	B.E.A.	Elizabethan	Paris
5.10	Sabena	Convair	Brussels
5.25	Alitalia	Convair	Milan / Rome
5.30	Air France	DC-4	Paris
5.40	B.E.A.	Elizabethan	Düsseldorf / Berlin
5.45	Swissair	DC-6B	Zürich
6.15	B.E.A.	Elizabethan	Amsterdam
7.00	P.A.A.	Stratocruiser	New York
7.00	K.L.M.	Convair	Amsterdam
7.00	B.E.A.	Elizabethan	Paris
7.00	B.O.A.C.	Argonaut	Tokyo
7.05	B.E.A.	Viscount	Glasgow
7.20	B.E.A.	Viscount	Belfast
7.30	P.A.A.	DC-6	New York
7.50	B.E.A.	Elizabethan	Brussels
7.55	B.E.A.	Viscount	Manchester
8.00	B.O.A.C.	Stratocruiser	New York
8.00	Air France	DC-4	Paris
8.15	B.E.A.	Viscount	Birmingham

NOTES:

The details were correct at the time of going to press and are liable to alteration. There will also be unscheduled services.

If, as is often the case, there is a westerly wind, landings will be on No. 5 runway, near the Garden Party area and just to the south of it, and take-offs will be from No. 1 runway near the Bath Road and about ¾-mile to the north.

16.11.61	The Oceanic building (re-named Terminal 3 in 1968) opened for use.
28.03.62	The northside passenger Terminal closed. The Royal suite, cargo operations and aircraft parking continued until the late 1960s.
08.02.63	The first of only four visits by the giant Tupolev Tu-114 turboprop - at that time the largest airliner in the world. BEA had to rig two sets of steps together to reach the door of CCCP-76481, chartered by Roy Thomson to collect 170 British businessmen on a visit to Moscow. The same Tu-114 returned with the party three days later.

The awesome Aeroflot Tupolev Tu-114 chartered by Roy Thomson in February 1963. (Brian Piket)

20.08.63	The first multi-storey car park was opened in the Central Area - 1,063 spaces.
23.03.65	The M4 motorway spur was opened.
18.05.66	Sheila Scott departed in Piper Comanche G-ATOY on a round the world solo flight. She arrived back at Heathrow on 20.6.66, gaining many point to point records in the process.
16.05.67	The world's first fully automatic landing by an aircraft in scheduled airline service was made by BEA HS.121 Trident 1 G-ARPP from Nice to Heathrow.
11.05.68	CCCP-86666, leased from Aeroflot by CSA, was the first Ilyushin IL-62 to visit Heathrow.
06.11.68	British Eagle International Airlines,, Heathrow's largest non-state carrier, went into liquidation and ceased operations. The fleet, mainly Bristol Britannias, BAC 1-11s, Vickers Viscounts and Boeing 707s, was parked up at their engineering base for several months before dispersal. Blocks 41 and 44 continued to be referred to as the 'Eagle taxiway' for several decades afterwards.
09.12.68	The cargo tunnel was opened by William Rodgers, the Minister of State at the Board of Trade.
07.05.69	Terminal 1 was opened for domestic services and BEA's European flights.
14.06.69	G-AVPD, a single seat Jodel D9 built by Stuart W.McKay at the BEA Engineering base, departed Heathrow on its maiden flight flown by Captain John Ellis. The BAA mowed a strip of grass north of 28L especially for the take-off. Its Special VFR clearance referred to 'turning right at the Brylcreem factory' en route for Booker.
12.01.70	The first visit by a Boeing 747 was made by Pan American's N735PA 'Clipper Constitution' on a proving flight.
22.05.70	The BEA/BOAC Cargo Centre was officially opened by HRH The Duke of Edinburgh.
13.09.70	UK Prototype BAC Concorde G-BSST, following its display at the SBAC Show, Farnborough, contrived to divert to Heathrow from its test base at Fairford. 1st visit of a supersonic transport to Heathrow.
20.05.74	The first Airbus produced type to land was F-BVGA, an Air France A300 - heralding the type's introduction on the Paris route 3 days later.
22.11.77	Scheduled supersonic flights finally gained access to New York using Concorde.

The sad sight of part of the British Eagle fleet and company vehicles crammed into the airline's maintenance base following their financial collapse in November 1968. (BAA)

18.11.80	Ex Heathrow ATCO Judith Chisholm departed in Cessna T210L G-BAGE on a round the world solo flight. She returned to Heathrow on 3.12.80 having gained 28 point to point records in a total elapsed time of 360 hrs 22 mins 23 secs.
30.01.81	Thick fog blanketed Heathrow all day. Of the 107 landings made in the 24 hours, 88 were made by British Airways HS.121 Tridents while Boeings contributed zero.
27.09.81	The last scheduled piston engined transport movement took place - Finnair Cargo DC-6ST operated by Karair's OH-KDA as AY033/034 Heathrow - Manchester -Helsinki.
05.06.83	The US Space Shuttle 'Enterprise' mounted on top of Boeing 747-123 N905NA made a low fly-past of 10L en route to Stansted.
11.07.85	Five Douglas DC-3s and a Piper Aztec camera ship G-FOTO made a formation approach to 28R, thence en route via Northolt to the Fairford Air Tattoo.
01.04.86	Terminal 4 officially opened by HRH The Prince of Wales and HRH The Princess of Wales.

Judith Chisholm - Heathrow ATCO 1972-78 and Aviatrix, departed Heathrow 18.11.80 on a record-breaking round the World flight in a Cessna T210L. She died from cancer at the all too early age of 41. (via Audrey Lowe)

The only Antonov An-22 to visit Heathrow, seen here on 18.12.88. It is parked behind one of several Antonov An-124s to visit the Airport. They were picking up urgent relief supplies for the Armenian Earthquake disaster. (Pete Bish)

14.12.88   First visit of the Antonov An-124 (CCCP-82008) - then the world's largest aircraft. Several further
            visits by An-124s were made during December 1988, collecting relief supplies for the Armenian earthquake.

16.12.88   The first and only visit of the Antonov An-22 (CCCP-09319) - the world's largest ever
            propeller aircraft - also picking up relief supplies for the Armenian earthquake.

16.08.89   Qantas Boeing 747-438 VH-OJA departed as QF7441 on a special non-stop proving flight to
            Sydney, Australia.Time en route was 20hrs 9mins and the distance 9,638 nautical miles. The aircraft
            was towed to the 27L holding point to maximise endurance.

20.10.94   During construction of the Heathrow Express rail link to Paddington the newly dug tunnel collapsed in the
            Central Area causing traffic chaos and flight delays which continued over a period of several days.

12.12.97   A major fire in an air-duct above a deep-fat fryer at Burger King in Terminal 1 in the early hours caused travel
            chaos for the rest of the day with hundreds of diversions and cancelled flights.

29.05.99   Heathrow recorded its busiest ever hour - 45 landings, 54 departures = 99 total.

27.10.02   SAA Boeing 747-344 ZS-SAU operating flight SA226 was the last movement on runway 23
            landing at 0746.

10.08.03   Thanks to its great expanse of concrete, Heathrow became the first place in the UK to ever record 100°F
            (37.8°C). Gravesend, Kent beat the record later the same day!

30.10.03   Heathrow's elevation officially increased by 3 feet to 83 feet.

21.07.04   The current highest daily movement record set at 1382.

GOODBYE CONCORDE

Although each event recorded above was noteworthy in its way nothing surpasses the immense public interest generated by British Airways' decision to withdraw its entire fleet of Concordes from service late in 2003. Although technically outside the period of this book it would be inexcusable not to pay tribute to this beautiful aircraft which graced our aprons for over 30 years. Three dates are particularly significant to ATC:-

22.10.03   The arrival of BAW2 from New York coincided with that of BAW9021 returning from a UK 'farewell' flight. Steve Dominic - Heathrow's Final Director - and his colleagues on 'X' Watch were able to sequence the pair onto parallel approaches to 09L and 09R using visual separation with the enthusiastic cooperation of the pilots involved. The touchdowns were just three seconds apart.

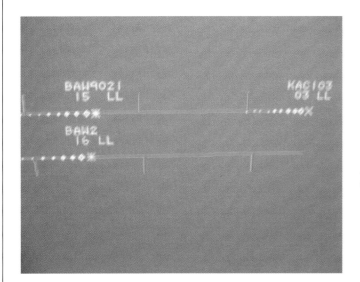

Radar picture of 09L/R approaches and parallel Concordes just under 5 miles from touchdown on 22.10.03. (Mike Inglis)

24.10.03   Three Concordes landed in stream on 27R marking the end of operations into Heathrow. Incredibly emotional for all present. Rather appropriately Ivor Sims was on Air Arrivals to clear the last Concorde, BAW2 from New York, to land as it had been he who cleared the first schedule for take-off for Bahrain back in 1976.

26.11.03   The day of the very last Concorde movement at Heathrow, Brian Ringrose cleared G-BOAF for take off as it departed for the Bay of Biscay en route to its final resting place at Filton, Bristol. The four other aircraft that were modified following the Air France disaster made their final flights out of Heathrow over the preceding month :-

31.10.03   G-BOAC to Manchester for display in the Aviation Heritage Park.
03.11.03   G-BOAG to New York en route to the Museum of Flight in Seattle.
10.11.03   G-BOAD to New York for the Intrepid Sea Air Space Museum, Manhattan.
17.11.03   G-BOAE to Barbados for display at Grantley Adams Airport.

     Of the 2 unconverted aircraft, G-BOAA was dismantled and transported by road and barge to the Museum of Flight, East Fortune, Scotland whilst G-BOAB remains at Heathrow for display - although its initial resting point, beside Runway 23, is out of view from anyone unless they are a window seat passenger using 27R!

Heathrow's last resident Concorde, 'AB in happier times taxying out for departure on the short lived Braniff interchange service to Washington and Dallas as G-N94AB in 1979. Note the Airport Fire Service's Canadair C-4 Argonaut under the nose. (Pete Bish)

APPENDIX C

THE STAFF LIST

The following list, collated over the past 7 or 8 years attempts to list every ATCO and ATCA/ATSA who has worked in the VCR and approach elements of the Control Tower building in the whole period 1946 - 2005. Not included are people who worked only in AIS, the Flow Unit, Thames Radar, Noise Monitoring or Approach after the move to TC at West Drayton. Ladies are listed by their family names on first arrival at Heathrow.

Old style trainees on Cadetships are not included as they were not posted in, only detached. Some of them gained unit endorsements. By contrast many recent students are included as Heathrow was their initial posting - even if they failed to validate and moved on quickly. This list does not differentiate between those who validated and those who did not - all are or were part of the (still) elite body of people who worked at Heathrow ATC - nearly 1200 over a period of 59 years! This list must be treated as a 'first attempt' at such a project. There will be names missed, particularly from the early years and accurate dates and subsequent histories are needed for some of the people who do appear. All updates are welcome as it is my intention to maintain this list for the future.

The list was compiled from the memories of a large number of individuals - especially Jimmy Birchall, Graham Bisset, Pam and Bill Broadmore, Bob Cook (ATCA), John Kiernan, Lucy Miller, Des and Winnie O'Connell, Mike Perry, Ron Toseland plus the many watch lists which have been unearthed in attics and files. My task has then been to put accurate information onto those names - which has been a wonderful opportunity to talk or correspond with many famous names - from my first and only meeting with the late Bill Woodruff downwards! Many thanks to all of you who have responded with your details or who have similarly joined in the spirit of this venture by pointing me towards your former colleagues and friends. My thanks too go to Mrs Lesley Gunn at the CAA Pensions Administration Department who added addresses to my named, stamped envelopes to many retired staff. Also to Roger Kunert who has been my 'main agent' at the Tower since my move to TC.

Finally my sincere thanks to Brendan McCartney who has kept the list tidy (and in alphabetical order) thanks to his word processing skills ….. If your memory of location indicators and abbreviations are a bit rusty then a de-code is at the end of this section.

I look forward to your updates using any of the following contact methods:-

Pete Bish, Hayward Cross, Hungerford, Berkshire, RG17 0QD
Tel / Fax 01488 681527
e-mail adverts@zebedeelist.co.uk

Handover of Power - On the Tower steps from Maurice Bennett to Ron Toseland in September 1981. (quo'tass via Ron Toseland)

THE BOSSES

ATCO I/C	Bill Rimmer	1946-47
	Jack Barringer	1947-52
	Roger Bulstrode	1952-56
	Bill Woodruff	1956-62
	Jack Barringer	1961
	(Returned temporarily whilst Bill Woodruff on Patch Committee)	
	Maurice Young	1962-64
	Ray Kirk	1964-69
Ch ATCO/Ch Officer	Basil Turner	1969-72
	Mac Pearson	1972-76
	Maurice Bennett	1976-81
	Ron Toseland	1981-83
	Mike Perry	1983-86
General Manager	Keith Williams	1986-90
	Gordon Doggett	1990-92
	Roger Budgen	1992-2001
	Steve James	2001-04
	Martyn Jeffery	2004-

Keith Williams became Heathrow's first General Manager in December 1986. (Pete Bish)

SURNAME	INIT	FIRST NAME/ KNOWN AS	DATES	START GRADE	END GRADE	COMMENTS
Abery	EH	Ernie	1949-55/1972-76	ATCOIII	ATCOI WS	>SATCC >School of ATC >HQ >Returned >EGHH (Ch Officer) >Retired 1981
Acton	DW	Dave/Ackers	1974-81	ATCOII	ATCOII	>HQ (C(R)7) >EGDM (>Man ATC, acting ATCOI) >LTCC >HQ(AP2) >Retired 1995 >Own clock/antique furniture business
Adams	MCC	Martin	1973-79	ATCAIII	ATCAII	>Resigned >Simoniz Int PLC (Buyer)
Adby	L	Les	1991-	ATSAII	ATSAII	C
Addiscott, Miss	MA	Margaret	1973-75	ATCAIII	ATCAII	>Mrs Sylvester-Thorne >OACC >Retired 1977
Adkins	CB	Chas	1979-80	ATCOII	ATCOII	>Resigned >EGJB
Aitchison	AB	Bud	1959-67	ATCOIII	ATCOII	>SATCC >ScATCC >ATCOI > Retired 1987
Albertini	AV	Tony	1940s	ATCOIII	ATCOI	>SATCC >HQ C(Ops)2B >Retired >Deceased
Alcock	N	Norman	1950s	ATCOIII	ATCOII	>N.Div >Retired
Alder	MG	Martin	1969-72	ATCAIII	ATCAII	>ATCOIV >EGNS >LATCC >Resigned 1978 >De Beers (Pilot HS125) >BCAL (Pilot BAC 1-11) >BA (Pilot A320.B747-400> Training Captain A320)
Alexander	IH	Iain	1973-98	ATCOIII	ATCOI RWM	>LTCC
Allen	SRJ	Sam/Derby	1950s	ATCAII	ATCA II	>
Allison	GJ	Guy	2003-	ATCOII	ATCOII	C
Allison	J	Jimmy	1950s	RC	ATCA	>ATCAI >Deceased
Allsopp	PJ	Pete	1975-85	ATCOC	ATCOII	>ATO >Thames Radar >ATC Ops >LATCC >LTCC >ATCOI >LATCC >LACC
Almond	RG	Richard	1974-79	ATCAII	ATCAII	>Cadetship >EGPH >CATC >LTCC >EGKK
Alterskye	JA	John	1973-77	ATCOIV	ATCOII	>Resigned >IAL (OMAD, OBBI, OMSJ, OMDB) >EGSS >LTCC >Retired 2002
Alty	NH	Norman	1960s	ATCO	ATCO	>EGCC >Deceased
Anderson	A	Andrea	1997	StATCO	ATCOII	C
Anderson	RJ	Andy	1972-75	ATCAIII	ATCAII	>EGPD >EGKK >ATSAIV
Anderson	S	Steve	1997-98	StATCO	StATCO	>EGKK >ATCOII >ATC Ops & Training
Anderson-Taylor	CE	Clifford	1959-63	ATCAII	ATCAII	>ATCOIII >PATCC >Hack Green >SATCC >ATCOI >LATCC >Retired 1997
Andrews, Ms	JM	June	1960s	ATCA	ATCA	>
Annable, Miss	DP	Deirdre	1966-68	ATCAIII	ATCAII	>SATCC >Mrs MacKay >LATCC >ATCOIV >ATCOII >Temp ATCOI >Retired 2004
Annett	VA	Viv	1972-85	ATCAII	ATCAII	>Retired 1985 >Deceased
Apps	CJ	Colin	?	ATCA	ATCA	>EGKK
Armstrong	DH	David	1999-	StATCO	ATCOII	C
Arnott	AC	Andy	1964-66/80-82	ATCAIII	ATSAIII	>AIS Pinner >NMU >Returned >LATCC >Deceased
Atkinson	HE	Pat	1950s-1960s	ATCOIII	ATCOII WS	>LATCC >Deceased
Austin	DR	Dennis/Bunny	1960-61/1977-93	ATCOIII	ATCOI WM	>LATCC >Returned >Dep ChATCO >Retired 1993
Austin, Ms	G	Gemma	2001-	StATCO	ATCOII	C
Austin	ND	Norman	1962-70	ATCAIII	ATCAII	>CATC >ATCAI >ATCEU >ATSAIV >CATC >Retired 1993
Austwick	B	Barry	1980s	ATCO	ATCO	>EGPH
Avogadro, Miss	S	Sonia	2003-03	StATCO	StATCO	>LTCC
Ayling, Ms	N	Nicky	1996-96	ATCOII	ATCOII	>Resigned >EGHI
Baber	PD	Paul	1989-	ATSAII	ATSAIV	C
Badger, Miss	KMA	Kate	1977-80	ATCAII	ATCAII	>EGSS >Caetship >EGPF >ATCOII >EGHH >Resigned >EGHI (IAL) >ELLX >Is of Scilly >EGMC >Rejoined >EGAA >CATC >ATCOI >Head of Training Standards >SATCO >Head of Ops >CTC (Head of Trg, Improvements and Developments)
Bain	GK	Gordon	1974-75	ATCOIV	ATCOIV	>EGKK >LTCC
Bainbridge	N	Neil/Spike	1989-	ATCOII	ATCOI	>Head of Operations. C
Baker	KP	Kevin	1972-	ATCAII	ATSAIV	C
Baker	MJS	Mick	1969-73/83-85	ATCAIII	ATCOII	>Cadetship >EGPD >Returned >LATCC >LTCC >ATCOI
Baker	RN	Robin	1970s	ATCA	ATCA	>SRG (College Regulation & Licensing Policy)
Baksh	J	Joynal	1999-2000/2003-	ATCOII	ATCOII	>EGSS >Returned. C
Ballantyne	LA	Lou	1958-58	ATCAIII	ATCAIII	>EGKK >SATCC >AIS Pinner >ATCAI >Retired 1986. >AIS EGLL as ATSAII >Retired 1992
Bannister	G	Geoff	1976-	ATCAII	ATSAIV	C
Barber	IC	Ian	1970s	ATCA	ATCA	>

SURNAME	INIT	FIRST NAME/ KNOWN AS	DATES	START GRADE	END GRADE	COMMENTS
Barber	MJ	Mark	*1970s*	ATCA	ATCA	>EGKK >Resigned
Barber	SJ	Stuart	2001-	StATCO	ATCOII	C.
Barnes	AE	Al	1982-93	ATCOII	ATCOII	>LTCC
Barnes	SL	Steve	1983-96	ATCAII	ATSAII	>EGCC >ATSAIII >Deceased 2004
Barringer	JH	Jack	1947-52/61-61	ATCOI I/C	ATCOI I/C	>ATCEU (North side EGLL) >Returned >Deceased
Barrows	CJ	Chris	1963-64/66-73	ATCOC	ATCOII	>Cadetship >Returned >ATCOIII >ATCOII >LATCC >CATO6 >ATCOI >LATCC >Head of CATO5 >DD Airspace Policy >LATCC(GM) >Director Airport Services >Retired 1998
Barsh, Miss	KF	Kathy/Basher	1989-2002	ATCOII	ATCOII	>Mrs Nuttall >ATCOI >LTCC
Batchelor	CM	Colin	*1960s*	ATCA	ATCA	>ATCO >EGHH >EGKK >Retired >France >Deceased 1996
Bate	JP	Jeremy	1986-93	ATCOII	ATCOII	>LTCC
Bateman		Taffy	*1950s*	ATCOIII	ATCO	>SATCC >Retired >Deceased
Batham	SP	Stevie	1971-	ATCAIII	ATSAII	C
Baty	GGM	Geoffrey/Geoff	1961-61/63-68	ATCOIII	ATCOII	>EGUF >Returned >ATCOII >Resigned >EGNT >Dep SATCO >Ops Coordinator >Retired 1998
Baxter	ECI	Eric	*1960s*	ATCA	ATCAII	>LATCC >ATCAI >AIS EGLL >AIS Pinner >Retired >Deceased 2003
Baxter	JG	Graham	1969-73	ATCAIII	ATCAII	>ATCOIV >EGPE >EGPH >CATC >ATCOI (Head of Studies Aerodromes >Head of External Training)
Bayes	GH	Gordon	1952-60	ATCOIII	ATCOII	>SATCC >LATCC >ATCEU >Retired 1981
Beames, Miss	MA	Mavis/Mave	1980-80	ATCOIV	ATCOIV	>EGKK >ATCOII >EGDM >Mrs Hardy-Gillings >CATC
Beards	CP	Chris	1978-93	ATCAII	ATSAIV	>AIS EGLL
Beckwith	R	Roger	*1960s*	ATCA	ATCA	>EO?
Beddard	MS	Mike	2003-04	ATSAII	ATSAII	>ATC Ops >Resigned >ATCO >EGHD
Bedford, Miss	S	Sheila	*1950s*	ATCA	ATCA	>HQ Typing grade
Beechinor	EG	Eric/Beech	1960-66	ATCOIII	ATCOII DWS	>SATCC >LATCC >Eastern Radar (Watton) >HQ (Joint Airmiss Section) >Retired 1986 >Sussex Archaeological Society (Fishbourne Palace)
Belcher	F or J?	John	*1960s*	ATCAIII	ATCAII	>
Bell	D	Daniel/Harry Potter/Dan	2001-03	StATCO	ATCOII	>EGNM
Bell	GJ	Graham	1966-66	ATCAIII	ATCAIII	>Cadetship >EGHH >ATCOII >LATCC >Retired 2002
Belsey		Jack	*1940s*	ATCO	ATCO	>
Benifer	LA?	Ben	*1960s*	ATCO	ATCO	>
Bennett	GC	Geoff	*1940s*	ATCO	ATCO	>
Bennett	MB	Maurice	1976-81	ChATCO	ChOfficer	>Retired 1981
Bennett, KSG	R	Reg/Ben	1952-57	ATCOIII	ATCOII	>ATCEU >LATCC >HQ(CP3) >Retired 1980
Bennie	GA	Graeme	1985-85	ATCOII	ATCOII	>EGBB >EGPF >ScATCC >EGPH >Resigned >IAL >West Freugh >EGNV
Berriman	DG	Dennis	1964-75	ATCOIII	ATCOII	>LATCC >Retired 1998
Berry, Miss	ED	Liz?	*1980s*	ATCA	ATCA	>
Bethel	ME	Matthew	1989-93	ATCAII	ATSAII	>Cadetship >ATCOII >LTCC
Betley	S	Stuart	*1970s*	ATCAIII	ATCA	>
Bickley, Miss	TJ	Teresa	1969-73	ATCAIII	ATCAII	>Mrs Excell >Resigned
Billing	WG	Bill	1972-74	ATCOII	ATCOII	>EGSS > HQ(CR6) > HQ(REQ4) >ATCOI >Retired 1992. >ATC Planning Consultant until 2000
Birchall	JW	Jimmy	1962-69/74-83	ATCOI WS	Dep ChATCO	>Asst ChATCO >Joint Services Staff College >S.Div >Returned (Dep ChATCO) >Retired 1983
Bish	PJ	Pete	1971-93	ATCO C	ATCOII	>LTCC
Bisset	AG	Graham	1961-61/65-78	ATCAII	ATCOII	>SATCC >ATCOIV >EGHH >EGBB >Returned >LATCC >ATCOI >Retired 2000
Black	GR	Gary	1979-86	ATCAII	ATCAII	>Cadetship >LATCC >ATC(DP) >DSS
Blakebrough	B	Basil	1956-58	ATCAIII	ATCAII	>EGKK >AIS EGKK >ATCAI >FBU Manager >Retired 1992. Also RAFVR(T) 1961-89
Blanchard	P	Pete	*1970s*	ATCA	ATCA	>EGKK >Resigned
Blott	W	William/Bill/ Blotto/Smudge	1952-57	ATCOII	ATCOI RWS	>SATCC >HQ >LATCC >HQ >Retired 1981
Boland	JB	Jeff	1999-2005	StATCO	ATCOII	>CATC
Bolinbroke, Miss	P	Pat	*1950s*	ATCAII	ATCAII	>Resigned >Australia?

SURNAME	INIT	FIRST NAME/ KNOWN AS	DATES	START GRADE	END GRADE	COMMENTS
Bolwell	JA	John	1993-93	ATCOII	ATCOII	>LTCC
Bonnett	SM	Steve	2001-	ATSAII	ATSAII	C
Booth	FJ	Frank	1970s	ATCAI	ATCAI	>AIS EGLL >Retired >Deceased
Borcherds	PD	Pete	1950s	ATCOIII	ATCO	>Resigned to breed Boxer dogs
Botfield	TB	Terry	1960s	ATCOIII	ATCOII	>Retired >Probation Officer >Mayor of Royston
Bothington	J	Jim	1969-70	ATCAIII	ATCAIII	>Resigned
Bougourd	RJ	Roy	1960s	ATCA	ATCAII	>LATCC >ATCAI >Retired
Boulter	RG	Ron	1964-78/80-88	ATCOIII	ATCOII	>LATCC >Returned >Thames Radar >EGLC >Retired 1996 >EGHL >EGLW >EGMH>
Bowdler	KM	Keith	1978-90	ATCAII	ATSAIII	>ATCEU
Boyd	MC		1970s	ATCAIII	ATCA	>
Boyes	EA	Eric/Bill	1948-49	ATCOIII	ATCOIII	>ATCEU >LATCC >CATC >LATCC >ATCOII >ATCEU >CATC >HQ(CG4) >Retired 1976 >Inland Revenue >Abbey Life Assurance Co (until 1980)
Braber, Ms	PD	Pascale Den	2003-?	StATCO	StATCO	>EGSS
Bradley	N	Nigel	1999-2000	ATCO	ATCO	>
Brassfield	G	George	1940s	RC	RC	>Deceased 1948
Brazier	P	Paul	1990s	ATCO	ATCO	>EGPB
Brealey	KI	Ken	1957-66	ATCOIII	ATCOII	>LATCC >ATCOI >Joint Field HQ >EGKK (Ch Officer) >Retired 1987. Lives Spain
Brewer	PW	Pete	1965-65	ATCAIII	ATCAIII	>EGVP >ATCEU >Cadetship >LATCC >ATCOI >LACC >Retired 2004
Bridge, Mrs	ME	Marilyn	1991-96	ATCOII	ATCOII	>Resigned >Spain >LSGG >LSZH
Bridgewater	C	Chris	1998-98	StATCO	StATCO	>EGLC >EGKK
Bright	AG	Andy	1979-90	ATCAII	ATCAII	>Cadetship >EGKK >ATCOII
Brighton	SJ	Stu	1969-71	ATCAIII	ATCAII	>Cadetship >LATCC >ATCOII >NERC Project >LATCC >LACC
Brindley	DGC	Darrell	1990-2004	ATCOII	ATCOII	>LTCC
Brisley, Miss	PS	Paula	1989-94	ATCAII	ATCAII	>Cadetship >LTCC >EGSS
Broadmore	WJ	Bill	1956-64	ATCOIII	ATCOII WS	>SATCC >LATCC >ATCOI >Retired 1983
Broderick	DJ	Dave	1980-93	ATCOIII	ATCOII	>LTCC >Retired 2004
Brooks	J	John	1970s	ATCO	ATCO	>EGCC >West Freugh?
Brown	BG	Bernard/Bernie	1952-56	ATCOIII	ATCOII	>SATCC >HQ >CATC >ATCOI >LATCC >Retired 1976 >Own business & other aviation interests
Brown	KV	Ken	1947-51?/1970s	ATCOIII	ATCOI WS	>?>Returned>Retired >Deceased 1988?
Brown	P	Pete	1950s	ATCA	ATCA	>EGSS(CAFU)
Brown	PG	Pete	1960s	ATCO	ATCO	>Australia
Browne, Miss	S	Simone	1994-95	ATCOII	ATCOII	>EGKK >Mrs Simpson >LTCC
Bruce, Miss	W	Wendy	1996-2004	ATSAII	ATSAII	>Mrs Turner >Resigned >EGHI
Bruce-Smith	PR	Pete/PBS	1959-70	ATCOIII	ATCOII	>LATCC >EGKK (WM) >Retired 1978
Bryan	WG	Glenn	1989-89	ATCOII	ATCOII	>LATCC >LACC
Buck	D	Dave	1968-69	ATCOC	ATCO	>Resigned >IAL
Buckingham	BA	Brian	1970s	ATCAII	ATCAI	>ATC Records >Deceased
Buckingham	D	Dave	2003-	ATSAII	ATSAII	>ATC Ops. C
Budd	AJ	Arthur/Art	1972-84/88-93	ATCO C	ATCOII	>CATC >Returned >LTCC >Retired 2005
Budgen	RE	Roger	1965-66/84-85/92-2001	ATCAIII	GM	>Cadetship >LATCC >ATCOII >CATO >Returned (ATCOI WM) >EGPK (GM) >DD Airport Services >Returned (GM) >Head of Customer and External Affairs
Bull, Miss	JA	Jenny	1967-72	ATCAIII	ATCAII	>Resigned >Mrs Prentice >PanAm >Govt Social Survey >Office of National Statistics
Bullock	GR	Geoff	1953-68/1972-85	ATCOIII	ATCOII	>Saudi Arabia >Returned >ATC Info Officer >Retired 1985
Bulstrode	RF	Frank/The Bull	1952-56	ATCOI I/C	ATCOI I/C	>CATC (Superintendent) >Retired >Deceased
Bunn	ND	Norman	1981-93	ATCOI	ATCOI WM	>Retired 1993 >Deceased 1997
Burgess	PL	Pete	1969-81	ATCAIII	ATSAII	>AIS EGLL >ATSAIV
Burlyn	ML	Mike	1969-72	ATCOIV	ATCOII	>Resigned >EGHI >OOMS >EGPW >EGGW >EGKK (& part time EGHR) >EGDM >SERCO Germany >IAL Bailbrook >EGHI >EGGW (Unit Trg Officer) >Also CHIRP Management Board & Past Editor GATCO Magazine 'Transmit'

The Tower Cricket Team, circa 1949.
L to R rear: Tim Rhys-Davies, Bill Boyes, Jock Frazier, Bob Waud, John Shuckburgh.
L to R front: Frank Butler, Bob Gregory, Charlie Fearn, Bob Cook, Dicky Manly, unknown. (via Bob Waud)

SURNAME	INIT	FIRST NAME/ KNOWN AS	DATES	START GRADE	END GRADE	COMMENTS
Bush, Mrs	AK	Ann	1965-67	ATCAIII	ATCAII	>Resigned >McAlpine Helicopters >Skyline Helicopters >Alan Mann Helicopters >CofE Ordained Minister >Chaplain Reading Prison > Lives Canada
Bush	DE	Doug	1966-87/90-92	ATCOC	Man ATC	>EGPH(GM) >Returned (Man ATC) >EGKK (GM) >Retired 2001 >South Africa (ATNS)
Bush	GL	Gordon	1964-66	ATCAIII	ATCAII	>Resigned >British Eagle >EGTK (StATCO) >Air Canada >Virgin Atlantic > Lives Canada
Butler	HM	Frank	1946-61+	RC	ATCAII	>SATCC >Deceased
Butler	KS	Kevin	2002-	ATSAII	ATSAII	C
Byne	J	John	1968-70?	ATCA	ATCA	>Resigned
Byrne	SG		1960s	ATCOIII	ATCO	>
Caddick	A	Andrew	1970-70	ATCAIII	ATCAIII	>Resigned
Caddington, Miss	A	Ann	1971-80/81-?	ATCAIII	ATCOII	>Resigned (Nurse) >Mrs Gardner >ATCOIV >EGFF >Returned >ATCOII >Mrs Quinton >Resigned >EGGD
Caira	JA	Joe	1956-60	ATCAII	ATCAII	>ATCOIII >EGBB >EGCC >EGDM >ATCOII >Retired 1990 >SATCO Netheravon (Airwork Ltd) until 1994
Callier	IM	Ian	1973-2002	ATCOIV	ATCOII	>Retired 2002
Campbell	GM	Malcolm	1960s	ATCA	ATCA	>LATCC >Deceased
Campbell	MJ	John	1977-87	ATCOC	ATCOII	>Resigned >Radio Broadcaster County Sound >Ocean Sound and ATCO EGTD >EGHH (WS) >EGNT >IAL Bailbrook >CATC
Campbell	PG	Graham	1969-75	ATCOIII	ATCOII	>CATO6 >CATO1 >ATCOI >LATCC >Retired 2001
Cant	AG	Tony	1956-63	ATCAIII	ATCAII	>Resigned 1963 >Runs own carpet & flooring shop, Slough
Cant	JR	John	1966-67/70-87	ATCAIII	ATCOII	>Cadetship >Returned >Resigned >Gama Aviation (Pilot BE200) >Oracle Aviation (Pilot) >DanAir (Pilot B737) >BA (Capt. B737) >Gama Aviation (Capt BBJ)
Capper	AJ	Al	1980s	ATCOII	ATCOII	>EGKK >EGGP
Card	AM	Alan	1963-76	ATCOIII	ATCOII	> LATCC >Retired 1993
Carder	SH	Sid	1960s	ATCO	ATCOII	>HQ >Retired >Deceased 1996

SURNAME	INIT	FIRST NAME/ KNOWN AS	DATES	START GRADE	END GRADE	COMMENTS
Carney	DJ	Dave	1966-84	ATCOC	ATCOII	>EGBB (WM) >Retired >ATCOIII NERC part time >Resigned >ATC Instructor
Carnie	T	Tom	1960s	ATCAII	ATCA	>Resigned >AEA
Carruthers	JR	Jack	1960s	ATCOII	Dep ChATCO	>Retired >Deceased
Carson	J	Jon	1989-	ATSAII	ATSAII	C
Carter	A	Alan/Al	1968-93	ATCO C	ATCOII	>LTCC >Retired 2002 >EGTB >Part time EGHL
Carter	J	John	1960s	ATCO	ATCO	>New Zealand
Carter	PNQ	Pete	1983-92	ATCOII	ATCOII	>Retired
Carter	RW	Roger	1979-80	ATCOII	ATCOII	>Retired 1980
Caush, Mrs	AF	Anna	1966-66	ATCOIII	ATCOIII	>Resigned 1966 >Shipbroking1980 >Retired 1995
Caush	DS	David/Dave	1975-80/98-99	ATCOII	ATCOI	>EGPD >CATO5 >Airport Services HQ >EGPD >ATCOI Airports HQ>Returned >EGLL Ops >Retired 1999
Chadwick	FL	Frederick/Chad	1950s	ATCO	ATCO	>
Challenger, Ms	LD	Lisa	2002	StATCO	ATCOII	C
Chambers	GL	George	1953-58	ATCOII	ATCOII	>SATCC >ATCEU (Heathrow) >ATCEU (Hurn) >ATCOI >Retired 1983
Chambers	PJ	Peter	1958-58	ATCA	ATCAII	>EGKK>
Chandler	K	Ken	1950s	ATCOIII	ATCO	>Deceased 1954
Channing	T	Trevor	1955-65+	ATCAII	ATCAI	>LATCC >Deceased
Chapman	BAG	Brandon	1976-90	ATCOC	ATCOII	>ATCOI >EGSS (Man ATC >GM) >Head of Operational Strategy & Performance >Manager Airport Services >Director Airport Services
Charles, Ms	S	Sharron	2004-	ATSAII	ATSAII	C
Chaudhary	M	Munawar	1997-	ATCOII	ATCOI+ WM	C
Chennell	LA	Lionel	1940s	ATCOIII	ATCO	>CATC
Cheyne	RJDL	Bob	1950s	ATCO	ATCO	>Cyprus >Eurocontrol >Deceased
Chiddy	PJ	Pete	1980s	ATCOII	ATCOII	>Resigned >EGBE >EGPK >North Sea Oil Rigs
Chillas	BF	Barry	1960s	ATCO	ATCO	>EGKK >LATCC (D/DP ATS) >Retired
Chisholm, Mrs	JM	Judith	1972-78	ATCOC	ATCOII	>Resigned >De Beers (Pilot HS125) > Flew solo round world C210 1980 > Deceased 1988
Clark	E	Elaine	1960s	ATCA	ATCA	>BCAL (Flight Attendant)
Clark, Mrs	J	Jenny	1960s	ATCA	ATCA	>
Clark	PJ	Peter/Pete	1978-86	ATCAIII	ATCAII	>Resigned >United Biscuits (Pilot Be200/300) >Brymon (Pilot Dash7) >BA (Pilot B737 >B747-400)
Clarke	L	Leigh	1999-2000	StATCO	StATCO	>EGKK >LTCC
Clarke	MA	Matt	2004-	StATCO	StATCO	C
Clarke	RD	Roger	1991-2005	ATCOII	ATCOI	>Head of Training. >LTCC
Clarkson	GK	Graham	1977-93	ATCOII	ATCOII	>LTCC
Cleary	M	Mike	1971-94	ATCAI	ATSAIV	>Retired 1994 >Part time uniformed chauffeur
Cleminson	CW	Clem	195?-73	ATCAII	ATCAI	>Retired >Deceased
Cliffe	DCFH	Dennis	196?-73	ATCO	ATCOII	>LATCC >Resigned >IAL (OBBI >Ras al Kaimah) >EGPF >Resigned >Scatsta >
Clifford	TR	Terry	1969-73	ATCOIII	ATCOII	>LATCC >CATO >LATCC >LTCC >Retired 1999
Coates	GB	Geoff	1972-	ATCOC	ATCOII	>ATC Ops. C
Coffey	GC	Gary	1987-92	ATCOIV	ATCOII	>EGCC
Coffin	A	Alistair	1999-?	StATCO	StATCO	>EGUF
Colby	EE	Eric	1950s	ATCOIII	ATCO	>ScATCC (WS) >Retired >Deceased
Collier	MJ	John	1967-68	ATCAIII	ATCAII	>Cadetship >LATCC >Retired
Collins	DAC	Tony	1956-64	ATCOIII	ATCOII WS	>SATCC >S Div >LATCC >ATCOI >CATO >SATCO >LATCC >DD >Insp ATC >Dir Trg & Licensing >Retired 1987
Collins, Mrs	SA	Sheila	1977-90	ATCAII	ATSAII	>EGCC >Ms Appleby
Colter, Miss	DP	Pam	1953-63	Tracker	ATCAII	>Mrs Broadmore >Resigned 1963
Constantine	RA	Richard/Dicky	1956-64/67-81	ATCOIII	ATCOII	>SATCC >Returned >Retired 1981 >Deceased 2002
Conway	MJ	Michael/Mick	1955-66	ATCAIII	ATCAI	>ATCOIV >LATCC >ATCOII >Retired 1991
Cook	JO	Bob	1959-69/1970s	ATCOIII	ATCOII	>LATCC >EGSS (I/C FTU) >Returned >RRE Malvern >Retired 1992
Cook	RV	Bob	1946-81	RC	ATCAI	>Retired 1981 >Deceased 2004

SURNAME	INIT	FIRST NAME/ KNOWN AS	DATES	START GRADE	END GRADE	COMMENTS
Cooke	JJ	Jeremy/Jez	1981-2003	ATCOII	ATCOII	>EGBB
Cooke, Ms	P	Pamela/Pam	1965-67	ATCAIII	ATCAII	>Mrs Rogers >Resigned >Bank >Charitable Trust, London >Hewlett-Packard Ltd
Coomber	CM	Colin	1967-79	ATCOIII	ATCOII	>OACC >FMU >Retired 1996 >Deceased 2004
Coombs	JA	Jack	1960s	ATCOIII	ATCO	>LATCC >Retired >Deceased
Cooper	J	Jason	2003-	ATCOIII	ATCOII	C
Cooper	J	John/Duff	1960s	ATCOIII	ATCO	>LATCC >Retired
Cooper, Ms	N	Nicky	1987-99	ATCOIV	ATCOII	>Mrs Winstanley >Ms Cooper >ATC Ops 2 >EGUF (Man ATS) >CATC (Head of Ops >Delivery Manager)
Copinger	WP	Pat	1960s	ATCO	ATCOII WS	>LATCC >EGSS (I/C FTU) >CATC
Cordy	J	John	1960s	ATCO	ATCO	>EGDM? >New Zealand Tower Chief Wellington
Corline, Miss	VM	Val	1963-71	ATCAIII	ATCAII	>LATCC >Mrs Halloway >ATSAIV >Retired 2002
Corne	DR	David	2004-	ATSAII	ATSAII	C
Cosgrave	CA	Chris	1973-88	ATCOC	ATCOII	>Resigned >Oracle (Pilot C421/C500) >Gama Aviation (Pilot BE200/LR35/Hawker 1000/G4/G5)
Coterril	F	Frank	1960s	ATCOIV	ATCO	>Resigned >Decca Radar
Cotsell	J	John	1950s	ATCA	ATCA	>
Cottam	AD	Tony	1965-68	ATCAIV	ATCAII	>Cadetship (inc EGLL validation) >EGKK >ATCOII >LATCC >Tony Bridger >Retired 2002
Cotter	DW	Dave	2003-	StATCO	ATCOII	C
Coulter	CRH	Jim	1970-76	ATCOIV	ATCOII	>ScATCC >OACC >ATCOI WM
Covell	PL	Peter/Pete	1965-76	ATCOIV	ATCOIII	>LATCC >ATCOII >Ops3 (ATC (DP)) >Retired 1992
Cowell	RA	Bob	1984-95	ATCOII	ATCOII	>LTCC >Retired 1999
Cox	DJ	Doug	1973-75	ATCOII	ATCOII	>EGPF >EGMH (Kent Radar) >LATCC >Retired 1993 >South East Coast College of Air Training
Cox, Ms	HM	Hilary	1999-	ATSAII	ATSAII	C
Crabb	DM	Dennis	1980-83	ATCOII	ATCOII	>LATCC >EGAA >EGCC
Craddock	AG	Graham	1960s	ATCO	ATCOII WS	>LATCC >Retired >Deceased
Craig	HTM	Tom	1958-65	ATCOIII	ATCOII	>ScATCC >Retired >Deceased
Crampton	GC	Geoff	1960s	ATCAI	ATCAI	>AIS EGLL >Retired
Crampton	M	Mike	?	ATCA	ATCA	>
Crawford	NJ	Nick	1992-93	ATCOII	ATCOII	>LTCC
Cree, Ms	JM	Josephine/Jo	1955-66	ATCAII	ATCAII	>ATCEU >CATC >Retired 1986
Crizzle	DP	Des	1976-91	ATCAII	ATSAIV	>AIS EGLL
Croft	AH	Tony	1977-95	ATCOII	ATCOII RWM	>LTCC >Retired 2005
Croft, Mrs	G	Gillian	1980s	ATSA	ATSA	>NERC Training
Crosswell, Miss	RE	Rachel	1991-97	ATSAII	ATSAII	>LATCC >LACC
Crouch	DN	Des	1963-68	ATCOIII	ATCOII	>LATCC >ATCOI >Chief Examiner CAA House >Regional Insp S Div >LATCC >Retired 1998 >Deceased 2001
Crowley	KCA	Kevin	1992-2005	ATCOII	ATCOII	>Resigned >New Zealand
Culley	AB	Tony	1960s	ATCO	ATCO	>CATC
Culley	IJ	Ian	1969-81	ATCOIV	ATCOI	>LATCC >CCF Planning (PE Req 1) >LATCC (WM) >LACC(WM)>Retired 2005
Curtis	R	Robert/Bob	1971-75/77-80	ATCAIII	ATCOIV	>'Special Leave' in Yugoslavia 1973-74 >Cadetship >Returned >EGPF >EGSS >
Curtis-Nuthall	C	Chris?	1960s	ATCA	ATCAII	>
Dack	JRW	John	1952-53	ATCAIII	ATCAII	>School of ATC (Tracker Instructor) >ATCOIII >Ghana >EGKK >ATCOII >LATCC >CATC >ATCOI (Head of Area Studies >Deputy GM) >Retired 1990 >Part-time instructor to 1995
Dacombe-Bird	LWS	Bill	1960s	ATCOIII	ATCO	>
Dallison	EN	Eric	1947-82	RC	ATCAI	>Retired 1982
Dalton	T	Tommy	1940s	ATCO	ATCO	>EGJJ (ATCO I/C)
Daly	HJ	Harold	1950s	ATCO	ATCOII	>CATC >Retired
Daly, Mrs	II	Irene	1972-74	ATCAII	ATCAII	>Resigned >Thames Valley Police
Daly	R	Ron	1971-93	ATCOC	ATCOII	>ATCOI >LTCC >Retired 2004
D'Ambrosio, Miss	CF	Caroline	1970s	ATCOIII	ATCOIII	>EGPH (WM)
Daniel, Ms	H	Hazel	1996-2001	ATSAII	ATSAII	>AIS EGLL >ATSAIV
Darling	MK	Matthew	1992-93	ATCOIV	ATCOII	>LTCC

SURNAME	INIT	FIRST NAME/ KNOWN AS	DATES	START GRADE	END GRADE	COMMENTS
Darling	R	Roger	1975-90	ATCAII	ATSAIII	>LATCC >ATSAIV >LTCC >Retired 2002
Datta	B	Bikash	1970-90	ATCAIII	ATSAII	>Resigned 1990 >Pursuing interests in Bodybuilding, Fitness, Tai Chi and Medical research
Davey, Miss	E	Edna	1951-57	ATCA	ATCAII	>Mrs Sweeting >Resigned 1957 >Lives Canada
Davey, Miss	JA	Jenny	1973-83	ATCAIII	ATCAII	>Mrs Ward >ATCEU >Resigned >Electronics Assembly >Brittany Ferries >Didcot Girls School >Tesco >Bartley Junior School >Redbridge School >Rejoined>LACC (ACPO)
Davidson	A	Alastair/Al	1993-97/98-2001/2003-	ATCOII	ATCOII	>Resigned >Spain >Returned >Resigned >EGBJ >Returned. C
Davidson	PFD	Pete	1954-69	RC	ATCAI	>ATCEU >Retired 1985
Davies	GR	Gordon	1960s	ATCOIII	ATCO	>S.Div >Returned >LATCC >Retired >Geests (bananas) Cardiff
Davies	ME	Mike	1967-97	ATCAI	ATSAIV	>AIS EGLL >Retired 2000
Davies	RA	Robert/Rob	1979-84	ATCAII	ATCAII	>Cadetship >EGPB >ATCOII >EGCC >ATCOI
Davis	ARJ	Jack	1950s-1960s	ATCOIII	ATCOIII	>LATCC >ATCOII >EGHH >EGHI?
Davis, MBE	JM	John	1965-73	ATCOIV	ATCOII	>LATCC >ATCOI >EGKK (WM) >Retired 1997
Davis, Ms	K	Kirsten	1999-	StATCO	ATCOII	C
Davis	WH	Bill?	1950s	ATCAI	ATCAI	>Resigned >Shop in Windsor >Deceased
Dawe	RA	Raymond/Dickie	1955-59/19??-76	ATCOII	ATCOI WS	>Cyprus Government (To set up Eastern Med ATC) >LATCC >ATCOI >Returned (WS) >ATC Ops >Retired 1976
Dawkins, Miss	AE	Ann	1966-73	ATCAIII	ATCAII	>Mrs Harris >Resigned
Dawson	REJ	Dick/Cowboy	1969-83/87-2002	ATCO C	ATCOII	>CATC >Returned >Retired 2002
Day	KD	Kevin	1987-2000/2001-01	ATCOII	ATCOII	>LATCC >Returned >LATCC >LACC
Dean	HB	Brian/Dixie	1956-63	ATCAIII	ATCAII	>ATCOIV >Mersey Radar (Hack Green) >PATCRU >CATC >ATCEU >CATC >Retired 1992 >Short period teaching English to Russian & Ukrainian ATCOs
Deane	J	John/Dixie	1964-76	ATCOIV	ATCOII	>LATCC >ATCOI >Retired 1997
Denchfield	AM	Tony	1977-86	ATCOC	ATCOII	>EGSS >ATCOI >EGKK (WM)
Dennis	JJ	Jeff	1980s	ATCO	ATCO	>EGFF >SRG (Regional Manager ATS Safety Regulation)
Dibdin	GJ	John/Jock/ Dibbers	1958-63	ATCOIII	ATCOIII	>EGVP >LATCC >ATCOII >Retired 1986
Dillon	J	Justin	2002-	StATCO	ATCOII	C
Dingle	SWH	Stuart	1994-2000	ATSAII	ATSAIV	>CACC
Dixon	GT	Gary	2004-	StATCO	ATCOII	C
Dixon	J	John	1960s	ATCO	ATCO	>
Dixon	KN	Keith	1958-60	ATCOIII	ATCOII	>Hong Kong >SATCC >Deceased
Dixon	PJ	Pete	1970s	ATCA	ATCA	>EGKK
Dobison	C	Chris	2003-04	StATCO	StATCO	>LTCC >Resigned >EGNV
Docwra	DA	Dan	1967-69	ATCA	ATCA	>Cadetship >Resigned >BAA EGPH >HM Immigration
Doggett	GW	Gordon	1990-92	GM	GM	>LATCC(GM) >LACC(GM) >Retired 2002
Dolan	A	Adrian	2001-	StATCO	ATCOII	C
Dominic	SJ	Steve	1982-93	ATCOIV	ATCOII	>LTCC
Doolin	J	Jonathan/Jon	2000-	ATSAII	ATSAII	C
Downey	TR	Terence	1950s	Tracker	ATCA	>
Dowse, Ms	S	Sue	2001-	ATSAII	ATSAII	C
Doyle	MJ	Mike	1988-	ATCOII	ATCOI+ WM	C
Doyle	P		1980s	ATSA	ATSA	>
Doyle	S	Simon	1990-91	ATSA	ATSA	>Resigned >Returned to stockbroking!
Drapper	J	John	1960-61	ATCAIII	ATCAIII	>SATCC >ATCOIV >LATCC >ATCOII >CATC >EGMH >LATCC >Retired
Dryden	MAP	Michael/Mick	1970-81	ATCOIV	ATCOII	>Resigned >EGJJ (WM) >Retired 2004
Dugan	BE	Brian/Dougal	1970-80	ATCAIII	ATCAII	>AIS Pinner >ATCAI >ATSAIV >AIS EGLL
Dunn	J	Jem	2002-04	ATOM	ATOM	Manager Safety & Performance >EGLC(GM)
Dunn	L	Lawrie	1980-88	ATCOI	ATCOI WS	>Head CG2 >Retired 1994
Durward	AM	Sandy	1960s	ATCO	ATCO	>LATCC >EGKK >Retired
Dyer	G	George	1968-75	ATCOIV	ATCOII	>ScATCC >ATCOI WM >Retired 2001
Dyer, Ms	M	Maggie	1950s	Tracker	ATCA	>
Dyer	MP	Mick	1983-	ATCAI	ATSAIV	C
Ebert	FN	Fred	1966-75+	ATCAII	ATCAII	>NMU >Retired >Deceased 1996

Royal Visit No 1: Bill Woodruff, HRH Duke of Kent, Pete Covell, Basil Turner (Chief Officer) and Phil Griffith 19.10.71. (via Phil Griffith)

SURNAME	INIT	FIRST NAME/ KNOWN AS	DATES	START GRADE	END GRADE	COMMENTS
Eckett	RD	Robert	1995-96	ATCOII	ATCOII	>EGBB >Thames Radar (ATC Ops) >LTCC
Ede, Miss	ME	Mary	1951-58	ATCAIII	ATCAII	>Mrs Tapsall >Resigned 1958 >School teacher later.
Edney, Ms	V	Vivien	1960s	ATCAIII	ATCA	>Scotland?
Edwards	MG	Mike	1982-88/93-93	ATCOII	ATCOI	>ATCOI >CATC >LATCC >Returned >LTCC >ATC Investigations LATCC >ATC Investigations LACC
Edwards	BD	Brian	1967-69?	ATCAIV	ATCAIII	>Cadetship >EGCC >LATCC >EGCC >Retired
Eggeling. Mrs	AC	Alice/Ali	2004-	ATSAIV	ATSAIV	C
Eldred	IB	Ian	1980s	ATCOC	ATCO	>EGSS >ATCA
Elliott	EW	Ted	1947-47/55-60	ATCOIII	ATCOII	>OAC Gloucester >ATCC Uxbridge >EGWU >Returned >SATCC >LATCC >ATCOI >Development of SSR >Retired 1976
Elliott, Miss	HL	Helen	1972-78/1984-86	ATCAIII	ATCOII	>Cadetship >EGAA >Mrs Lees >Returned >EGKK >LTCC >Mrs Rhind
Elliott	WAE	Bill	1960s	ATCAII	ATCAII	>Retired
Ellis	WJ	John	1988-93	ATCOII	ATCOII	>LTCC >ATCOI >LACC (Flow Control Manager)
Ellison	JA	John	1960s	ATCOII	ATCO	>Cayman Is (DCA)
Elves, Ms	M	Maggie	1960s	ATCA	ATCA	>
Endersby	CG	George	1940s	ATCOIII	ATCO	>HQ >West Freugh >Deceased
Ennis	GC	George	1967-77/87-90	ATCOIV	Man ATC	>CATO >LATCC >ATCOI >EGBB (Chief Officer) >Returned (Man ATC) >ATO (Head of ATM Policy & Performance) >Retired 2003
Erl	CEG	Clive	1956-62	ATCOIII	ATCOII WS	>LATCC >ATCOI >Retired 1984
Evans, Miss	LA	Lillian	1960s	ATCO C	ATCO	>Mrs Pring >EGPB
Everest	RH	Robert/Bob	1967-71	ATCAIII	ATCAII	>Resigned >Air Canada >Saudia >TWA >Emirates
Every	AF	Fred	1950s	ATCOII	ATCOII	>LATCC >ATCOI >ScATCC >HQ >Retired >Deceased 2003
Excell	RW	Ron	1969-73	ATCAIII	ATCAII	>Resigned >ATCO >OMDB >EGTK >IAL Bailbrook >EGHH >IAL Head Office >SITA (EU Air/Ground Comms Manager)
Fallows	TM	Tony	1983-92	ATCAII	ATSAIV	>LATCC >LACC(FISO)
Farnell	E	Eddie	1950s	ATCO	ATCO	>
Fearn	CWJ	Charlie	1940s	ATCOIII	ATCO	>HQ >Retired >Deceased
Feltham	PJ	Paul	1970s/81-83?	ATCA	ATCO	>Cadetship >Returned >EGBB
Fennell, MBE	RA	Paddy	1960s	ATCAII	ATCAI	>Retired

SURNAME	INIT	FIRST NAME/ KNOWN AS	DATES	START GRADE	END GRADE	COMMENTS
Ferguson	DW	Doug	1974-84	ATCAI	ATCAI	>AIS Pinner >AIS EGLL >Deceased 2003
Ferguson, Miss	SRCF	Sharon	1973-90	ATCAIII	ATSAIII	>Mrs Louden >Mrs Thorpe >LTCC >ATSAIV >LATCC >Retired 2002
Ferguson	WJ	Bill	1974-92	ATCOIV	ATCOI RWM	>LATCC >LACC
Fielder	AD	Andy	1989-	ATSAII	ATSAII	C
Filmer, Ms		Teddy	1950s	ATCA	ATCA	>Resigned
Finch	R		1969-70	ATCAIII	ATCAIII	>Resigned
Findlay, Mrs	ES	Elaine	1982-2002	ATCAII	ATSAIV	>Ms Blake >Resigned
Finlay	IMS	Ian	1968-76	ATCOIV	ATCOII	>LATCC >ATCOI >FMU (Setting up >Flow Manager > Hd Ops >Man ATFMD >Traffic Manager) >LACC (Flow Control Manager)
Fisher	EHG		1970s	ATCAII	ATCA	>Cadetship
Fisher, Miss	AL	Alison	1970s	ATCAIII	ATCAII	>
Fishpool	CL	Colin	1981-88	ATCAII	ATSAII	>Loganair (Pilot Twin Otters) >British Regional Airlines >British Airways CitiExpress (Pilot ATP)
Fitch	CJ	Chris	1964-65	ATCOC	ATCOC	>Resigned >IAL(Rhodesia) >OBBI(WM) >EGPD >EGGP(GM) >OBBI (Advisor to Head of Aviation) >Retired
Fitch	CM	Chris	1950s	ATCA	ATCA	>Cadetship >Resigned
Fitch	WWD	Walter/Wally	1956-67	ATCAIII	ATCAI	>EGSS >EGKK >AIS Pinner >Retired 1982. Also PPL 1963 >CPL >Own business Instrument Flight Training until 2003.
Fitzwilliam	JT	Jeremy/Jerry	1966-68	ATCOIV	ATCOIV	>EGKK >RAE Llanbedr/EGUF >EGPF >Retired 1996
Fleming	AJ	Alec	1984-	ATCOII	ATCOII	C
Flood, Miss	MJ	Mel	2000-	StATCO	ATCOII	>Mrs Gates >ATC Ops. C
Flower	AG	Tony	1990-99	ATSAII	ATSAII	>ATCO > EGKA >EGJA
Flynn	PS	Pat	1975-98	ATCOC	ATCOII	>ATC Ops >Special Projects >LTCC
Foley	A	Alan/Al	1994-94	ATCOII	ATCOII	>EGKK
Foley	GA	Grant	1983-88	ATCAIII	ATSAII	>Resigned >BT
Foley, Miss	SE	Sue	1978-83	ATCAII	ATCAII	>Mrs Field >Trg Office >Cadetship >ATCOII >EGKK >LATCC >LTCC
Ford	AH	Adrian	1956-57	ATCAII	RC	>ATCOIII >EGLK >Croydon >SATCC >LATCC >ATCOII >CATO6 >ATCOI >ScATCC (WM) >OACC(ACS) >Resigned 1991 >IAL/SERCO Instructor >Retired 1996
Ford	RA	Reg	1966-68	ATCAIII	ATCAII	>LATCC >Cadetship >EGUF >LATCC (DP SADO(F)) >EGDM >EGUF >CATC. Also JP for Dorset >Retired 2004
Forster	I	Ian	1995-	ATSAII	ATSAIV	C
Forster	SW	Steve	1980-91/92-99	ATCOII	ATCOII	>CATC >Returned >LTCC >ATCOI
Foster	TE	Terry	1960s	ATCOIII	ATCO	>
Foster	N	Norman	1960s	ATCA	ATCA	>
Foster, Miss	PJ	Petra	1992-94	ATCOII	ATCOII	>EGPD
Fotheringham	G	George	1970s	ATCAI	ATCA	>AIS Pinner >Retired
Foulkes	GP	Graham	1978-86/88-93	ATCAII	ATCOII	>Cadetship >Returned >LTCC
Fowler	K	Ken	1989-97	ATCOII	ATCOII	>CATC >LACC >ATCOI
Fox	KW	Ken	1950s	RC	ATCAII	>SATCC
Fox	QJ	Quillon/Q	1991-92	ATCOII	ATCOII	>EGSS >EGPD >LACC >EGSS
Foyston	AL	Andrew/Andy	1992-93	ATCOII	ATCOII	>Resigned >EGBE >LXGB >EGTD >EGUF
Frajzek	M		1998-98	ATCO	ATCO	>ATSA >Resigned >EGBE
Francis	AE	Ted	1960s	ATCOIII	ATCOII	>LATCC >CATC >Retired
Francis	DE	Derek	1967-73	ATCOIV	ATCOIII	>EGBB >ATCOII >CATC >Thames Radar >LFMU >Retired 1996
Franklin		John	1960s	ATCAIII	ATCAII	>LATCC
Frazier		Jock	1940s	ATCO	ATCO	>
Freakes, Miss	WG	Winnie	1953-60	ATCAIII	ATCAII	>Mrs O'Connell >Resigned 1960
Freedman, Miss	LS	Lesley	1980s	ATCAIII	ATCAII	>Resigned >Kibbutz in Israel >Mrs Micheali
Freeman	AL	Arnie	1955-55/1958-66	ATCAIII	ATCOII	>ATCOIV >Returned >LATCC >Retired 2002
Freeman, Miss	BM	Brenda	1971-72	ATCOIV	ATCOIV	>EGKK >ATCOII >Mrs Evans >ATCOI Head of Ops & Trg >WM >Retired
Freeman, Miss	JE	Jane	1995-99	ATSAII	ATSAII	>Resigned
Friendship	AHB	Basil	1960s	ATCOIII	ATCOII	>HQ >EGSS >Retired 1980? >Deceased 2001
Frith	JE	Jack	1964-72	ATCOIII	ATCOII	>LATCC >ATCOI >Retired 1988 >Lives France
Frost	FW	Freddie	1958-58	ATCOIII	ATCOIII	>EGHI >EGHH >SATCC >LATCC >Retired 1993 >EGHL

SURNAME	INIT	FIRST NAME/ KNOWN AS	DATES	START GRADE	END GRADE	COMMENTS
Fullard	N	Nigel	2001-	ATSAII	ATSAII	C
Gale	TE	Terry	1969-70/83-84	ATCOC	ATCOII	>EGSS >LATCC >Returned >LATCC >ATCOI >LTCC
Gallagher	PL	Pat	1993-93	ATCOII	ATCOII	>LTCC >Retired 2004
Gallop	RJW	Dick	1988-89	ATCOII	ATCOII	>Thames Radar >LTCC >Retired 2004
Gardiner	R	Richard	1960s	ATCA	ATCA	>Cadetship
Gardner	PG	Paul	1970s	ATCAIII	ATCAII	>Resigned >BMA
Garratt	P	Paul	1971-78	ATCAIII	ATCAII	>Resigned >BAA
Garrett	AD	Andy	1992-93	ATCOII	ATCOII	>LTCC >ATCOI. Also pilot Gama Aviation (BE200/LR45)
Gatfield	RA	Rob/Blobby	1981-	ATCAII	ATSAII	C
Gell	JPC	Clive	1974-83	ATCOIV	ATCOII	>CATOI >LATCC >LTCC >ATCOI >LATCC >LACC
George	CE	Eric	1970-80	ATCAI	ATSAI	>ScATCC >Head of ATSA Trg >Sim Support Manager >Retired
George	CH	Clive	1967-2004	ATCAIII	ATSAII	>Retired 2004
Gibbons, Miss	MI	Mary/Wendy	1952-81	TCII	ATCAII	>Retired 1981 >Deceased 1997
Gibson, Miss	K	Kay	1950s	ATCAII	ATCAII	>Mrs Frost >Mrs Buckingham >Retired
Gilbert	JB	John	1969-72	ATCOIV	ATCOII	>EGCC >Retired 2003 >MACC Part-time
Gilchrist	K	Keith/Grommit	1990-	ATSAII	ATSAIV	C
Giles	DED	David	1992-94	ATCOII	ATCOII	>EGPD
Gilhespy	JM	Jonathan	2004-	ATSAIV	ATSAIV	C
Girdler, Miss	TL	Tina	1984-91	ATCAII	ATSAII	>AIS EGLL >ATSAIV >Mrs Smith >Resigned 1997
Gleave	JH	John	1970s-99?	ATCAI	ATSAIV	>AIS EGLL >Retired 2004
Gleaves	DA	Dave	1967-69	ATCA	ATCA	>Cadetship >EGSS >Resigned >Abbey National >Wine company
Glynn	RHJ	Rohan	1990-	ATCOII	ATCOI+ WM	C
Goddard	R	Roger/Tiny Tim	1991-98	ATCOII	ATCOII	>Resigned >BMA (Pilot F70/F100) >bmibaby (Pilot B737)
Godden	DA	Dave	1970s	ATCA	ATSA	>ATCEU
Golds	RE	Ron	1956-65	ATCAII	ATCAI	>AIS EGLL >EGSS (CAFU Ops Officer) >Retired 1988
Goldstraw	NH		1970s	ATCAII	ATCA	>
Goodman	R	Ron	1960s	ATCO	ATCO	>EGGD
Goodman	SJ	Steve	1974-74	ATCAII	ATCAII	>Cadetship >EGPH >OACC >ATCOI WM
Goodyear	JB	Johnny	1960s	ATCOII	ATCO	>LATCC >ATC(DP) >Deceased
Gorse, Miss	IM	Irene	1971-73	ATCAIII	ATCAII	>Resigned >Britannia Airways (Flight Attendant) >Mrs Baxter >Rejoined >ATCEU(ACPO)
Gorst	DI	David/Dave	1963-71	ATCOIII	ATCOII	>LATCC >ATCOI >Head Ops3 >ATCEU (Head ASA Group) >Retired 1993
Gosling, Miss	MJ	Jean	1967-71	ATCAIII	ATCAII	>Resigned >Mrs Townsend >Civil Service >Local Government Officer
Goulding, Miss	YDF	Yvonne/Vonne	1960s	ATCAIII	ATCAII	>Mrs Chandler >Resigned
Graham	LE	Len	1940s	ATCOIII	ATCO	>
Granata	MA	Marco/Marc	1986-88	ATCAII	ATCAII	>MACC >ATSAIV
Granger	M	Mark	1990-94	ATSAII	ATSAII	>LATCC>
Granger, Ms	L	Linda	1982-84	ATCOII	ATCOII	>Resigned >EGCD (SATCO >Airfield Manager) >EGMH
Grant	T	Tommy	1960s	ATCO	ATCO	>Retired
Graves	DA	Dave	1966-78?	ATCO	ATCOII	>LATCC >Resigned >IAL Bailbrook >Retired >Wrote book "United Kingdom Air Traffic Control: A Layman's Guide" > Deceased
Gray, Miss	D		1950s	ATCA	ATCA	>Resigned
Gray	GP	Gary/Gary Glitter	1973-80	ATCAIII	ATCAII	>Cadetship >LATCC >LTCC
Gray	KAT	Ken	1960s	ATCA	ATCA	>ATCO >LATCC >ATCOI >Retired 1997
Green OBE	EGH	Egerton/Edge	1962-68/70-72	ATCOIII	ATCOII	>Tech Advisor to Ghana Govt >Returned >Ops Section >LATCC >ATCOI >Head CATO5/1/2 >Dir ATC Licensing (DD Grade) >Dir ATS Standards (Dir Grade) >Retired 1992 >ATC Consultant
Green, Miss	ES	Sue	1970s	ATCA	ATCA	>Lindholme >Resigned >Probation Service
Green, Miss	JM	Jackie	1986-	ATSAII	ATSAII	>Mrs Mitchell >Mrs Jackson. C
Green	KJ	Keith	1974-76	ATCAIII	ATCAII	>Cadetship >LATCC >ATCOI >LACC
Green	MR	Mel	1970s	ATCAII	ATCA	>
Green	SJ	Steve	1994-94	ATCOII	ATCOII	>LTCC
Greenfield	C	Craig	1995-	ATCOII	ATCOI+ WM	C
Gregory, Ms	A	Anna	1970s	ATCAII	ATCAII	>Resigned

SURNAME	INIT	FIRST NAME/ KNOWN AS	DATES	START GRADE	END GRADE	COMMENTS
Gregory	EJ	John/Eddie the Orbit	1980-84	ATCOII	ATCOII	>CATO >LATCC >ATCOI >LACC (WM)
Gregory	RW	Bob	1948-53	ATCOIII	ATCOIII	>SATCC >ATC Ghana >SATCC >RRE Malvern >CATC >HQ >CATC >Retired 1980 >Deceased 2005
Gribble	AC	Andrew/Andy	1982-83	ATCOII	ATCOII	>EGPD >ScATCC
Griffin	CE		1960s	ATCOIII	ATCO	>
Griffith	PS	Phil	1970-74	ATCOIV	ATCOII	>Examination Branch >LATCC >Inspector of ATC >ATCOI >Chief ATC Examiner >Asst Dir of I & L >SRG (Head ATC Regulation) >Head of ATSSD >Head of Aerodrome and ATSSD >Retired 2003
Griffiths	JW	John	1950s	ATCO	ATCO	>HQ >LATCC
Griffiths	RDM	Dick	1981-2000	ATCAIII	ATSAIV	>AIS EGLL
Groholski, Ms	S	Sue	1970s	ATCA	ATCA	>
Guilbride	SF	Steve	1970s	ATCAIII	ATCAII	>Canada ?
Gunston	MJ	Mike	1969-70/82-87	ATCAIII	ATCOII	>Cadetship >EGPF >EGPB >Returned >LATCC >LTCC
Haddock	S	Stanley/Stan	1965-66	ATCOIV	ATCOIV	>EGKK >Resigned >EGNM (WS) >Retired 2002
Hadfield	DM	David/Birdy	1990s	ATSAII	ATSAII	>Resigned >Australia
Haines	ACC	Alan/Al	1972-85/88-01	ATCOC	ATCOI WM	>ATC Ops >LATCC >ATCOI >Returned >Head ATC Ops & Trg >WM >LTCC
Haines, Mrs	JI	Jane	1973-74	ATCAII	ATCAII	>Resigned >CAA Surveys >Scandinavian Airline System
Hall	AJ	Tony	1974-80	ATCAI	ATCAI	>EGCC >ATSAIII >ATSAIV
Hall	G	Gary	2002-?	StATCO	StATCO	>
Hall, Miss	MM	May	1950s	ATCA	ATCA	>Retired
Hall	PV	Peter	1959-68	ATCOIII	ATCOII	>LATCC >Retired 1983> Lives USA
Hall	SWC	Steve	1976-78	ATCOIV	ATCOIV	>EGKK >ATCOII >HQ(CAP2)>LATCC >ATCOI >LACC (ATC Planning and Development)
Hall, Miss	VE	Rona	1974-76?	ATCAIII	ATCAII	>Resigned
Halliday, Miss	JH	Joan	1970s	ATCAII	ATSA	>ATSAIV >LATCC >Retired
Halloway	VJ	John	1959-66	ATCOIII	ATCOII	>LATCC >Retired >EGTF (Flying Instructor)
Hall-Willis	AN	Tony/THW	1965-77	ATCOII	ATCOII	>LATCC >Retired 1995
Halverson	MR	Martin	1986-87	ATCOII	ATCOII	>EGKK >EGCC >ATCOI >LATCC (WM) >LACC (WM)
Hamer	N	Norman	1960s	ATCO	ATCOII	>EGSS
Hamer	PB	Pete	1986-93	ATCOII	ATCOII	>LTCC
Hanbury, Miss	JC	Julie	2004-04	ATCOII	ATCOII	>EGLC
Hanbury	JF	Joe	1967-68/77-93	ATCAIII	ATCOII	>Cadetship >EGKK >Lindholme >Returned >LTCC >ATCOI >NERC ATC Trg >Business Development >Retired 2003 >JFH Associates Ltd
Hancock	CWJ		1960s	ATCOIII	ATCO	>
Handley	DJ	Doug	1964-72	ATCO	ATCOII	>EGBB >LATCC >CATC >Deceased
Harben	SP	Steve	1981-2000	ATCAII	ATSAIV	>ATC Trg >AIS EGLL >Head of Trg & Development AIS
Harborne	JL	John	1970-85	ATCAIII	ATSAII	>EGUF >ATSAIV >AIS EGLL
Hardcastle	M	Martin	1997-98	StATCO	StATCO	>EGFF
Harding	JB	John	1953-57	ATCOIII	ATCOIII	>St Just & Isles of Scilly (ATC Manager) >ATCOII >SATCC >HQ >ATCOI >LATCC >SATCO >DDATC >Dep Centre Supt >Retired 1981 >Voluntary work
Hardwick	PG	Philip/Phil	1993-2000	ATCOII	ATCOII	>EGFF
Harkins, Mrs	P	Paula	1986-99	ATCAII	ATSAII	>LATCC >LTCC >CACC
Harris	CR	Chris	1967-80	ATCOC	ATCOII	>LATCC >ATCOI >LACC
Harris	N	Neil/Bandaid	1999-2001	StATCO	ATCOII	>Resigned >EGNX
Harrison, Ms	K	Karen	2000-?	ATSAII	ATSAII	>EGCC
Harrison	RL	Richard	1976-93	ATCO C	ATCOII	>LTCC
Harriss	D	Derek	1970-98	ATCOII	ATCOI WM	>Head ATC Ops & Trg. >Retired 1998 > Deceased 1999
Hart, Ms	S	Sue	1960s	ATCA	ATCA	>Resigned >Nurse
Hatch	MA	Margaret	1950s	ATCA	ATCA	>Resigned >TCA
Hatfield	R	Ron	1959-67	ATCOIII	ATCOII	>LATCC >Retired 1987
Hawkins	AR	Andy	1987-93	ATCOII	ATCOII	>LTCC
Hawthorne	F		1960s	ATCOII	ATCO	>
Hawthorne, Miss	C	Carolyn	2001-	ATSAII	ATSAII	>Mrs Stear. C

Idle moment - northside Tower: Joan Ivory, Graham Stevens, Bill Blott and Dicky Manly, circa 1953. (John Harding)

Pam Brewer (née McLean) became Miss CAA in 1975 - in the days before political correctness would bar such competitions. She is seen here with Lord Boyd-Carpenter (the first CAA Chairman) and Sheila Scott (see Appendix B, 18.5.66) (via Pam Brewer)

SURNAME	INIT	FIRST NAME/ KNOWN AS	DATES	START GRADE	END GRADE	COMMENTS
Hay	AR	Andy	1984-85	ATCOII	ATCOII	>LATCC >ATCOI >LACC
Hay, Miss	SRS	Sheena	1973-75	ATCAII	ATCAII	>LATCC >EGPD >EGFF >LTCC >Mrs Cowell
Haycock	TGC	Paddy	1960-79	ATCOIII	ATCOII	>Retired 1979 >Deceased 2001
Hayes	FW	Fraser	*1980s*	ATSA	ATSA	>Resigned >Botanist in Manchester
Hayes	HC	Bert	1974-90	ATCO C	ATCOII	>Regional Trg Unit >SRG (Inspector of ATS) >SRG (Regional Manager ATS Safety Regulation)
Hayes	PA	Paul	1967-74	ATCAIII	ATCAII	>Resigned >Air Claims Ltd
Hayes	PW	Paul	1976-79/82-87	ATCAII	ATCAII	>EGGP >Returned >HQ >LATCC >LTCC (Business Analysis)>CATC (Head of Business Support) >CTC (Business Support Man)
Hayes, Miss	S	Suzy	1997-	ATCOC	ATCOII	C
Hayward	EW	Eric	*1950s*	ATCOIII	ATCOIII	>SATCC
Heard	BEJ	Bryan	1951-57	ATCOIII	ATCOIII	>School of ATC >EGDM >ATCOII >Min of Technology (Flying ATC) >ATCOI >LATCC >WS >Retired 1981
Hebron	RS	Ralf/Bluey	*1950s*	ATCO	ATCO	>EGUF >EGHH >LATCC >Australia?
Heffer	HM	Harry/Michael/ Mike	1964-75	ATCOIII	ATCOII	>LATCC >ScATCC >EGVW >HQ (CAP5) >Retired 1990
Hemming	MP	Malcolm/Mini-Malc	1986-2004	ATCOII	ATCOII	>LTCC
Hemming	PH	Pete	1952-55	ATCOIII	ATCOIII	>School of ATC >ATCOII >ScATCC >CATO2 >HQ (C(Ops)2B) >ATCOI >ScATCC (WM, Dep Centre Supt, Centre Supt) >DDCATO2 >DDCATO1 >DC(R) CAA House >Retired 1985
Hendry	R	Roy	1972-93	ATCOII	ATCOII	>LTCC >Resigned 2000 >Gama Aviation (Pilot BE200/ LR35/ LR45/ G4)
Herbert	CK	Chris	1967-72/76-	ATCAIII	ATCOI	>LATCC >Cadetship >Returned. C
Hewitt	G	Gerry	1967-68/80-93	ATCAIII	ATCOII	>Cadetship >EGFF >Returned >ATCOI >LTCC
Hewitt	MW	Mark	1998-	StATCO	ATCOI	C
Hewitt, Miss	V	Vickie	1994-94	ATCOII	ATCOII	>Resigned >EGSC

SURNAME	INIT	FIRST NAME/ KNOWN AS	DATES	START GRADE	END GRADE	COMMENTS
Hickman	AM	Al	1967-76	ATCOIV	ATCOII	> LATCC >ATCOI >Retired 2002
Hickson	D	Donald/Don	1976-82	ATCOII	ATCOI WS	>EGUF (SATCO) >Manager ATC Farnborough & Ranges >Retired 1983 >Church Organist >President Berks Organists Assoc
Hide	S	Stuart	1961-67	ATCAIII	ATCAII	>Resigned >Air Canada >Retired
Hill, Miss	CA	Celeste	1999-2000	ATCOII	ATCOII	>Resigned >EGHH >OMDB
Hillyer	RW	Bob	1987-93/94-2004	ATCOII	ATCOII	>LTCC >Returned >LTCC
Hilton	DR	Dave	2004-	StATCO	StATCO	C
Hoar	PFA	Pete	1960s	ATCA	ATCA	>Flying >Retired as Swissair Captain
Hobbs	LN	Len	1958-73	ATCO	ATCOII	>Retired >Deceased
Hobbs	SC	Steve	1980-2000	ATCOII	ATCOII	>LATCC >LACC
Hockin, Miss	ME	Marie	1990-2005	ATCOII	ATCOII	>Mrs Yendall >LTCC
Hodge, Ms	MH	Mary	1960s	ATCA	ATCA	>
Hodson	AG		1980s	ATCAII	ATCA	>
Hoey	L	Laurence	1979-83	ATCAII	ATCAII	>EGFF >Cadetship >ATSAII >EGFF
Holdstock	MP	Mike	1989-	ATCOII	ATCOII	C
Holland	CF	Chris	2003-04	ATSAII	ATSAII	>EGCC
Holland, Miss	SJ	Sandra	1980s	ATCAII	ATSAII	>CATC >Resigned >Barclays Bank
Hollis	JA	Jack	1954-56/67-81	ATCOIII	ATCOI WS	>ATCOII >ScATCC >HQ >Returned >Retired 1981 >Deceased 2004
Holt, Ms	C	Clare	2004-05	StATCO	StATCO	>
Holt	P	Phil	1978-79	ATCOII	ATCOII	>EGPH >Resigned >Manchester Airport Authority >Rejoined >EGCC >CATC
Holton	RN	Ron	1954-59	ATCOIII	ATCOII	>EGPK >ScATCC >Scottish Div >ATCOI >EGPH (Ch Officer) >Retired 1983
Holyoak, Miss	GM	Gabby	1952-76	Tracker	ATCAII	>LATCC >Retired
Hooper	MA	Mark	197?-96	ATCA	ATSAII	>Resigned >USA
Hooper	PJ	Paul	1965-70	ATCAIII	ATCAII	>Eurocontrol EBBR >Maastricht UAC
Hooper	PR	Paul	1994-	ATCOII	ATCOII	C
Hopkins, Miss	P	Pam	1950s	ATCAII	ATCAII	>Resigned
Horner	E	Eric	1961-71	ATCOIII	ATCOII	>LATCC >ATCOI >Retired 1985
Hornsby	DG	Dave	1961-70	ATCOIII	ATCOII	>LATCC >Retired 1992
House	DJ	Dave	1992-93	ATCOII	ATCOII	>LTCC
Houston, Ms	S	Sue	1989-2000	ATSAII	ATSAII	>AIS EGLL >Mrs Veevers >ATSAIV
Howard-Allen	WM	Wendy	1991-93	ATCOII	ATCOII	>LTCC >ATCOI
Howell	JA	Johnny	1960s	ATCOIII	ATCO	>
Howell, Miss	R	Rachel	1999-2003/2004-	StATCO	ATCOII	>Mrs Ware >Resigned >Canada >Returned. C
Howlett	GD	Gareth	1986-88	ATCOII	ATCOII	>Thames Radar >LTCC
Huckle	TR	Terry	1970-73	ATCAIII	ATCAII	>Cadetship >EGPF >LATCC >LACC >CATC
Hudson	W	Win/Winston	1954-62	ATCOIII	ATCOII	>ScATCC & OACC >EGDM >Retired
Huggett	CC	Chris	1981-93	ATCOII	ATCOII	>LTCC
Hughes	JJ	Jon	1999-	ATSAII	ATSAIV	C
Hughes	PJ	Peter	1959-66	ATCOIII	ATCOIII	>Resigned >BAA (Air Cargo Manager) >MoD >Retired 1998
Hughes	SRA	Steve	1970-75	ATCAIII	ATCAII	>Resigned >Canada >Flight DIspatcher (Transair, PWA, Canadian Airlines Int)
Hughes	W	Barney	1940s	ATCO	ATCO	>DD CATO (Aerodromes) >Retired
Humphreys	D	Dave	1970s	ATCAII	ATCA	>AIS Pinner >Retired
Hunt	BJ	Brian	1978-82	ATCAII	ATCAII	>ATCEU >ATSAIII >ATSAIV (Data Manager) >Retired 1995
Hunt, Mrs	J	Jules	1991-	ATCOII	ATCOI+ WM	>Miss Stafford. C
Hunt, Miss	JA	Judi	1969-71	ATCAIII	ATCAII	>Cadetship >EGAA >LATCC >Retired
Hutchings	A	Alan	1991-	ATSAII	ATSAII	C
Hutchings	RP	Ray	1991-2001	ATSAII	ATSAII	>Resigned >Train Driver
Hutchins, Miss	SF	Sue	1975-80	ATCAII	ATCAII	>Mrs Bannister >Resigned >Ran shop >BA
Ibell	CD	Cliff	1981-90	ATCAII	ATSAIII	>LATCC >ATSAIV >OSS >DSS
Ibell	K	Ken	1961-67	ATCOIII	ATCOII	>LATCC >ATCOI >ScATCC >SATCO >DD >LATCC (Centre Supt) >CAA House (Dir Planning LATCC) >DGATO >Retired 1990
Illingworth	C	Chris	1989-91	ATSAII	ATSAIII	>CACC

SURNAME	INIT	FIRST NAME/ KNOWN AS	DATES	START GRADE	END GRADE	COMMENTS
Ingham	I	Irene	*1950s*	ATCA	ATCA	>
Ingleton	A	Pete?	*1950s*	ATCAII	ATCA	>ATCO >Retired
Inglis	MJB	Mike	1982-93	ATCOII	ATCOII	>LTCC >ATCOI
Ingram	VF	Vic	*1960s*	ATCAI	ATCAI	>Retired >Deceased
Innes	DM	Dave	*1960s*	ATCO	ATCO	>CATC >Retired
Irwin	PW	Paul	1981-89	ATCAII	ATSAIV	>Cadetship >EGVW >EGLC
Ivory, Ms	J	Joan	*1950s*	ATCAII	ATCAII	>EGKK >CATC >ATCEU >Retired >Deceased
Jack	AW	Alan	1969-83	ATCOC	ATCOII	>LATCC >ATCOI >Head of ATCP NERC >Manager ACP&P >Director Service Development & Investment
Jackman	RA	Rod	1987-91	ATCOII	ATCOII	>LATCC >ATCOI >LACC
Jackson, Ms	RA	Rachel	2001-	ATSAII	ATSAII	C
Jakes	AG	Tony	1966-66	ATCOIII	ATCOII	>LATCC >HQ DC(R) >EGDM >EGUF >Retired 1991 >IAL Bailbrook until 1995
James		Joe	*1970s*	ATCA	ATSA	>AIS EGLL >AIS EGKK >Retired 1986 >Deceased
James	BPV	Barry	1961-66	ATCOIII	ATCOIII	>Resigned >New Zealand
James	DJ	Derek	*1960s*	ATCOIII	ATCO	>
James	SV	Steve	1981-92/96-98/2001-04	ATCOII	GM	>ATCOI >ATO >D of ATC Ops >Returned (WM) >Civil Air Attache, Washington USA >Returned (GM) >GM European Development
Jarrett, Miss	SJ	Sue	1974-76	ATCAIII	ATCAII	>EGKK >Mrs Hills >ATSAIII >ATSAIV
Jarvis	GW	Graham	1974-	ATCAIII	ATSAII	C
Jaskolkowski	SJP	Stan	1978-79	ATCAIII	ATCAIII	>Resigned >Various jobs >EGBE (Senior ATCA)
Jeens	IWB	Ian	1956-65	ATCAII	ATCAI	>AIS EGLL >AIS EGKK >AIS Pinner (Editor UKAIP) >AIS EGLL >Retired 1991
Jeffery	MJ	Martyn	2004-	GM	GM	C. Also London Group Manager
Jeffries	P	Paul	2002	StATCO	StATCO	>
Jellard, Miss	PB	Patricia	*1970s*	ATCA	ATCA	>
Jellett	WA	Bill	*1960s*	ATCOIII	ATCO	>LATCC >Retired >Deceased
Jenkins	DA	Derek	1969-80	ATCOIV	ATCOII	>CATC >Resigned >Landlord "The Cottage Inn", Wellingborough, Somerset >IAL (EGHH) >EGGP >Rejoined >EGCC >Retired 2004
Jennings	FD	Dave	1973-1990	ATCAIII	ATSAIV	>AIS EGLL
Jermey	AR	Andy	1967-71	ATCAIII	ATCAII	>Cadetship >EGKK >ATCOII >LTCC >TC Trg >Deceased 2002
Jess	AS	Alec	1949-55	ATCOII	ATCOII	>SATCC >CATC >PATCC >Deceased
Johnson	PG	Paul	1977-93/2003-	ATCOC	ATOM	>LTCC >Returned >Development Manager. C
Johnson	RC	Richard/Dick	1978-82	ATCOIV	ATCOII	>EGPB >EGPE >Airspace Policy, CAA House >Retired 1995
Johnson	RA	Richard	2003-04	StATCO	StATCO	>LTCC
Johnston, Mrs	M	Margaret	*1980s*	ATCA	ATSAII	>Retired
Johnstone	RA	Ray	1948-52	ATCOIII	ATCOIII	>SATCC >ATCOII >RAF Wartling >SATCC >HQ (Airspace planning) >LATCC >ATCOI (Software Manager FPPS) >Database Manager FPPS >9020 Test Section >Retired 1983
Jones	BT	Brian	1987-	ATCOII	ATCOII	C
Jones, Ms	C	Carol	2001-	StATCO	ATCOII	C
Jones	C	Chris	2000-	StATCO	ATCOII	C
Jones	GA	George	1949-55	ATCOIII	ATCOII	>ScATCC >PATCC (ATCO I/C) >Retired
Jones, Ms	K	Kumi	1999-2000	StATCO	StATCO	>LATCC >LACC >Mrs Aiken
Jones	P	Paul	*1980s*	ATSA	ATSA	>Eurocontrol
Jones	PG	Pete	1972-72	ATCOIII	ATCOIII	>LATCC >EGAA (WM) >Retired 1996
Joyce	DG	Derrek	1961-69	ATCOIII	ATCOII	>LATCC >ATCOI >N Div ATC2 >Retired 1984 >Training Advisor IANS Luxembourg >ATC Consultant Pakistan 1986
Judge	M	Malcolm/ Big Malc	1981-	ATCAI	ATSAIV	C
Julian, Ms	A	Audrey	*1960s*	ATCA	ATCA	>BUA as Flight Attendant?
Karai	F	Phil	*1960s-86+*	ATCAI	ATSAIV	>AIS EGLL >Retired
Kavanagh	FJ	John	*1950s*	ATCA	ATCA	>SATCC >Deceased
Keeble	JC	John	*1960s*	ATCAII	ATCAI	>AIS EGKK >LATCC >AIS EGLL >Retired >Deceased
Keel	MDR	Mike	*1970s*	ATCA	ATCA	>ATCO >
Kehoe	RT	Richard	1975-2002	ATCAII	ATSAII	>Retired 2002
Keightley, Mrs	LG	Linda	1974-84	ATCAIII	ATCAI	>Cadetship>LATCC>ATSAIV>ATCOIII>EGSS>ATSAIV>LATCC> ATCOIII>EGSS>Aberporth>EGLC>Retired 2003

SURNAME	INIT	FIRST NAME/ KNOWN AS	DATES	START GRADE	END GRADE	COMMENTS
Kelly	BW	Brendan	1987-2000	ATCOII	ATCOI	>Head ATC Ops >LTCC (WM)
Kelly	EAW	Eric	*1960s*	ATCAI	ATCAII	>Deceased
Kemp	G	Greg	1996-	ATCOC	ATCOI	C
Kemp	GP	Pete	1964-2001	ATCAIII	ATSAIV	>Retired 2001
Kennedy, Miss	JA	Juliet	1991-92	ATCOII	ATCOII	>EGSS (Man Ops & Trg) >EGKK (Man ATC >GM)
Kenny, Miss	GV	Gillian	2004-	StATCO	StATCO	C
Kerr, Ms	A	Alice	1947?-68	ATCAII	ATCAI	>LATCC >Retired >Deceased
Kerr	J	Jim/Uncle Jim	1965-73	ATCOIV	ATCOII	>LATCC >Retired
Kerswell	PE	Pete	*1960s*	ATCO	ATCOII	>HQ (DC(R)) >Deceased
Kiernan	JC	John/JK	1958-60/61-77/77-88	ATCOIII	ATCOII	>ICAO Belgian Congo >Returned >LATCC >Returned >EGLC >Retired 1995
Kimber	CJ	Chris	2003-	ATSAII	ATSAII	>ATC Ops. C
Kimber	CGM	Gordon	1957-68	ATCAII	ATCAII	>CATC >ATSAIII >Retired 1992
King	A	Antony	2001-02	ATSAII	ATSAII	>Cadetship >EGKK
King	J	Jonathan/Jon	1990-98	ATSAII	ATSAII	>LATCC >LACC >ATSAIII
King	K	Kathy	*1960s*	ATCA	ATCA	>Mrs Mirfield >Resigned
King	RAS	Robert/Bob	*1980s*	ATCO	ATCO	>LATCC >ATCOI >Resigned >Safeway?
Kingman	L	Len	*1960s*	ATCO	ATCOII	>LATCC >ATCOI >Retired >Deceased
Kinnon, Miss	E	Elayne	?	ATCA	ATCA	>Cadetship
Kirby, Miss	LA	Annette	1971-78	ATCAIII	ATCAII	>Resigned >BAA >Mrs Cullen >Sir Robert McAlpine Ltd
Kirk	AR	Ray	1964-67	ATCO	SATCO I/C	>LATCC (Centre Supt) >Retired
Kirkland			*1960s*	ATCAII	ATCA	>
Knife	NB	Nigel	1969-76	ATCAIII	ATCAII	>Cadetship >LATCC >Retired 2001
Knight	D	Damon	1998-2000	ATCOII	ATCOII	>EGSS (WM)
Knight	G	Graham	*1960s*	ATCA	ATCA	>ATCO >IAL Bailbrook
Knight	GT	Trevor	1963-73	ATCOIII	ATCOII	>LATCC >ATC Ops3 (ATC DP) >Retired 1992
Kunert	R	Roger	1966-	ATCAIII	ATSAIV	C.Heathrow ATC's Longest ever serving member!!
Kurzman, Miss	F	Francesca/ Check	1974-76	ATCAII	ATCAII	>Resigned >Mrs McEwen >Administrator at Utility Auditors (own business)
Kyle	JL	Les	1958-60/62-63/70-71	ATCAIII	ATCOII	>RAF National Service >Returned >ATCOIV >R&D >Returned >LATCC >ATCOI >Retired
Lake	GC	Graham	1970-71	ATCAIII	ATCAII	>ATCEU >Cadetship >LATCC >Resigned >EGJJ >EGHH (IAL) >Controller Internat. Aviation Marketing (IAL) >SITA (Asst VP Air/Ground Services) >ARINC UK
Lambert	G	Gerald/Gerry	1955-57	ATCOIII	ATCOII	>PATCC > >Manchester Radar, Antrobus >Hack Green >PATCRU >EGCC >Retired 1977. Extensive travelling & sailing
Lambert	SW	Steve	1976-93	ATCO C	ATCOII	>LTCC
Lamont	DI	Dave	*1980s*	ATCO	ATCO	>EGSS >Resigned
Lander	M	Malcolm	1996-	ATSAII	ATSAII	C
Lander, Miss	M		*1970s*	ATCA	ATCA	>
Lane	R	Roger	*1990s*	ATCO	ATCO	>
Langley	DC	Dean	1996-	ATSAII	ATSAII	C
Langton	WE	Tim	*1960s*	ATCO	ATCO	>LATCC >Retired
Large	GA	Geoff	1961-63/67-81	ATCOII	ATCOI WS	>LATCC >HQ >Returned >Retired 1981
Latimer, Miss	BK	Bernie	1979-93	ATCAII	ATSAIII	>LTCC >Mrs Allen >LACC (Ops Resource Office)
Laurence, Miss	K	Kay	*1970s*	ATCAIII	ATCAII	>Resigned >BAA >Dog breeder
Lavelle	LA	Leonard/Len	1955-63	ATCOIII	ATCOII	>SATCC >LATCC >ATCOI >Retired 1981
Lawrence, Miss	A	Angie	2000-	ATSAII	ATSAII	>ATC Ops >Mrs Cain. C
Lawrence	RH	Laurie	1955-58	ATCOIII	ATCOIII	>EGKK >EGVW >LATCC >CATC >Retired >Deceased 1997
Lawson	CM	Clive	1971-76	ATCAII	ATCAII	>ScATCC >ATSAIII. Also Voluntary Lifeboat Crewman, RNLI Troon
Lawson	EW	Ted	*1960s*	ATCO II	ATCOII	>LATCC > ATCOI >Retired
Lawson, Miss	M	Margo	1973-76	ATCAIII	ATCAII	>ScATCC >ATSAIII.
Layton	PD	Phil	1986-91/2005-	ATCOII	Man ATC	>ATCOI >LTCC >Head TC Ops >Man TC Ops and Service Provision >Returned (Man ATC)
Leather	PK	Pete	1971-81	ATCAIII	ATCAII	>Cadetship >EGCC >ATCOII >ATC Ops
Lee	PA	Pete	1999-	ATSAII	ATSAII	C
Legge, Miss	JM	Joy	1976-79	ATCAI	ATCAI	>Mrs Alexander >Resigned 1979
Leggett, Ms	CG	Cherry	*1960s*	ATCAIII	ATCA	>Resigned

Runway Inspection! - Jack Carruthers and Mac Pearson (Chief Officer) on the 28L runway centreline in the mid 1970s (via Mac Pearson)

Royal Visit No 2: Mac Pearson (Chief Officer), HM Queen Elizabeth The Queen Mother and Paddy Haycock 7.5.76. (via Colin Haycock)

SURNAME	INIT	FIRST NAME/ KNOWN AS	DATES	START GRADE	END GRADE	COMMENTS
LeGros	NP	Pete	1985-90	ATCOII	ATCOII	>CCF Planning >LATCC >ATCOI >LACC Head of Airspace and Service Planning
Lennon, Ms	VE	Elaine	1981-	ATCAII	ATSAII	>Mrs Cosgrave. C
Lewis	M	Malcolm	*1950s*	ATCA	ATCA	>Resigned >EGGW >ATCO >Flying HS125s?
Lewis	MW	Mike	1973-93	ATCOIII	ATCOII	>LTCC >Retired 1995 >Deceased 2004
Linton	IM	Ian	1970-75	ATCOC	ATCOII	>HQ (DC(R)) >LATCC >ATCOI >EGLC (Man ATS) >EGBB (GM) >LTCC(DGM >GM)
Lister	DA	Dave	1971-73	ATCAIII	ATCAIII	>Resigned >Hamble >Britten-Norman (Pilot BN-2) >Air Anglia (Pilot F27) >Air UK >Monarch (Pilot 737, Capt 757/A321/A330)
Lloyd	PN	Pete	*1970s*	ATCA	ATCA	>
Lloyd	TA	Trevor	*1970s*	ATCA?		>
Locker	M	Martin	2004-	ATSAII	ATSAII	C
Lockley	MWB	Martin	1974-81	ATCOII	ATCOII	>CATO5 >LATCC >ATCOI >LACC >Retired 2002
Lockton, Miss	L	Lilly	*1950s*	ATCAII	ATCAII	>Resigned >Canada
Lodge	RJ	Robin	1987-	ATCOII	ATCOII	C
Lofting	C	Chris	1997-	ATSAIV	ATSAIV	C
London	DT	Des	1979-89	ATCA	ATSAII	>Resigned >Family building business
Looby, Miss	CE	Carol/LoobyLoo	1971-75	ATCAIII	ATCAII	>ScATCC >Resigned >EGNM
Louden	PA	Paul	1971-90	ATCO C	ATCOII	>EGPH(GM) >EGPF(GM) >Manager Airport Services >LTCC(GM) >LACC(GM)
Love	A	Alan	1954-58	ATCOIII	ATCOIII	>SATCC >ATCOII >ATCOI >LATCC >Retired 1983 >Deceased 2002
Lovell	IHJ	John	*1960s*	ATCO	ATCO	>
Low	FJ	Frank	1952-60	ATCOIII	ATCOII	>LATCC >CATO1 >ATCOI >Head of CATO2 >Head of CR5 >LATCC (WS >DCS) >Retired 1984
Lowman, Ms	YEL	Yvonne	*1950s*	ATCA	ATCA	>SATCC >ATCEU >ATCAI >LATCC >Deceased
Lucas	P	Phil	1989-96	ATSAII	ATSAII	>EGPD
Luck	SC	Stuart	*1970s*	ATCAIII	ATCA	>Resigned >Ford Air (Chief Pilot)
Luff	RJ	Reg	*1960s*	ATCAII	ATCAII	>NMU >Deceased

SURNAME	INIT	FIRST NAME/ KNOWN AS	DATES	START GRADE	END GRADE	COMMENTS
Lyden	J	John	*1980s*	ATCOC	ATCO	>LATCC >Resigned >Gulf >Own company
Macauley	NJ	Neil	*1950s*	ATCA	ATCAII	>ATCAII >LATCC
MacClean, Ms	F	Fiona	*1960s*	ATCA	ATCA	>British Eagle as Flight Attendant
MacCormick	AC	Angus	1992-	ATCOII	ATCOI RWM	C
MacDermot	J	John	1968-93	ATCOIV	ATCOI	>LTCC >ATCOII (Voluntarily!) >Retired 1996
MacDonald	AR		*1970s*	ATCAIII	ATCA	>
MacDonald	J	John/Mac	1947-48/54-60	ATCOIII	ATCOII WS	>?>Returned>S.Div >HQ >ATCOI >ATC Insp & Licensing >Min of Technology >SATCO >LATCC (DCS) >DD Aerodromes >DD Area >Retired 1976 >Chairman & Director Freight Forwarding Company. Qualified pilot for 56 yrs to 1995
Mack	NJ	Nigel	1970-83	ATCOC	ATCOII	> IATC (ATC Examiner & Pilot) >SRG ATS Standards (ATC Examiner & Pilot) >Principal Inspector ATS South >Regional Manager ATS South >Retired 2003
MacKay	IJ	Ian	1969-79	ATCOIII	ATCOII	>LATCC >LACC >Retired 2002 >Part-time EGLK
MacKinnon	I	Ian	1970-71	ATCAIII	ATCAII	>Cadetship >EGSS >ATCOII >LATCC >Retired 2001
MacKinnon	MS	Stewart	1960-67	ATCOIII	ATCOIII	>LATCC >ATCOII >ATCOI >DCATO >JFC >Retired 1987. >Deceased 1999
Maclean	A	Andrew	*2000s*	StATCO	StATCO	>EGPH
MacLean, Miss	AM	Angela/Angie	1972-80	ATCAIII	ATCAII	>Cadetship >LATCC >Mrs Slann >Resigned >IT Lecturer in Belgium
MacMahon, Miss	CA	Carol	1973-77	ATCAII	ATCAII	>Cadetship >EGKK >LTCC
MacPherson	JB	John/Mac	1946-82?	ATCAIII	ATCAI	>Retired >Deceased
Magner, Miss	DA	Debbie	1994-94	ATCOII	ATCOII	>LTCC >Mrs Orme
Makein, Miss	SL	Sandra/Scragg	*1970s*	ATCA	ATCA	>Resigned >Swissair >HM Customs & Excise
Male	MV	Mike	1976-88	ATCOIV	ATCOII	>Resigned >Own computer software company
Maley, Miss	AC	Anne	1951-80	ATCAIII	ATCAII	>Mrs MacDonald >ATC Records Office >Retired 1980
Manly, MBE	RE	Dicky	1946-49/53-60	ATCOIII	Dep ATCO I/C	>S.Div >Returned >Deputy ATCO I/C >Staff Officer MoA HQ >Deceased 1965
Manning	J	Jack	*1950s*	ATCOIII	ATCOII	>CATC >Retired
Mapleson	RD	Ray	*1960s*	ATCAII	ATCAII	>ScATCC >Retired
Marks	P	Pete	*1970s*	ATCA	ATCA	>FMU >LATCC >Eurocontrol
Marlowe	AG	Tony	*1960s*	ATCAII	ATCAI	>Resigned >Air Canada
Marsh	A	Andy/Swampy	1981-	ATCAI	ATSAIV	C
Marsh	P	Peter	*1950s*	ATCO	ATCO	>Deceased
Martin	DE	Dave	*1960s*	ATCO	ATCO	>EGBB
Martin-Bishop	PJ	Paul	1975-82	ATCOC	ATCOII	>CATO > ATCOI >LATCC >Paul Bishop >LACC >Retired 2004
Maslin	BR	Bernard	*1950s*	ATCAII	ATCA	>ATCAI >LATCC >Resigned >Antique shop?
Mason	B	Barry	*1960s*	ATCOIII	ATCOIII	>Deceased
Mason	GA	Geoff	*1960s*			
Mason	I	Ian	1975-93	ATCOC	ATCOII	>LTCC >CATC >Retired
Mason	P	Phil	*1940s*	ATCOIII	ATCO	>Deceased
Masterton			*1960s*	ATCAIII	ATCA	>
Mather	EG	Eric	*1950s*	ATCOII	ATCOI WS	>CATC (Supt) >Deceased 2004
Matthews	DJ	Dave	1979-86	ATCAII	ATCAII	>Cadetship >EGSS >ATCOII >LTCC
Matthews	EVF	Eric	1946-48	ATCOIII	ATCOII	>EGWU (I/C GCA) >ATCOI >Scottish Div HQ >MoA HQ >SATCC >EGCC (ATCO I/C) >SATCO >PATCC (Centre Supt) >DD Personnel >S.Div IATC >Retired 1976
Matthews	JL	Jimmy	*1960s*	ATCOII	Dep ATCO I/C	>HQ >S.Div >Deceased
Mawdsley	J	John	1970-72	ATCAIII	ATCAII	>Resigned >Wine Importer Liverpool
May, Ms	M	Molly	*1950s*	ATCA	ATCAII	>
Maynard, Miss	LM	Lynne	2005-	StATCO	StATCO	C
McBride, Miss	T	Terry	*1950s*	ATCAII	ATCA	>South Africa
McCarthy	DE	Derek	*1950s*	ATCA	ATCAII	>ATCAI >LATCC >FMU EGLL >Retired 1993
McCartney	BJ	Brendan/Bren	1972-93	ATCOIV	ATCOII	>LTCC >Retired 2002
McClelland	CR	Colin	1975-79/89-93	ATCO C	ATCOII	>EGPE >ScATCC >Exam Branch >Returned >LTCC >Also pilot C500
McCloy	R	Rob	1999-	StATCO	ATCOII	C

SURNAME	INIT	FIRST NAME/ KNOWN AS	DATES	START GRADE	END GRADE	COMMENTS
McColl	WB	Bill	1965-74	ATCOIII	ATCOII	>CATC >LATCC >ATCOI >Retired 2000 >Canford Aviation Shop >Airborne Aviation as Flying Instructor >CATC Part-time
McConnell	IJ	Iain/IMC	1968-79	ATCOIV	ATCOII	>EGPI >Resigned >Radio Solway >Scottish Newcastle Breweries >Wimpey
McCormack	J	Jim	1974-75	ATCOII	ATCOII	>ScATCC >DCR >LATCC >LTCC >ATCOI >LTCC WM >LATCC >Retired
McDermot	P	Pete	1982-83	ATCOII	ATCOII	>EGUF >Retired
McDonald, Miss	W	Wendy	1972-73/76-92	ATCAIII	ATCOII	>Cadetship >Returned >Mrs Campbell >CATC >ATCOI >Mrs G Wilson >Resigned >Cawdor Castle Tourism Ltd >ATC Consultant
McDonnell	BA	Bernard/Mac	1952-63	ATCOIII	ATCOII	>SATCC >LATCC >Retired 1979
McDowell	L		1980s	ATSA	ATSA	>
McGhee	ND	Neil/Cpt Peacock	1990-2002	ATSAII	ATSAIV	>ATC Ops 3 >Resigned
McGinley	B	Brian	1960s	ATCA	ATCA	>Resigned >Heinz Ltd
McGregor	AJM	Andy	1970-74/79-	ATCAIII	ATSAIV	>Cadetship >ATSAIV >AIS EGLL >Returned. C
McGregor	W	Bill	1958-60/64-73	ATCAIII	ATCOII	>Renfrew >ScATCC >ATCOIII >Returned >ATCOII >LATCC >ATCOI >S.Div Inspectorate >EGVW(SATCO) >EGDM(SATCO) >Head of Flying ATC(MoDPE) >Resigned 1993 >Hong Kong (Senior Safety Officer ATC & Airport) >Retired 1997
McKee	SJ	Shane	1992-	ATCOII	ATCOI	C
McKenzie	M	Mike	1977-90	ATCAII	ATSAIV	>AIS EGLL
McKinna	ID	Dave	1979-99	ATCOII	ATCOI WM	>Retired 1999
McKinnon	J	John	1960s	ATCO	ATCO	>
McKnight	A	Andrew/Andy	2003-	StATCO	ATCOII	C
McLean	A	Alastair	1968-88	ATCOIV	ATCOII	>ATCEU >Retired 1992 >Continues as Magistrate, Musician, Part-time estate agent and general market trader!
McLean	G		1990s	ATSA	ATSA	>
McLean, Miss	PE	Pam	1972-74	ATCAII	ATCAII	>Mrs Brewer >LATCC >Miss CAA 1975 >Retired 2002
McLeod	J	John	1960s	ATCAII	ATCAII	>Resigned
McLeod	KJ	Ken	1960s	ATCOIII	ATCO	>Aberporth >Llanbedr >Deceased
McLeonard, MBE	VBM	Victor/Vic	1954-60	ATCOIII	ATCOIII	>ScATCC >EGPF >ScATCC >ATCOI >OACC (WS) >Retired 1980
McMahon	K	Kevin	1984-93	ATCOII	ATCOII	>LTCC >ATCOI
McQuaker	RG	Mac	1960s	ATCO	ATCO	>
Meakin, Mrs	EA	Elisabeth/Liz	1980-83	ATCAIII	ATCAII	>Resigned
Meakin	KP	Keith	1980-90	ATCOII	ATCOII	>ATCOI >EGPB (Man ATS) >EGFF(Man ATS) >EGPH (GM and Scottish Group Manager)
Mealing	PDS	Pete	1960s	ATCO	ATCO	>LATCC >Retired >Deceased
Meek	JD	John	1960s	ATCO	ATCO	>EGHH
Mercer	AJ	Andy	1991-	ATCOII	ATCOII	C
Metcalfe	RC	Rod	1969-2003	ATCOC	ATCOII	>Retired 2003
Metherell	P	Pete	1950s	ATCA	ATCA	>Cadetship >SATCC >EGFF >LATCC >Resigned >EGTG (SATCO) >Deceased c2000
Michael	TJE	Gene/Mike	1950s	ATCOIII	ATCOII	>LATCC >EGMH
Michelle, Miss	AC	Mandy	1970s	ATCA	ATCA	>Resigned >Swissair
Middlemas, Miss	HF	Helen	1991-2000	ATSAII	ATSAII	>ATSAIV >CACC
Miles, Miss	E	Betty	1950s	ATCA	ATCA	>Retired
Miles	RC	Rod	1965-70	ATCAII	ATCAI	>LATCC >ATSAIII >ATSAIV >OSS FDP >Retired
Millar	GJO	Geoff	1960s	ATCA	AICA	>LATCC >ScATCC >EGPK
Miller	KH	Keith/Keefy	1977-95/96-2004	ATCOC	ATCOII	>SRG >Returned >LTCC
Miller, Mrs	LP	Lucy	1971-91/91-97	ATCAIII	ATSAII	>CATC >Returned >AIS EGLL >Retired 2005
Millett	DE	Dave	1970-73	ATCOIV	ATCOIII	>EGSS >ATCOII >LATCC >Temp ATCOI >LACC >Retired 2002
Milliner, Ms	SA	Sandra	1960s	ATCA	ATCA	>Mrs Braund
Milliner, Miss	SE	Liz	1966-75+	ATCAIII	ATCAII	>AIS EGLL >AIS Pinner >AIS EGLL >ATSAIV
Mills	DR	Dave	1975-81	ATCAIII	ATCAII	>Cadetship >EGBB >ATCOII >LTCC
Mirfield	WE	Ted	1950s	ATCOIII	ATCO	>Retired >Deceased
Mobbs	DJ	Dave	1970-72	ATCAIII	ATCAII	>Cadetship >EGPF >Resigned >Oil Rig >EGGP >EGPK (Dep SATCO/WM)
Moffat	AM	Archie/Jock	1950s	ATCOIII	ATCOIII	>LATCC(WS) >Deceased
Montgomerie	I	Ian/Monty	1992-99/2003-	ATCOII	ATCOII	>Resigned >Returned. C

SURNAME	INIT	FIRST NAME/ KNOWN AS	DATES	START GRADE	END GRADE	COMMENTS
Montgomery, Miss	L	Lynn	2000-03	ATSAIV	ATSAIV	>ScATCC
Moody, Miss	HM	Hilary	1957-64	ATCAII	ATCAII	>Resigned >Mrs Davies >Frazer-Nash Ltd (Sales & Marketing) >Retired 1992
Moody	SJ	Steve	1976-78/81-82	ATCAII	ATCOIII	>Cadetship >Returned >EGPH >Resigned >Paramount (Pilot MD80) >Other flying jobs >easyJet (Pilot B737)
Moor	IR	Ian	1966-78	ATCOIV	ATCOII	>Ian Frankeiss-Moor >LATCC >SRG >ATCOI >EGKK (WM) >Retired 2000 >EGLW
Moore	BTE	Brian	1954-59	ATCAII	ATCAII	>ATCOIV >EGSS >EGJB >SATCC >LATCC (WM) >Man CATO >Retired 1989
Moore, Miss	JE	Jane	1973-85	ATCAIII	ATCAII	>Resigned >Mrs Williams >Own business Antiquarian Book Dealer
Morehouse	G	Gordon	1956-58/85-87	ATCAIII	ATCOII	>Resigned >EGGW >ATCOIII >ATCOIV >SATCC >ATCOIII >LATCC >ATCOII >Returned (ATC Ops 2) >Retired 1987 >Deceased 2002
Morris	PA	Paul	2003-	ATCOII	ATCOII	C
Morton	RJ	Rick	1986-88	ATCOII	ATCOII	>ATCOI >LATCC >LACC
Moss	DJ	Pete	1957-86	ATCAII	ATCAI	>Retired 1986
Mosses	JP	Julian/Jules	1970-73	ATCAIII	ATCAII	>ATCOIV >LATCC >ATCOII >LACC >Retired 2002
Mothershaw	MJ	Mike/Mothercare	1982-93	ATCOII	ATCOII	>LTCC >EGCC
Mould	D	Dan	1990-96	ATSAII	ATSAII	>AIS EGLL >ATSAIII >Eurocontrol
Mount	S	Stan	1950s	ATCOII WS	ATCOII WS	>Deceased
Mundy	ME		1950s	ATCA	ATCA	>
Mundy	RWG	Dickie	1960s	ATCOII	ATCOII WS	>SATCC >ATCOI (WS) >Retired >Deceased 1998
Munson, Miss	J	Judy	1970s	ATCAIII	ATCA	>
Murdoch, Miss	EM	Libby	1984-89	ATCAII	ATSAII	>Mrs Shoesmith >ScATCC >ATSAIII >Ms Murdoch >OACC
Murphy	AN	Tony	1992-96	ATSAII	ATSAII	>ScATCC
Napier, Miss	MJM	Moira	1965-73	ATCAII	ATCAII	>ATCAI >AIS EGLL >Mrs Potter >AIS Pinner >AIS EGLL >Retired 1997
Nash	GF	Geoff	1976-80/1982-86	ATCOIV	ATCOII	>EGPB >Returned >Resigned >EGJB >IAL Bailbrook >CATC
Neale, Miss	JE	Jo	2003-	ATSAII	ATSAII	C
Neale, Mrs	P	Pat	1983-	ATCAII	ATSAII	C
Neale	SM	Steve	1983-	ATCAII	ATSAII	C
Nedbolsky, Miss	RG	Nedda	1954-60	ATCAIII	ATCAII	>Retired >Mrs Spratt
Nelson	JC	Steve	1980s	ATCAII	ATCAII	>
Neville	RM	Bob	1973-93	ATCOC	ATCOII	>LTCC
Newlands	LJ	Lance	1968-69	ATCOIII	ATCOIII	>LATCC >ATCOII >Resigned 1981 >SERCO >Kuala Lumpur ACC >OMDB >Eurocontrol, IANS Luxembourg >HQ Brussels, Examiner >Chairman European Licensing Task Force >Safety Regulator >European ATM Programme Training Co-ordinator >Delivering courses to member states on Human Error Analysis in ATM Technique.
Newman, Ms	AE	Angela	1955-67/68-71	ATCAIII	ATCAI	>LATCC >Returned >LATCC >Retired 1983
Newman	ME	Malcolm	1967-68	ATCAIII	ATCAIII	>Cadetship >EGKK (ATCAIII) >ATCAII >ATCAI >EO Finance, Aviation House >Telecomms Establishment, Finance >SRG >Retired 2002
Newns	RQT	Richard	2003-04	ATCOII	ATCOII	>EGKK
Newton	R	Ron	1950s	ATCO	ATCO	>HQ >Retired
Nicholas	DG	Gerry	1981-93	ATCOII	ATCOII	>LTCC
Nicholson			1960s	ATCAIII	ATCA	>
Nisbett	AV	Alec	1951-56	ATCOIII	ATCOII	>SATCC >HQ >ATCOI >LATCC >SATCO> Retired 1980
Nisbett	KO	Ken	1960s	ATCAIII	ATCAII	>Resigned >Metropolitan Police
Nixon, Miss	AH	Audrey	1948-49	TCII	TCII	>Mrs Gregory >Resigned >Rejoined >EGLK (ATCAIII) >Resigned 1958
Nobbs	PH	Paul	1982-86	ATCAII	ATCAII	>Cadetship >ScATCC >ATCOII >NSC Project >Eurocontrol
Nolan	M	Michael/Moose	1994-96	ATSAII	ATSAII	>Resigned >HIAL >EGPB
Norris	AV	Tony	1973-76	ATCAIII	ATCAII	>Cadetship >EGPB >ATCOII >EGKK >LTCC
Norris	NG	Nigel	1970s	ATCA	ATCA	>Cadetship >LMML
Nutcher	C	Chris	1981-81	ATCOIV	ATCOIV	>EGMD? >BMA (Pilot A320)
O'Connell	DA	Des	1955-60	ATCOII	ATCOII	>SATCC >LATCC >Retired 1980

Evening in the Tower 11.1.59 shows left to right Jock Dibden (Co-ordinator), Len Hobbs (GMC) and Ron Holton (Air)
(Maurice Peall)

SURNAME	INIT	FIRST NAME/ KNOWN AS	DATES	START GRADE	END GRADE	COMMENTS
O'Connell	TPD	Tom	1969-77	ATCAIII	ATCAII	>Resigned >Air Anglia (Pilot F27) >Leisure International (Capt B767) >Air2000 (Capt B767)
O'Connor, Ms	HC	Helen	1970-71	ATCAIII	ATCAIII	>Cadetship >LATCC >IATC >LTCC >ATCOI >LATCC >LTCC
O'Connor, Ms	IP	Penny	1950s	TCII	ATCA	>Mrs Hayward >Resigned >Deceased
O'Connor	TRG	Rupert	1960s	ATCO	ATCOII	>SATCC
O'Doherty	MS	Michael	2002-	ATSAIV	ATSAIV	C
O'Donnell, Miss	M	Rita	1971-79	ATCAIII	ATCAII	>Mrs Leather >Resigned >Mars Ltd >Own business
Ogilvie	JA	Julian	1996-99	ATCOC	ATCOII	>Resigned >LSGG
O'Neill, Ms	P	Paula	1998-98	ATCOII	ATCOII	>EGKK >Mrs Clarke
Oram	JD	John	1983-91	ATCOII	ATCOII	>NERC Project >ATCOI (FSP Head of ATC Transition) >Service Development & Investment (ATC Requirements Manager) >LTCC
O'Regan	KC		1960s	ATCOIII	ATCO	>
O'Rourke	RP	Rory	2000-	ATSAII	ATSAIV	C
Oswick	KJ	Kevan	1978-87	ATCAII	ATCAII	>LATCC >Resigned >Own business
Overton	J	John	1960s	ATCO	ATCOII	>LATCC >EGMH >Deceased 2000
Owen	NS	Nigel	1981-83	ATCO	ATCOII	>EGPD >EGKK (WM)
Oxenford	JD	John	1960-65	ATCOIII	ATCOIII	>EGSS >Resigned >BEA (Pilot Viscount/BAC 1-11) >EGSH >Retired
Paine	TGS	Trevor	1960-88	ATCOIII	ATCO	>Resigned >CYYZ
Paintin	AR	Tony	1973-81	ATCOIV	ATCOII	>Resigned >EGJJ
Palmer	F	Fred	1940s	ATCOIII	ATCO	>
Pancholi	AK	Ashwin	2002-	ATSAII	ATSAII	C
Pargeter, Miss	RMM	Ruth	1975-80	ATCA	ATCAII	>Mrs Saunders >Resigned
Parker	AS	Alan	1961-62/1967-67	ATCAIII	ATCOIV	>SATCC >ATCAII > ATCOIV> Returned >LATCC >ATCOII >CAA House >ATCOI >LATCC >Retired 1989 >Consultancy work to 1995
Parker	ERG	Eric	1950s	ATCOIII	ATCOIII	>CATC >LATCC >CATC >Retired >Deceased
Parkes, Ms	J	Jane	198?-96	ATCA	ATSAII	>EGPD
Parry	N	Neil	1970s	ATCA	ATCA	>
Partridge	N	Neil	1996-	ATSAII	ATSAIV	>ATC Ops. C

SURNAME	INIT	FIRST NAME/ KNOWN AS	DATES	START GRADE	END GRADE	COMMENTS
Partridge	R	Richard	*1960s*	ATCA	ATCA	>Resigned >Local newspaper
Pascoe	JW	John	*1950s*	ATCO	ATCO	>Deceased
Patching	S	Stuart	*1960s*	ATCA	ATCA	>ATCOIV >EGSS >Resigned >BT
Paterson	JW	Pat	*1960s*	ATCOIII	ATCO	>EGCC
Patrickson	PC	Pete	1976-78	ATCAIII	ATCAII	>Resigned >BAA >EGBB (Airfield Ops Man > GM Airfield Services)
Payne	DJ	Dave	*1960s*	ATCO	ATCOII	>LATCC >Retired >Deceased
Payne	HWC	Henry	*1960s*	ATCA	ATCA	>SATCC >Cadetship >EGKK (WS)
Pazera, Miss	JE	Jo	1973-90	ATCAIII	ATSAII	>Mrs Lambert >Mrs Darling >LATCC >ATSAIII >Retired 2002
Peake	CA	Arthur	1983-9?	ATCAII	ATSAII	>Retired
Peall	MJ	Maurice	1954-69	ATCAII	ATCAII	>EGHH >LATCC >ATSAIV >Retired 1994
Pearson	KI	Ken/Mac	1972-76	Ch Officer	Ch Officer	>Retired 1976
Peasley	FRW	Fred	1955-64	ATCOIII	ATCOII	>SATCC >LATCC >ATCOI >Retired 1976
Pemberton	JB	John	1963-73+	ATCO	ATCOII	>LATCC >ATCOI >HQ >Retired >Eurocontrol
Pendrey	KW	Bill	*1960s*	ATCOIII	ATCOII	>Retired >Deceased
Pepall	RA	Raymond/Pep	1953-58	ATCOII	ATCOII WS	SATCC>Tavistock(ChATCO)>LATCC>ATCOI>CATO>LATCC(ACS Ops,SATCO)>HQ(DDC(R))>Retired 1982
Percival	EW	Eric/EP	1960-92	ATCAIII	ATSAIV	>Retired 1992
Perry	MJJ	Mike	1961-69/1983-86	ATCOIII	Ch Officer	>LATCC >ATCOII >HQ (C Ops 14) >EGCC >ATCOI >EGPF (Ch Officer) >Head CATO5 >Returned >Consultancy work >IAL Bailbrook >SERCO/IAL Deputy Principal & Manager Aviation Training >Retired 1995
Peters, Miss	C	Carole	*1990s*	ATCO	ATCO	>LTCC >EGBB >EGFF
Pettigrew	JF	Jim	*1960s*	ATCA	ATCA	>LATCC >Resigned
Pettit	MH	Martin	1970-70	ATCAIII	ATCAIII	>Cadetship >LATCC >ATCOII >LACC >Retired 2003
Phelps	R	Ralph	*1970s*	ATCA	ATCA	>
Phipps	PJ	Paul	*1960s*	ATCA	ATCA	>Resigned >BAA >Guest House IoW
Pickford, Miss	VJ	Vicky	1971-82/90-90	ATCAIII	ATSAII	>Resigned >Nanny USA >AA Business Travel Unit >Mrs Potts >Returned >Resigned 1990
Picton	AM	Tony	1979-83/95-	ATCAII	ATCOII	>Cadetship >EGKK >ATCOII >LTCC >Returned. C
Pierce	RV	Robin	1969-69	ATCO	ATCO	>EGBB >ScATCC >ATCOII >Retired
Piket	BA	Brian	1961-65/65-98	ATCAII	ATCOII	>ATCOIV >Returned >Retired 1998 >Author!
Pincott	AE	Tony	1989-92	ATSAII	ATSAII	>Cadetship >EGLC
Pirzada	AR	Johnny	*1950s*	ATCAII	ATCA	>Pakistan
Pitman	PC	Pete	1967-70	ATCAIII	ATCAII	>Cadetship >LATCC >ATCOI >Simulator Manager LATCC >Head of ATC Training >LACC
Plant	RJ	Ray	1970-83	ATCOC	ATCOII	>Resigned >EGJB (Man ATS)
Platt	C	Chris	*1970s*	ATCO	ATCOII	>EGKK >HQ >EGLC (Man ATS) >Deceased
Platt	LW		*1960s*	ATCOIII	ATCO	>
Plint	M	Mike	*1960s*	ATCAIII	ATCA	>Sopley >Eurocontrol >CAA House (Clerical Officer) >Resigned
Pocock	MH	Maurice	*1960s*	ATCO	ATCOI WS	>S.Div >Retired >Deceased
Pope	AJP	Andrew	2004-	ATSAIV	ATSAIV	C
Pope	D	Dave	1992-2000	ATSAII	ATSAII	>CACC >Retired 2004
Pope, Mrs	YE	Yvonne	*1960s*	ATCO	ATCO	>EGKK >Morton Air Services (Pilot) >Dan Air (Pilot HS748/ BAC 1-11) >Mrs Sinters >Retired >Lives Spain
Powell	RM	Meyrick	1958-59	ATCOII	ATCOII	>School of ATC >ATCOI >Head of ATC2 >Linesman/Mediator Project Authority >CP6 (DG(P)) >CR4 (DC(R)) >Retired 1976 >Lecturer IAL Bailbrook >Deceased 1999
Power	AJP	Angelo		ATCA	ATCA	>LATCC >HQ
Prentice	CR	Chris/CP	1967-93	ATCOC	ATCOII	>Regional Trg Unit >LTCC >Retired 2002
Prescott	DN	Des	*1950s*	ATCA	ATCAII	>ATCO >PATCRU >Retired 1994
Price	AW	Andy	*1980s*	ATCO	ATCO	>Retired >EBBR FMU
Price	FC	Frank	1957-65	ATCOIII	ATCOII	>LATCC >EGSS (Ch Officer) >EGCC (Ch Officer) >Retired 1986
Price	JD	Dave	1985-86	ATCOII	ATCOII	>EGPF >CATC >Retired 1995
Price, Mrs	JS	Janine	1981-1996	ATCO	ATCOI WM	>Mrs Smout >Resigned >EGJB >Resigned >Mrs Chamberlain
Price, Miss	MS	Sheila	1965-73	ATCA	ATCAII	>LATCC >Resigned
Prior, Miss	BA	Barbara	1955-62	ATCAII	ATCAII	>Mrs Dean >Resigned
Pritchard	W	Bill	*1960s*	ATCAII	ATCAII	>Resigned >BEA (Pilot) >Caledonian (Pilot L-1011) >BA (Capt B747-400)

SURNAME	INIT	FIRST NAME/ KNOWN AS	DATES	START GRADE	END GRADE	COMMENTS
Pritchard-Jones	B	Berwyn	*2000s*	ATSAII	ATSAII	>LTCC >ATSAIII
Prosser	AJ	Hank	1973-93	ATCOIII	ATCOII RWM	>LTCC Ops >Retired 1996
Proudfoot	BD	Brian	1970-73	ATCAI	ATCAI	>AIS EGPK >AIS EGPF >ATC Ops, ScATCC/OACC >Retired 1995
Przygrodski	JEEJ	Eryk/Jeep	1983-2004	ATCOII	ATCOI WM	>Retired 2004
Pullen	GD	Graham	*1970s*	ATCAIII	ATCA	>
Purvis, Miss	A	Ann	1968-71?	ATCA	ATCA	>Resigned >BKS >Mrs Radford >BMA >BA >Mrs Murray
Quantrill	TGC	Terry	1967-94	ATCOC	ATCOII	>ATC Ops >Retired 1994
Quest, Mrs	SM	Sue/Susie Q	1978-94	ATCAIII	ATSAII	>LTCC >Retired
Quinn	M		2002-?	StATCO	StATCO	>
Quinton	SP	Steve	1975-83	ATCAII	ATCAII	>EGFF >Resigned >EGGD (ATCA then ATCO)
Rackham	AL	Albert/Alan	1959-66	ATCOIII	ATCOII	>HQ (To plan for Maplin Airport Project) >CATC >LATCC >ATCOI >Retired 1985
Randall	RG	Russell/Russ	1968-72	ATCOIV	ATCOII	>RSRE Pershore >OACC >VHHH >CATC >LATCC >CATC >Retired 2004
Rattigan	T	Rastus	*1940s*	ATCOIII	ATCO	>CATC >Deceased
Rawsthorne	SJ	Steve	*1980s*	ATCAII	ATCAII	>Resigned >Saab Cars
Reading	SK	Keith	1946-65	ATCA	ATCAII	>Deceased
Reavely	P	Pete/Nutty Slack	*1950s*	ATCA/RC	ATCAII	>ATCO >SATCC>Resigned >Decca (GPS) >Ass Dir KMIA
Redhead, Miss	C	Celia	1970-79	ATCAIII	ATCAII	>Mrs Hall >Resigned >Saudia >Mrs Kunert >Raque Foods Ltd >Zebedee Balloon Service Ltd
Reed	NE	Nigel	1991-92	ATCOII	ATCOII	>Resigned >EGTC >EGUW >CATC
Reeson	D	Dale	2001-	StATCO	ATCOII	>ATC Ops. C
Reid	AWC	Alastair/Al	1966-67	ATCOIII	ATCOIII	>EGJB >ATCOII >SATCC >LATCC >ATCOI+ (WM) >ATC Investigations >Retired 2002
Reid	PW	Paul	1996-98	ATCOII	ATCOII	>EGLC (Man ATS) >EGKK(GM) >LACC (DGM ATC Services)
Revis	OC	Owen	*1970s*	ATCA	ATCA	>AIS Pinner >AIS EGLL >Retired 1996
Reynolds, Ms	GM	Gladys	1952-60+	ATCAII	ATCA	>Resigned >Windsor Castle Guide >Deceased
Reynolds	JN	John	1970-73?	ATCAIII	ATCAII	>Cadetship >EGPD >ATCOII >MACC
Rham	DA	Derek	1981-93	ATCOII	ATCOII	>LTCC >ATCOI
Rhys-Davies	T	Tim	*1940s*	ATCOIII	ATCO	>
Richards	DP		*1980s*	ATCO	ATCO	>
Richards	F	Frank	*1950s*	RC	ATCA	>CATC >Deceased
Richardson	HJ	Harry/The Colonel	1952-63/1973-77	ATCOIII	ATCOII	>IATC Heston >LATCC >Returned >IATC Heston >EGPA >Retired 1982 >Lives USA
Richardson	LT	Les	1967-68/1971-73	ATCAIII	ATCAII	>Cadetship >Returned as ATCA >LATCC >Resigned
Richardson	N	Kim	1972-74	ATCAIII	ATCAII	>Resigned
Richardson	PM	Pete	1978-83	ATCAII	ATCAII	>Cadetship >LATCC >ATCOII>ATCOI >LACC
Riches	GC	Graham	1972-83	ATCAIII	ATCAII	>Cadetship >EGSS >ATCOIII DWM. Also part-time AFISO Duxford
Rigby	HSC	Harold	1947-47/65-70	ATCOIII	Dep CO	>Formed GCA School, Aldermaston then EGHH >SATCC (WS) >HQ >ICAO Pakistan >HQ >Formation of Eurocontrol >Returned (Dep CO) >Seconded Hong Kong >Head OSO1 >Resigned >Plessey Co (Operational Consultant) >Independent Aviation Consultant
Rimmer	W	Bill	1946-47	ATCO I/C	ATCO I/C	>Ops >Renfrew(?) (Airport Commandant)
Ringrose	B	Brian	2000-	StATCO	ATCOII	C
Robbins	H	Harold/Robby	1947-75+	RC	ATCAII	>Deceased
Roberts	DH	Derek	*1970s*	ATCA	ATCA	>AIS?
Roberts, Miss	JS	Jan	1969-73+	ATCA	ATCA	>AIS
Robertson	JA	Cockney Robbie	*1950s*	ATCO	ATCO WS	>SATCC >LATCC >Retired >Deceased
Robinson	G	Gavin	2003-	ATSAII	ATSAIV	C
Robinson	RA	Bob	1982-	ATCOII	ATCOII	C
Rodger	RM		*1970s*	ATCAIII	ATCA	>
Rodway	R	Rick	1992-93?	ATCO	ATCOII	>EGPD >CATC
Rogers	JF	Joe	*1950s*	ATCOIII	ATCO	>CATC >Deceased
Rogers	MJ	Mike	1963-71	ATCOIII	ATCOII	>LATCC >Retired
Rolfe	NA	Neil	1973-83	ATCAIII	ATCAII	>Cadetship >EGDM >ATSAII >AIS EGLL >ATSAIV
Rose	DA	David	2005-	StATCO	StATCO	C

SURNAME	INIT	FIRST NAME/ KNOWN AS	DATES	START GRADE	END GRADE	COMMENTS
Rose	I De F	Ian de Francis	*1960s*	ATCA	ATCA	>ATCAI >LATCC >ATCO >CATC?
Rosenthal	P	Paul	1969-71	ATCAIII	ATCAII	>Resigned >RAF (Pilot Helicopters)
Ross	MP	Malcolm/Malcy	1974-90	ATCOC	ATCOII	>EGCC >ATCOI
Rowe	EC	Eric	*1960s*	ATCO	ATCO	>SATCC >Retired
Rowed	AV	Tony	*1960s*	ATCO	ATCOII	>EGKK >EGPB >Retired
Rowland-Rouse	RA	Bob/R³	1971-72/81-83	ATCAIII	ATCOII	>Cadetship >EGSS>ATCOII >Returned >LATCC >DAP >ATO >D of ATC Ops >ATCOI >LACC
Rudge, Miss	DE	Diane	1974-83	ATCAIII	ATSAII	>Mrs Woodhouse >Cadetship >LATCC >ATSAII >ATSAIV >Mrs Tod >Resigned >Eurocontrol
Ruffell	AW	Arthur	*1950s*	ATCOII	ATCO	>Responsible for Heathrow's famous "Reds & Greens" >S.Div
Rundell	P	Paul	*1960s*	ATCOIII	ATCO	>LATCC
Rushworth	D	Duncan	1969-70	ATCAIII	ATCAIII	>Resigned >Air Canada
Rymill	JS	John/JSR	1967-87	ATCOIII	ATCOII	>Thames Radar >Retired 1994 >Part-time EGTF
Sabourin	AV	Alan	1950-64+	ATCOIII	ATCOII	>SATCC >LATCC >Retired 1983 >Deceased 1993
Saker	J	John	*1950s*	ATCO	ATCO	>LATCC >Deceased
Sallaway	JD	John	1974-79	ATCAIII	ATCAII	>Cadetship >EGCC >ATCOI
Sanderson	JH	Sandy	*1950s*	ATCOIII	ATCOII	>RAF Watton >EGKK >Retired >Deceased
Sargent	JP	Phil	1947-50?	ATCOIII	ATCOIII	>EGKK
Saul	TH	Tom/Tommy	1949-52/54-55/68-70	ATCOIII	ATCOI WS	>EGWU >Returned >EGCC >ATCOII >HQ >LATCC >Returned >Sopley >HQ (Heston) >Retired 1976
Saunders	IJM	Ivan	1964-68/70-85/88-97	ATCAII	ATSAIV	>CATC >EGHH FTU >ATCAI >Returned >AIS Pinner >Returned >Retired 1997
Savidge	S	Simon	2001-?	ATCO	ATCO	>
Savill	GA	Geoff	*1950s*	ATCA	ATCAII	>ATSAIV >ATCEU >Retired
Sayers	JA	Tony	1965-73	RC	ATCAI	>AIS >Resigned >BAA >Retired
Saynor	J	Jack	1949-55	ATCOII	ATCOII WS	>ScATCC >S.Div >LATCC >DD CATO2 >DDCAP >DCATO >DCNATS >Retired 1983 >Deceased 2003
Scanlon	AJ	Tony	*1960s*	ATCA	ATCA	>ATCO >CATC >EGPH >EGPK >EGOY(SATCO) >Retired
Scott	GE	Graham	1998-2004/2004-	StATCO	ATCOII	>Resigned >CYYZ >Returned. C
Scott	PE	Pat	*1950s*	ATCAII	ATCA	>
Scroggie	JMF	John	1967-67	ATCAIII	ATCAII	>ATSAIV >LATCC >Eurocontrol >LATCC >LTCC Data Processing
Scuffel, Mrs	S	Sara	2003-04	StATCO	StATCO	>EGLC
See	DW	Don	*1960s*	ATCOIII	ATCO	>LATCC >Retired
Seed	R	Bob	1952-63	ATCOIII	ATCOII	>PATCC >EGCC >ATCOI >RRE Pershore (SATCO) >Retired >Deceased 2002
Selley, Miss	Y	Yvonne	*1970s*	ATCAIII	ATCAII	>Resigned >Deceased
Selly	SG	Stan	*1960s*	ATCOIII	ATCOII	>Lands End >CATC >Retired >Deceased
Settle	MS	Mike	1986-88	ATCAIII	ATSAIV	>LATCC >LACC (FISO)
Settle	S	Stewart	1990-91	ATCOII	ATCOII	>EGPH >Resigned >EGGD
Sharland	RE	Richard	2004-	StATCO	StATCO	C
Sharman	RR	Roy	*1960s*	ATCO	ATCO	>LATCC >Retired
Sharp, Mrs	C	Carol	*1980s*	ATSA	ATSA	>
Sharpe	SH	Steve	1987-87	ATCOII	ATCOII	>LATCC (ATC Ops then Head of ATC Ops 1) >ATCOI >LACC
Shaw	C	Chris	*1990s*	ATSA	ATSA	>
Shawe	DC	Dave	1977-2002	ATCO C	ATCOI WM	>LTCC
Shepperd	C	Chris	1999-2002	StATCO	ATCOII	>EGCC
Shiers, Ms	S	Sheila	*1950s*	ATCA	ATCA	>SATCC >Returned >EGKK >LATCC >ATCOIV >Retired 1968 >Mrs Freeman
Shuckburgh	JS	John	1947-53	ATCOIII	ATCOIII	>Ops Officer >Resigned>BAA Fire Service >Retired 1983
Shurlock	PR		*1950s*	ATCO	ATCO	>HQ? >Deceased
Siddell	JC	John/Sid	1977-97	ATCOC	ATCOII	>Freelance pilot Gama Aviation (BE-200) >Resigned 1997 >VHHH
Silk	ET	Eric	*1950s*	ATCO	ATCO	>EGKK >SATCC >Deceased
Sillence	CF	Clive	*1960s*	ATCAII	ATCA	>EGKK >Resigned >EGTI >SATCC?
Simmonds, Miss	KAE	Karen/Kaz	1999-	ATSAII	ATSAII	>Mrs Dodkin >ATC Ops >Ms Simmonds. C
Simmonds, Miss	KJL	Kate	2001-04	ATSAII	ATSAII	>ATC Ops >Resigned >Canada >UK Teaching Pilates
Simmonds	RK	Reginald/Reg	1978-79	ATCOII	ATCOII	>LATCC >ATCOI >Seconded ICAO 1986 plus GATCO posts >Retired 1990 >IAL Bailbrook >ATC Consultant until 2002

'D' Watch Training review 1970.
L to R: Jack Hollis (Watch Supervisor), Alan Hickman, Brian Smith, Judi Hunt, Graham Bisset.
Foreground: Alan Card training John Cant on No2 Director, with Sue Williams (now Clifford) and Chris Prentice looking on.
(via Graham Bisset)

SURNAME	INIT	FIRST NAME/ KNOWN AS	DATES	START GRADE	END GRADE	COMMENTS
Simmonds, Miss	SPJ	Steph	1983-95/97-	ATCOII	ATCOI WM	>SRG >Returned. C
Simmons, Miss	KT	Karen	2004-	ATCOII	ATCOII	C
Simpson, Miss	KN	Kym	1988-91/93-	ATCAII	ATCOII	>Cadetship >Returned >Mrs Sampson >Ms Simpson >Mrs Glynn. C
Sims	IG	Ivor	1976-84/94-2004	ATCOC	ATCOII	>Resigned >EGJB >Returned >LTCC
Sinclair	B	Basil	*1950s*	ATCOIII	ATCO	>
Sinclair	P	Pete?	*1990s*	ATSA	ATSA	>
Singfield	TR	Tom	1969-78	ATCAIII	ATCAII	>Cadetship >EGKK >ATCOII >LTCC>Retired 2005
Slade	L	Les	1961-62	ATCAII	ATCAII	>ATCOIV >SATCC >CATC >ATCOII >EGUF >Retired
Smart	D	Dave	*1960s*	ATCOIV	ATCO	>Resigned >Northeast Airlines (Pilot Viscounts)
Smeath	JM	John/ The Captain	1965-73?	ATCOIII	ATCOII	>LATCC >Deceased 1988
Smellie	D	Dave	1981-81	ATCOIV	ATCOII	>Resigned >IAL(Dubai) >EGPK >EGBJ >Cumbernauld >
Smith	A	Alan	*1950s*	ATCO	ATCO	>St Just (ATCO I/C) >Deceased
Smith	A	Tony	*1960s*	ATCO	ATCO WS	>ScATCC
Smith	BT	Brian	1963-73/84-84	ATCOIII	ATCOII	>LATCC >ATCOI >Head CAP5 >Returned (Head ATC Org) >EGFF (Ch Officer) >EGKK (GM) >Manager Airport Services >Retired 1997
Smith, Mrs	E	Liz	1971-73	ATCA	ATCAII	>
Smith	KD	Ken	1963-68?	ATCO	ATCOII	>Deceased
Smith	KJC	Kevin	1989-93	ATSAII	ATSAII	>Cadetship >LATCC >
Smith	MP	Mike/Smiler	1974-78	ATCAIII	ATCAII	>Resigned >BAA

SURNAME	INIT	FIRST NAME/ KNOWN AS	DATES	START GRADE	END GRADE	COMMENTS
Smith	RS	Dick	1963-78	ATCAIII	ATCOII	>ATC1 >LATCC >ATCOI >LTCC(WM) >Retired 2000 >Lives France. Part-time Eurocontrol EBBR in 2004
Smith. Miss	VM	Valerie/Val	1970-75	ATCAIII	ATCAII	>EGPD >Mrs Anderson >Mrs Melvin >OMDB
Smith	W	Wayne	1997-98	ATSAII	ATSAII	>ATSAIII >CACC
Smy	P	Paul/Small Pie	1992-2004	ATCOII	ATCOI RWM	>LTCC
Snow	A	Adrian	2000-	StATCO	ATCOII	C
Snow	OL	Tony?	1950s	ATCA	ATCA	>ATCAI >SATCC >Resigned >Postman >Magistrate
Sood	SN	Surinder/Sandy	1970s	ATCA	ATCA	>HQ
Soper	J	Joe	1950s	ATCOII	ATCO	>ATCEU (Northside EGLL) >Deceased
Spalton	B	Bert	1969-76	ATCOII	ATCOI	>EGCC >Retired 1984
Spink	AF	Adam	1999-	ATCOII	ATCOII	C
Spooner	RK	Robert	1979-2002	ATCOII	ATCOI	>Manager Operational Development
Spott, Miss			1970s	ATCA	ATCA	>
Spouse	RA		1970s	ATCAIII	ATCA	>
Spragg	DM	Doug	1980s	ATCO	ATCO	>LATCC >Eurocontrol >Retired
Spratt	KA	Ken	1950s-1960s	ATCO	ATCOII	>EGUF >Retired 1976 >Part-time pilot >Deceased 1997
Staley	RV	Roy	1961-69/1977-81	ATCOIII	ATCOI	>LATCC >ATCOII >ATCOI>Returned> D.ATC(SL) (Editor MATS Pt 1) >Head of ATC Licensing >Dir. ATC (Inspection & Licensing) >SRG (ATS Standards) >Retired 1993 >Consultancy work
Stammers	ML	Martin	1960s	ATCA	ATCA	>ATCO >IAL >EGMC?
Stanley	AA	Stan	1950s	ATCOIII	ATCOIII	>EGKK >EGSS (ATCO I/C)
Stanton	HPM?	Mike	1960s			>
Staunton	KWA	Kevin	1960-72/1974-78	ATCOIII	ATCOII	>LATCC >Returned >Resigned >IAL >OBBI >Brunei >OMAD >Eurocontrol >Luxembourg >Russia >TACIS Project >ANS Prague >Retired 2001
Steel	IW	Iain	1982-86/1991-96	ATCAII	ATSAII	>EGVW >Cadetship >ATSAII >Returned >LTCC >ATSAIII
Steele	D	David	1990s	ATSA	ATSA	>Eurocontrol
Stemp	J	James	1995-	ATSAII	ATSAII	C
Stephens	PG	Pete	1970s	ATCA	ATSAIV	>ATC Ops >Retired
Stephenson	AD	Tony/Zero	1970s	ATCA	ATCA	>RAF Lindholme >Eastern Radar >Highland Radar
Stevens		Bob	1960s	ATCA	ATCA	>
Stevens	G	Graham	1954-61	ATCOIII	ATCOII WS	>S.Div >EGSS(ATCO I/C) >ATCOI >PATCC >LATCC >Retired 1982
Stevens	J	John	1989-95	ATSAII	ATSAIV	>ATC Ops >CACC (Signals WM) >Scotland
Stewart	P	Paul	1998-	ATSAII	ATSAIV	C
Stewart-Taylor, Miss	A	Andrea	1997-	StATCO	ATCOII	>Mrs Anderson. C
Still	K		1990s	ATSA	ATSA	>
Stock	TW	Terry	1958-66	ATCOIII	ATCOII	>LATCC >DORA >CATO >LATCC >EGSS >LATCC >Retired
Stockley	KB	Kevin	1990s	ATSAII	ATSAII	>CATC >Resigned >ATCO >EGHH >Canada
Stokes	R	Dicky	1950s/70s	ATCO	ATCOII	>Retired >Deceased
Stratford	MJ	Martin	1993-94	ATCOII	ATCOII	>Thames Radar >LTCC
Street	G	Gerry	1960-68	ATCAIII	ATCAI	>ATCOIV >EGKK >ATCOII >EGUF >Retired 1996
Street, Miss	MA	Margaret	1970-72	ATCAIII	ATCAII	>Mrs Moore >EGCC >LATCC >ATSAIV >Retired 2001
Stretton	WAC	Bill	1963-72	ATCOIII	ATCOII	>LATCC >ATCOI >RSRE Malvern (Senior Civil ATCO) >Retired 1993 >Consultant for CAA >Part-time jazz musician
Strutt	GG	Geoff	1960s	ATCOIII	ATCOII	>ScATCC? >ATCEU
Stuart	JG	Jock (now Jim)	1956-62	ATCOIII	ATCOII	>ScATCC >Border Radar (ATCO I/C) >CAP4 >Retired 1989
Stubbs	PA	Phil	1994-96	ATCOII	ATCOII	>Resigned >EGTD >EGKK (Man ATC)
Sturrock, Miss	J	Jean	1960s	ATCA	ATCA	>AIS EGLL >Retired
Sullivan	DG	Don	1950s	ATCO	ATCOII	>SATCC >LATCC >Retired 1996?
Summerhayes	G	Geoff	1960s	ATCO	ATCOII WS	>Retired
Swan	C	Christopher/ Chris	1968-79	ATCOIV	ATCOII	>OACC >CATC >Retired 1995
Swann	MD	Martyn/Swanny	1973-	ATCAIII	ATSAIV	>ATC Ops2. C
Sweetapple	G	Gordon	1950s	ATCOIII	ATCO	>Ops branch (Liverpool) >Manchester Airport Managing Director 1970?
Swift	J	John	1990-90	ATCOII	ATCOII	>EGAA >EGPD(WM) >OMDB

SURNAME	INIT	FIRST NAME/ KNOWN AS	DATES	START GRADE	END GRADE	COMMENTS
Sylvester-Thorne	NB	Nigel	1973-75	ATCAIII	ATCAII	>ScATCC >Cadetship >LATCC >ATCOII >CAA House (LATCC Development) >Eurocontrol Experimental Centre
Tabbron	JW	John	1991-92/2004-	ATCOII	ATCOI	>EGSS >LTCC >TC Ops >Returned Head of Safety. C
Tapsall	TE	Trevor	1952-79	ATCAII	ATCAI	>Deceased 1979
Tarring	AF	Alan	1950s	ATCA	ATCA	>AIS >LATCC >EGKK >Retired
Taylor, Miss	CG	Carol	1974-76	ATCAII	ATCAII	>OACC >ATSAIII
Taylor, Mrs	K	Kathy/Marje	1999-2000	ATSAII	ATSAII	>Resigned
Taylor	MD	Malcolm	1979-82	ATCOIV	ATCOII	>EGPD >EGKK
Taylor, Ms	R	Ros	1960s	ATCA	ATCA	>
Taylor	RK	Richard	1981-95	ATCOII	Man ATC	>LTCC (WM) >SRG (Head of ATS Standards)
Tayte	MA	Mike	1986-87	ATCAII	ATCAII	>Resigned >ATCO >EGTK >EGBE >EGGW >EGBE >EGNX >EGJB >EGGD >EGBE
Temple	PJ	Pete	1950s	ATCOII	ATCOII WS	>ATCEU
Templeton, Miss	H McL F	Helen	1968-72?	ATCAIII	ATCAII	>EGDM
Tennent	BP	Brian	1960s	ATCAIII	ATCAII	>Cadetship? >EGPF
Theaker, Miss	JB	Joy	1966-71	ATCAIII	ATCAII	>Resigned >BA >Mrs Franklin >Probation Service
Theaker	RH	Roger	1964-68	ATCAIII	ATCAII	>ATCOIV >EGKK >ATCOII >LATCC >LTCC >Retired 2002
Thirde, Mrs	BJ	Barbara	1980s	ATCA	ATCA	>Resigned
Thomas	CH	Chris	1977-80	ATCOII	ATCOII	>LATCC >NERC (Head of ATC Training) >Retired 2002
Thomas	H	Howard	1972-79	ATCOC	ATCOII	>LATCC >CATO >ATCOI >Chief Scientists Dept >SRG International Services >Resigned
Thomas	T	Tommy	1940s	ATCOIII	ATCO	>EGLK >Retired >Landlord "Dog & Partridge", Yateley >Deceased
Thompson	K	Ken	1950s	ATCA/RC	ATCA	>ATCO >CATC >Chief Instructor (Area) >Dundridge >Deceased
Thompson	RF	Dick	1970s	ATCOII	ATCOII	>EGKK (WM) >Retired 1991
Thompson	WE	Eric	1970s	ATCOI	ATCOI WM	>Head ATC Ops >Retired >Deceased
Thorpe	AP	Andy	1980-82	ATCAII	ATCAII	>Cadetship >LATCC >ATCOII >LACC
Tilley	RH	Dick	1986-93	ATCOII	ATCOII	>ATCOI >LTCC >ATCOII
Tipping	PB	Paul	1994-	ATCOII	ATCOII	C
Toakley	IM	Ian	1978-93	ATCOIV	ATCOII	>LTCC >Deceased 1998
Tolson	F	Frank	1964-69/1973-74	ATCOI	Dep ChATCO	> ? >Returned (Dep ChATCO) >LATCC (WS) > Retired
Tomlinson	PG	Peter	2002-03	Man ATC	Man ATC	>Directorate Strategy & Regulation
Tong	G	Gary	1980s	ATCAII	ATCA	>Cadetship?
Toohey	S	Steven/Skippy	2000-2003	StATCO	ATCOII	>Resigned >Australia >OMDB
Took, Miss	ME	Mary	1971-77	ATCOIV	ATCOII	>Mrs Foster >Retired 1977
Toseland	JN	John/JNT	1960s	ATCO	ATCOI WS	>EGUF >Deceased
Toseland	RJ	Ron	1961-69/81-83	ATCOIII	Ch Officer	>LATCC >ATCOI >CATO1 >Returned >DCATO >JFC >DCNATCS >Retired 1991
Towers-Perkins	W	Bill/TP	1947-49	ATCOIII	ATCOII	>SATCC >ATCOI >HQ >SATCO >Retired >Deceased 2001
Townend	CK	Chris	1960s	ATCA	ATCA	>ATCEU >Deceased
Townsend	J	John	1964-68	ATCAIII	ATCAII	>Resigned >Esso Petroleum (Computer Operator/Programmer) >Bland Payne >Bolton & Paul >Norfolk CC
Toy	JM	Tom	1981-91	ATCOI	ATCOI WM	>LTCC (WM) >TC Business Efficiency Manager >Retired 2001
Treacy	DPJ	Paddy	1960-94	ATCAII	ATSAIV	>Retired 1994
Trickett, Ms	MC	Margot	1955-65	ATCAII	ATCAI	>LATCC >Retired >Deceased
Trickett	MJ	Marty	1970-76	ATCO C	ATCO II	>CATC >EGPB >EGDM >LATCC >LACC >Retired 2003 >Lives New Zealand
Turner	BA	Basil	1969-72	ChOfficer	ChOfficer	>ATCEU(Supt) >Retired 1976 >Consultant on Aviation English. Valid PPL to age 75 >Deceased
Turner, Miss	BJ	Beverley	1970-81	ATCOIV	ATCOII	>Mrs Hull >Resigned 1981 >Canada >Hong Kong >Lives France
Turner	LG	Tubby	1940s	ATCOIII	ATCO	>
Turner	MR	Mike	1989-95	ATCOC	ATCOII	>LTCC
Turnidge	BR	Bill	1940s/1960s	ATCOII	ATCOI WS	>HQ >Retired
Tyler	FG	Frank	1967-68	ATCAIII	ATCAII	>LATCC >ATCOIV >ATCOII >LTCC >Retired 2002
Vagg	RE	Ron	1955-58	RC	ATCA	>EGKK >CATC >Retired 1982 >Deceased 2001
Van der Merwe	D	Van	1960s	ATCO	ATCOII	>EGKK >Resigned >IAL
Van Dort	EA	Ted	1975-79	ATCOI WS	ATCOI WS	>EGUF (SATCO) >MoD(PE) Head of ATC >Retired 1989
Vening, Mrs	C	Carol	1973-73	ATCOIII	ATCOIII	>EGKK >ATCOII >Retired 2002

SURNAME	INIT	FIRST NAME/ KNOWN AS	DATES	START GRADE	END GRADE	COMMENTS
Venn, Miss	MC	Mary	1990-94	ATCAII	ATCAII	>Mrs Bishop >LATCC >Retired 2002
Vidler	AE	Tony	1950s	ATCOIII	ATCO	>SATCC >Deceased
Vidler	ME	Mark	1981-81	ATCOIV	ATCOIV	>EGSS >ATCOII >LTCC
Virden, Miss	LJ	Lucy	2004-04	ATCOII	ATCOII	>EGSS
Vringer	P	Pieter	2000s	ATCO	ATCO	>FGPF
Wade	EK	Eric/Rick	1954-58	ATCOIII	ATCOII	>SATCC >LATCC >ATCOI >Directorate of Data Processing >DD >Retired 1983
Wade	WW	Wally	1960s	ATCA	ATCAI	>LATCC >Deceased
Wadley	R	Rob	1968-91	ATCOC	ATCOI WM	>LTCC (WM >AC Resource Management)
Wagstaff	J	John	1960s	ATCAIII	ATCA	>
Wales	NK	Norman	1976-92	ATCAII	ATSAII	>CACC >Retired 1994
Walker	MS	Mike	1985-	ATCOII	ATCOII	C
Wallace, Miss	R	Robina	195?-75?	ATCAII	ATCAII	>EGPK >Retired 1982 >Deceased
Waller	NC	Neil	1970s	ATCAIII	ATCAII	>Cadetship >AIS EGLL >Aberporth
Wallis	AS	Wally	1962-68	ATCOIII	ATCOII WS	>SATCC >LATCC >ATCOI >SATCO >Retired 1976
Walton	RP	Bob	1956-67?	ATCA	ATCAI	>ATCO >CATC >PATCRU >Retired >Deceased 2002
Ward	CM	Colin	1967-89	ATCOIV	ATCOII	>EGUF >CATC >Retired 2004
Ward	L	Lou	1960s	ATCO	ATCO	>EGGW?
Ward	N	Norman	1960s	ATCO	ATCO	>CATC?
Ward	PA	Phil	1970s	ATCA	ATCAI	>ATCOIV >EGKK >ATCOII >LTCC >SRG (ATSI Investigator)
Ward	TM	Terry	1979-83	ATCAI	ATCAI	>CATC >ATSAIV >LATCC >NERC Project Team >PR Manager >LACC >ATC Operational Support LACC
Ward-Hunt	P	Peter	1948-52	ATCOIII	ATCOIII	>Uxbridge >SATCC >ATCOII >ATCEU >ATCOI >EGVW (ATCO I/C) >Retired 1977
Ware	BJ	Bernard	1950s	ATCOII	ATCOI WS	>SATCC >EGKK (ATCO I/C) >Retired >Deceased
Wareham	RD?	Roy?	1960s	ATCAIII	ATCAII	>Cadetship
Warner	CJ	Chris	1959-84/1985-96	ATCAII	ATSAIV	>AIS Pinner >Returned >ATC Ops >Retired 1996
Warren	JM	John	1970-79	ATCAIII	ATCAII	>Resigned >Saudia >
Warwick, Miss	JE	Janet	1974-78?	ATCAIII	ATCAII	>Resigned >Mrs Patrickson >Radiographer
Waterfield	PG	Pete	1954-57/1970-81	ATCAII	ATCOII	>CATC >EGHH >ATCOIII >EGKK >Returned >ATCOII >EGSS >LATCC LFMU >Retired 1992
Waterton	GW	Graham	1960s	ATCO	ATCO	>CATC >OACC >Retired
Watkins	AS	Tony	1973-89	ATCOIV	ATCOII	>Resigned >Runs own computer business
Watkins	DW	Dennis	1940s	ATCOIII	ATCO	>
Watkins, Miss	JME	Janie	1983-90	ATCAII	ATSAII	>Cadetship >LTCC >ATCOII>Mrs Barnes
Watson	A	Alan	1956-60	ATCOIII	ATCOIII	>ATCOII >SATCC >HQ >ATCOI >LATCC >SATCO >Retired 1991
Watt	G	Gerry	2004-	StATCO	ATCOII	C
Watt, Miss	SB	Sheila	1960-61	ATCAIII	ATCAIII	>SATCC >EGKK >AIS EGLL >EGKK >ATCAII >Retired 1988
Watts	RK	Rod	1966-80	ATCAIV	ATCAII	>Resigned >Saudia
Waud	AHG	Bob	1946-50	ATCOIII	ATCOIII	>SATCC >School of ATC >SATCC >ATCOII >Watling (ATCO I/C) >ATCOI >S.Div >LATCC (WS) >Head of CATO6 >Head of CATO2 >SATCO >LATCC (WS) >Retired 1977 >Deceased 2003
Waud	KM	Keith	1968-77/92-99	ATCOIV	ATCOII RWM	>Resigned >IAL (OBBI, EGHH, EGGP, EGMC) >BAA Airports UK (EGKB) >Returned >Deceased 1999
Way	FA	Frank	1979-81	ATCOI	ATCOI WS	>LATCC >SATCO >Retired 1994 >LATCC Training ECT
Wayman-Hales, Miss	CSF	Sarah	1995-	ATSAII	ATSAII	>Mrs Hooper. C
Webb	RM	Roy	1976-86?	ATCAIII	ATSAII	>Resigned >Brymon (Pilot Dash 7) >BA (Pilot B747-400)
Webber	DSR	Don	1940s	ATCOIII	ATCO	>CATC >Exam Branch >Deceased
Webber	TR	Terry	1992-93	ATCOII	ATCOII	>EGKK >LTCC
Weiler, Miss	TM	Trace	1981-85	ATCAIII	ATCAII	>Cadetship >Mrs Duncan >LATCC >ATCOII >CATC >LATCC >LACC >Mrs Carvall
Weir, Miss	AE	Anthea	1990-	ATCOII	ATCOII	>Mrs McKie. C
Welch	WJ	Wilfred/Wilf	1954-60	ATCOIII	ATCOII	>CATC >Teheran, Iran (Training of ATCOs on radar and introduction of radar simulator) >Kent Radar, Manston >Retired 1980 >Libya (Installation of radar simulator for Plessey) >Beijing until 1982 (to write radar simulator requirements for ICAO)
Wellard	LHT	Len	1960s/1986-?	ATCO	ATCOII	>LATCC >Returned >Retired
Welton, Miss	P	Pam	1950s	ATCA	ATCA	>USA

"C" Watch   Air Traffic Control

Heathrow   March 1982

C Watch. Key : 1. Alan Haines, 2. Chris Cosgrave,
3. Mike Male, 4. Kevin Baker, 5. Bert Hayes, 6. Tony Picton,
7. Laurence Hoey, 8. Keith Williams (Watch Manager),
9. Steve James, 10. Ray Plant, 11. Andy Bright, 12. Dave
Broderick, 13. Brian Piket (Author), 14. Elaine Lennon,
15. Clive George, 16. Doug Bush, 17. Pete Kemp,
18. Jez Cooke, 19. Mac MacPherson, 20. Graham Jarvis,
21. Janine Price, 22. Ron Daly, 23. Tony Denchfield,
24. Tom Toy, 25. Brandon Chapman, 26. Rob Spooner,
27. Roger Darling, 28. Mike Williams, 29. Pete Clark,
30. Roy Hendry, 31 Steve Quinton.
(Photo montage by Ron Daly)

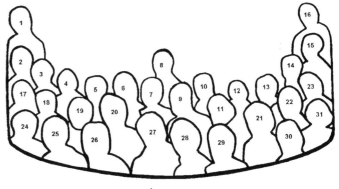

SURNAME	INIT	FIRST NAME/ KNOWN AS	DATES	START GRADE	END GRADE	COMMENTS
West	DJ	Dave	1973-78	ATCAIII	ATCAII	>Cadetship >LATCC >ATCOI >NERC Planning >LACC
West	L	Les	1950-57/67-83	ATCOIII	ATCOI WS	>SATCC >CATO >HQ >Returned >Retired 1983
Whale, Miss	EC	Emma	2004-	StATCO	StATCO	C
Wheatley	JR	Jim	*1960s*	ATCO	ATCO	>EGPF >Deceased
Wheatley	IAM	Ian/Dennis	1991-2004	ATCOII	ATCOII	>LTCC
White, Ms	J	Jacqui	1996-96	ATCOII	ATCOII	>EGBB
White, Miss	LG	Linda	1955-1970s	ATCAIII	ATCAII	>LATCC >Resigned >Inland Revenue
White, Miss	M	Morna	*1950s*	ATCAII	ATCAII	>Resigned

SURNAME	INIT	FIRST NAME/ KNOWN AS	DATES	START GRADE	END GRADE	COMMENTS
Whitehead	G	Gordon	1960s	ATCO	ATCO	>Canada
Whitehead	RA		1970s	ATCAII	ATCA	>LATCC
Whitehouse, Ms	S	Samantha/Sam	1990s	ATSA	ATSAII	>Cadetship >EGPH
Whitelock	NH	Norman	196?-75	ATCO	ATCOI WS	>LATCC >Retired >Deceased
Whiting	AW	Alf	1960s	RC	ATCAI	>
Whitmarsh	J	Justin	1978-81	ATCAIII	ATCAII	>Resigned >American Airlines (Capt B767s)
Whitney	RJ	Ralph	1969-75	ATCAIII	ATCAII	>EO Stats Branch, HQ >HEO, Commercial Svcs, SRG >Retired 1995
Whyte	D	Don	1990s	ATCO	ATCO	>EGPD >OMAA
Wicks, Ms	H	Heather	2000-01	ATSAIII	ATSAII	>EGCC
Wilcox, Miss	TA	Theresa	1979-	ATCAII	ATSAIV	C
Wild	G	Geoff	1973-78	ATCOII	ATCOII	>CATC >LATCC >LACC >CATC
Wildey	BT	Brian	1986-93/1994-2001	ATCOII	ATCOII	>LTCC >Returned >Retired 2001
Wilkie	D	Don	1940s	ATCOII	ATCOII	>ATCOI
Williams	CG	Cyril	1950s	ATCO		>
Williams	DG	Dave	1980-90	ATCAII	ATSAII	>Cadetship >EGKK >ATCOII >EGUF >ATCOIII >ATSAII >AIS EGLL >FMU >LATCC(OSS) >ATSAIV >LTCC (Current Systems)
Williams, Mrs	JE		1970s	ATCAII	ATCAII	>Resigned
Williams	KC	Keith	1979-83/86-90	ATCOI WM	GM	>Dep ChATCO >JFHQ DD (CATO Aerodromes) >Returned (GM) >DCATO >Director ATO (NATS) >Retired 2002
Williams	MFB	Mike	1980-90	ATCAII	ATSAII	>LATCC >LTCC(OSS)
Williams	RT	Richard	1968-69	ATCOII	ATCOII	>LATCC >ATCOII >EGPF (WM) >CATC
Williams, Mrs	SP	Sue	1968-2004	ATCOIV	ATCOII	>Mrs Clifford >Retired 2004
Williamson	SL	Steve	1993-94	ATCOI	ATCOI	>EGPH (Man ATC) >EGFF (Man ATS) >EGBB(GM ATS and Contract 2 Group Manager)
Wilson	CJ	Chris	1985-2005	ATCOC	Man ATC	>Manager Ops & Training >Man ATC >ATCOI >LTCC
Wilson	DK	Denis	1978-81	ATCAIII	ATCAII	>Cadetship >EGKK >LTCC >ATCOI
Wilson	GP	Gary	1989-	ATSAII	ATSAIV	>ATC Training. C
Wilson	P	Paul	1973-73/75-91/95-99	ATCO C	Man ATC	>Cadetship >Returned >ATO >ATCOI >Returned (Man ATC) >EGSS (Manager ATS) >Eurocontrol
Wilson	R	Bob	1950s	ATCA	ATCA	>Resigned >Furniture business
Winch	B	Barry	1978-81	ATCOII	ATCOII	>Resigned >Toronto ATCC (Data Systems) >Ottawa (CAATS Project) >Manager Ops Systems Requirements (Comms Facilities)
Winch	FE	Frank	1958-63	ATCOIII	ATCOII	>SATCC >Retired 1983 >EGTB
Winch, Mrs	L	Lyn	1978-81	ATCAII	ATCAII	>Resigned >Canada >Local Hardware Store
Winks	DJW	Dave	1970s	ATCO	ATCO	>Hong Kong >Deceased
Winstone	HE	Ted	1962-75	ATCOIII	ATCOII	>CATC >EGUF >RAE Larkhill >Retired 1991 >Airwork/Short Bros/SERCO EGDN >Is of Scilly
Winter	S	Steffan	2000s	StATCO	StATCO	>Scotland
Wise	RM	Bob	1978-86	ATCOII	ATCOI RWS	>Retired 1986 >Deceased 2001
Wishart	N	Neil	1999-2000	StATCO	StATCO	>EGBB
Wood	H	Harold/Harry	1940s	ATCO	ATCOII WS	>CATO >Retired >Deceased
Wood	HE	Eric	1960-67/1984-87	ATCOIV	ATCOI	>LATCC >EGCC >CAOS (Inspector of ATC Scotland & N. Ireland) >Returned (Head Org) >Retired >IAL Bailbrook
Wood	JC	John	1959-91	ATCAII	ATSAIV	>Retired 1991
Wood	NE	Norman	1981-	ATCOII	ATCOI	C
Woodbridge	EJ	Edward		ATCO	ATCO	>Deceased
Woodhouse, Ms	SM	Sarah	1993-	ATCOII	ATCOII	>Mrs Bate >Ms Newland. C
Woodley, Miss	EA	Liz	1960s	ATCO C	ATCO	>Mrs Bowler >ATMDC
Woodruff, CBE	WC	Bill	1956-62	ATCOI I/C	SATCO I/C	Valid PAR >Master GATCO >DD CATO >DCATO >JFC >DCNATS >CNATS >Retired 1981 >Various committees including specialist advisor to Parliamentary Select Committee on Transport >Deceased 2003
Wooldridge	AP	Tim	1940s	ATCOIII	ATCO	>Exam Branch >Deceased
Wooley	D	David	1960s	ATCOIV	ATCOIV	>Resigned >Flight International
Woolgar	CJ	Chris	1960s	ATCA	ATCA	>ATCOIV >EGSS >CATC >EGSS >Retired
Woolsey	FW	Frank	1940s	ATCO	ATCO	>

SURNAME	INIT	FIRST NAME/ KNOWN AS	DATES	START GRADE	END GRADE	COMMENTS
Wornham	J	Jon	1976-81	ATCAIII	ATCAII	>Cadetship >EGPK >Resigned >EGNS
Wraight	BJ	John	1980-80	ATCOIV	ATCOIV	>Resigned >EGSH
Wright	AJ	Alan	1963-98	ATCAII	ATSAIV	>Retired 1998
Wright	DB	Barry	2004-	ATSAII	ATSAII	C
Wright, Mrs	IJ	Isobel	1992-93	ATCOII	ATCOII	>Mrs Pope >FMU >LTCC
Wright	NW	Nick	1981-90	ATCOII	ATCOII	>ATCOI >FMU >LTCC >FMU >Retired 2002
Wyre	PF	Pete	1954-59	ATCOIII	ATCOII	>SATCC >ATCOI >EGDM (SATCO) >SATCO >LATCC (WS & ACS-Ops) >DDCAP1 >Retired 1983 >Deceased 2005
Youlton	A	Andy	1990s	ATSA	ATSA	>LATCC
Young	D	Don	1950s	ATCOIII	ATCOII	>SATCC (WS) >Deceased
Young	MA	Maurice	1962-64	ATCOI I/C	ATCOI I/C	>DD Personnel >Retired >Deceased
Young	R	Roger	1960s	ATCO	ATCO	>ScATCC? >ATCOI >Retired

ABBREVIATIONS IN STAFF LIST

Location Indicators

CYYZ	Toronto		EGNX	East Midlands
EBBR	Brussels		EGOY	West Freugh
EGAA	Belfast / Aldergrove		EGPA	Kirkwall
EGBB	Birmingham		EGPB	Sumburgh
EGBE	Coventry		EGPD	Aberdeen
EGBJ	Gloucestershire / Staverton		EGPE	Inverness
EGCC	Manchester		EGPF	Glasgow
EGCD	Manchester / Woodford		EGPH	Edinburgh
EGDM	Boscombe Down		EGPI	Islay
EGDN	Netheravon		EGPK	Prestwick
EGFF	Cardiff		EGPW	Unst
EGGD	Bristol / Lulsgate		EGSC	Cambridge
EGGP	Liverpool		EGSH	Norwich
EGGW	Luton		EGSS	London / Stansted
EGHD	Plymouth		EGTB	Wycombe Air Park / Booker
EGHH	Bournemouth		EGTC	Cranfield
EGHI	Southampton		EGTF	Fairoaks
EGHL	Lasham		EGTG	Bristol/Filton
EGHR	Chichester / Goodwood		EGTK	Oxford / Kidlington
EGJA	Alderney		EGUF	Farnborough (now EGLF)
EGJB	Guernsey		EGUW	Wattisham
EGJJ	Jersey		EGVP	Middle Wallop
EGKA	Shoreham		EGWU	Northolt
EGKK	London / Gatwick		ELLX	Luxembourg
EGLC	London / City		KMIA	Miami
EGLK	Blackbushe		LMML	Malta
EGLL	London / Heathrow		LSGG	Geneva
EGLW	London Heliport / Battersea		LSZH	Zurich
EGMC	Southend		OBBI	Bahrain
EGMD	Lydd		OMAA	Abu Dhabi International
EGMH	Manston		OMAD	Abu Dhabi Bateen
EGNM	Leeds Bradford		OMDB	Dubai
EGNS	Isle of Man		OMSJ	Sharjah
EGNT	Newcastle		OOMS	Muscat / Seeb
EGNV	Teesside		VHHH	Hong Kong

Other Abbreviations

ACPO	Aircraft Control Position Operator
ACS	Assistant Centre Superintendent
AEA	Atomic Energy Authority
AIS	Aeronautical Information Service
ANS	Air Navigation Services
ARINC	Aeronautical Radio Inc
Ass Dir	Assistant Director
Asst VP	Assistant Vice President
ATCEU	Air Traffic Control Evaluation Unit. Later became ATMDC then part of DAT and S 2003
ATCOC	ATCO Cadet
ATFMD	Air Traffic Flow Management Department
ATM	Air Traffic Management
ATMDC	Air Traffic Management Development Centre
ATO	Air Traffic Operations
ATOM	Air Traffic Operations Manager
ATS	Air Traffic Services
ATSI	Air Traffic Service Investigations
ATSSD	Air Traffic Service Standards Department, Gatwick
BA	British Airways
BAA	British Airports Authority
BBJ	Boeing Business Jet (B737)
BCAL	British Caledonian Airways Ltd
BEA	British European Airways
BMA	British Midland Airways
BT	British Telecom
BUA	British United Airways
C	Current
CAA	Civil Aviation Authority
CACC	Civil Aviation Communications Centre, Heathrow
CAFU	Civil Aviation Flying Unit. Became CAA Flying Unit
CAOS	Civil Aviation Office Scotland
CATC	College of Air Traffic Control, Hurn. Became part of DAT and S 2003
CATO	Civil Air Traffic Operations, Hillingdon. Became ATO
CC	County Council
CCF	Combined Control Function, West Drayton. Became Terminal Control, then LTCC.
Ch	Chief
CHIRP	Confidential Human Factors Incident Reporting Programme
CPL	Commercial Pilot's Licence
CTC	Corporate and Technical Centre, Whiteley, Hampshire
DAP	Directorate of Airspace Policy
DAT and S	Department of Air Traffic Training and Simulation
DCA	Department of Civil Aviation
DCS	Deputy Centre Superintendent
DD	Deputy Director
DGATO	Director General Air Traffic Operations
Dir	Director
DORA	Department of Operational Research and Analysis
DP	Data processing
DSS	Data Systems Specialist
DWM	Deputy Watch Manager
ECT	Emergency Continuation Training
EO	Executive Officer
FBU	Flight Briefing Unit
FDP	Flight Data Processing
FISO	Flight Information Service Officer
FMU	Flow Management Unit
FPPS	Flight Plan Processing System
FSP	Future Systems Planning
FTU	Field Training Unit
GATCO	Guild of Air Traffic Control Officers
GCA	Ground Controlled Approach

GM	General Manager
HEO	Higher Executive Officer
HIAL	Highlands and Islands Airports Ltd
HM	Her Majesty's
HQ	Headquarters - various London locations including The Adelphi, CAA House, Aviation House etc.
I/C	In Charge
IAL	International Aeradio Ltd
IANS	Institute of Air Navigation Services, Luxembourg
IATC	Inspector Air Traffic Control
ICAO	International Civil Aviation Organisation
Insp	Inspector
IoW	Isle of Wight
IT	Information Technology
JFC	Joint Field Commander
JFHQ	Joint Field Headquarters
JP	Justice of the Peace
LACC	London Area Control Centre, Swanwick
LATCC	London Air Traffic Control Centre, West Drayton
LFMU	London Flow Management Unit / Various locations LATCC>EGLL>LATCC>LACC
LTCC	London Terminal Control Centre, West Drayton
MACC	Manchester Area Control Centre
Man	Manager
Min	Ministry
MoA	Ministry of Aviation
MoD(PE)	Ministry of Defence (Procurement Executive)
N Div	Northern Divisional Office, Liverpool
NATS	National Air Traffic Services
NERC	New Enroute Centre. Became LACC.
NMU	Noise Monitoring Unit, Heathrow
NSC	New Scottish Centre, Prestwick
OACC	Oceanic Area Control Centre, Prestwick
Ops	Operations
OSS	Operational Support Staff
PAR	Precision Approach Radar
PATCC	Preston Air Traffic Control Centre, Barton Hall
PATCRU	Preston Air Traffic Control Radar Unit, Manchester Airport
PPL	Private Pilot's Licence
PWA	Pacific Western Airlines
RAE	Royal Aircraft Establishment
RAF	Royal Air Force
RC	Runway Controller (ATCA grade)
REQ	Requirements
RNLI	Royal National Lifeboat Institution
RRE	Royal Radar Establishment
RSRE	Royal Signals and Radar Establishment
S Div	Southern Divisional Office, Heston
SADO	Support and Development Organisation
SATCC	Southern Air Traffic Control Centre, Bath Road, Heathrow
SATCO	Senior Air Traffic Control Officer
ScATCC	Scottish Air Traffic Control Centre, Prestwick. Became Scottish Area Control Centre
Sim	Simulator
SITA	Societe Internationale de Telecommunications Aeronautiques
SRG	Safety Regulation Group
SSR	Secondary Surveillance Radar
St ATCO	Student ATCO. Previously known briefly as Trainee ATCO
Supt	Superintendent
TC	Air Traffic Clerk. Became ATCA grade
TCA	Trans - Canada Air Lines
Trg	Training
TWA	Trans World Airlines
UAC	Upper Air Centre
UKAIP	United Kingdom Aeronautical Information Publication
WM	Watch Manager
WS	Watch Supervisor

INDEX